Ecology of Aquatic Systems

Ecology of Aquatic Systems

Mike Dobson
and
Chris Frid

LONGMAN

Addison Wesley Longman Limited
Edinburgh Gate, Harlow
Essex CM20 2JE
England

and Associated Companies throughout the World

First published 1998

ISBN 0 582 29804 0

Visit Addison Wesley Longman on the World Wide Web at
http://www.awl-he.com

British Library Cataloguing in Publication Data
A catalogue record for this book is available from the British
Library.

Sabon and News Gothic.
Produced by Addison Wesley Longman Singapore Publishers (Pte) Ltd.

Contents

Preface

Aquatic ecology has traditionally been split into separate marine and freshwater components, each of which progressed more or less independently of the other for many years. This fundamental division is reflected in the way that the discipline is often taught, the two being treated as completely separate subjects, but it masks two very important features of aquatic systems: their incredible diversity, both in the variety of distinguishable habitat types and in the heterogeneity within a single water body, and the fact that, throughout this diversity, there are common themes, determined by the physical properties of water and by the mechanisms by which organisms interact with each other and with the environment. A major research initiative in aquatic ecology today, therefore, is emphasis upon the common properties underlying its diversity, an approach which recognises that, from an ecological perspective, there is no fundamental difference between marine and freshwater systems.

In this book, we attempt to give a flavour of these features. While emphasising the diversity and unique features of the major aquatic habitats by treating them under separate chapter headings, we also show that the same underlying themes crop up again and again, in every field of aquatic ecology. There is, of course, no way that a book of this size can do justice to the subject encompassed by its title, but it is our hope that it introduces enough of the excitement of aquatic ecology to stimulate further, more detailed study. To this end, we have tried to keep our explanations simple and, wherever appropriate, to define the terms and ideas which the reader may come across elsewhere.

Although written primarily as an undergraduate textbook, we hope that the book will be of wider use. Therefore, we expect from the reader some basic ecological knowledge, but no prior experience of aquatic ecology, in either of its disciplines. We hope that some will read the book from cover to cover, but accept that many will not, but will dip into it as a source of specific information, and we have designed its layout accordingly. We appreciate that some may find this 'reference book' format annoying, but trust that, for the majority of our target audience, it will be a positive feature.

Even though we aim to stimulate further integration of the two sciences of aquatic ecology, not even two of us can claim to possess all the required expertise. We wish, therefore, to acknowledge all those aquatic ecologists who have provided us with inspiration, either in person or through their writings. More specifically, the Marine Ecology Research Group at the Dove Marine Laboratory and the small but vocal Freshwater Group at Manchester Metropolitan University each provided stimulating intellectual environments and lively discussions, while Lisa Belyea, Susan Clark, Helen Fletcher, John Hall, Kirsty Nicholas and Richard Thompson all introduced us to various pieces of the literature which would otherwise have been missed. We wish to thank Martin Attrill for generously supplying the unpublished data used in Figure 3.11, and Stan Dobson and Margaret Gill, who each provided a photograph for our use. Tina Cadle, Kate Henderson and Alex Seabrook at Addison Wesley Longman pushed us along. Finally, special personal thanks to our partners, Deirdre and Susan, for support and understanding and, from MD, to Hannah and Lawrence for their patience.

Acknowledgements

We are grateful to the following for permission to reproduce copyright material:

Academic Press for Figure 4.13; American Society of Limnology and Oceanography for Figure 5.6; Backhuys Publishers for Figure 6.5; Blackwell Science Ltd for Figures 2.5b, 5.9 and 6.6; Butterworth Heinemann for Figure 5.3; Cambridge University Press for Figures 6.2 and 7.9; Chapman and Hall for Figure 3.10; Ecological Society of America for Figures 2.6, 4.10 and 7.11a; E. Schweizerbart'sche Verlagsbuchhandlung for Figures 2.7, 2.13, 6.8 and 7.6; Freshwater Biological Association for Figures 2.11a and 6.14b; John Wiley and Sons Limited for Figure 3.7; Kluwer Academic Publishers for Figure 7.13; Kluwer Academic Publishers and Prof. P. Denny for Figure 7.5b; Kluwer Academic Publishers and M-L Meijer for Figure 6.13; Munksgaard International Publishers Ltd for Figure 7.8; National Research Council of Canada for Figure 2.12; Nederlands Diekundige Vereinigung for Figure 6.14a; Oxford University Press for Figure 4.14; Plenum Publishing Corporation for Box 5.1, Fig. 1; Taylor and Francis for Figure 4.4.

Whilst every effort has been made to trace owners of copyright material, in a few cases this has proved impossible and so we would like to offer our apologies to any copyright holders whose rights may have been unwittingly infringed.

1
Life in Aquatic Systems

1.1   Introduction

Aquatic systems are those in which the primary medium inhabited by organisms is water, whether as an open water body or dominating the spaces between particles in a substrate. This broad definition covers a wide variety of habitat types, although generally they are divided into two separate groups: marine and fresh water systems. Research into aquatic systems has generally reflected this division, limnology (the study of fresh waters) and oceanography (the study of marine systems) proceeding more or less independently for many years.

This division masks two important features of aquatic systems. First, they are extremely diverse, with a wide range of aquatic habitat types distinguishable, each with its own unique components and processes. Some systems are transitional between marine and freshwater environments, yet, at the same time, show unique, distinctive features. Of these, estuaries and saltmarshes are generally classed as marine environments, while saline lakes are largely ignored. Second, there is much overlap among marine and freshwater systems: ecologically, a turbulent river may have more in common with a rocky marine coastline than with a garden pond, while there are many broad similarities between large freshwater lakes and the open sea. Despite these common features, the separation of the two disciplines has meant that, even now, limnologists and oceanographers use different terminology for the same processes, and even the same terminology for different processes!

The aim of this book is to explore these two features. We wish to emphasise the great diversity of aquatic systems, while demonstrating that all operate within the same functional principles, deriving from the physical properties of water. We also wish to show that the fundamental division between marine and freshwater systems is untenable from an ecological perspective. Taxonomically, they are very different, but ecologically, similarities across the freshwater–marine divide outweigh the differences. Furthermore, the fundamental and dominant determinant of aquatic community structure, across all aquatic habitats, is the physical environment generated by the movement of water. Biotic processes, such as competition and predation, can be important locally or over the short term, but the physical environment dominates overall. Other abiotic features of water, such as salinity, acidity and pollution load, have major effects upon the taxonomic components of water bodies, but their effect upon ecological processes is more muted. In contrast, similar ecological processes can be identified in aquatic habitats whose water chemistry is very different but whose patterns of water movement are similar.

Throughout the diversity of aquatic habitats, therefore, a common and recurring feature is movement of water, relative both to the substrate that contains it and to water masses within other parts of the same water body. It is this movement which will be returned to throughout the book, as it is the physical similarities and differences among water bodies which determine the ecological comparisons and contrasts which can be made

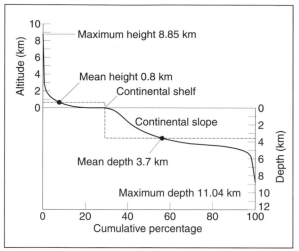

Figure 1.1 A hypsographic curve illustrating the cumulative percentage of the Earth below a given elevation. Features to note are that about 71% of the Earth's surface is below sea level and a rise in sea level of only 100 m would flood more than 5% of the current land area.

Table 1.1 Distribution of the world's water. The approximate volume of water in various aquatic systems is given, along with the percentage of the total water available

	Volume (km^3 × 10^3)	%
Oceans	1 338 000	96.5
Glacial ice	24 400	1.8
Groundwater	23 400	1.7
Freshwater lakes	105	0.008
Saline lakes	85	0.006
Atmosphere	13	0.001
Rivers	2	0.0001

between different aquatic systems. Some of these ecological similarities will be introduced later in this chapter (**Section 1.6**), while others are to be found in appropriate habitat chapters, although similarities between habitats are emphasised by cross-referencing where appropriate. Before these ecological themes are referred to, however, it is important to appreciate the diversity of aquatic environments and of the life which inhabits them, as well as the chemical components of that environment which impinge upon living organisms.

1.2 Distribution of the world's aquatic habitats

1.2a THE HYDROLOGICAL CYCLE

The Earth's surface and atmosphere contain about 1.5×10^9 km^3 of water, the overwhelming majority of which is in the oceans, which cover around 71% of the world's surface and average 3.7 km in depth (Figure 1.1). If the ice sheets and glaciers of polar and mountainous regions and the water within the ground are added, this accounts for approximately 100% of the water (Table 1.1).

This simplistic appraisal neglects, however, the importance of water movement on a global scale. The world's water is in a very dynamic state, with all of its aquatic features connected in an active hydrological cycle (Figure 1.2), generated by processes which lead to the evaporation of surface water, its transport by atmospheric circulation and its subsequent precipitation. Between this

Figure 1.2 The hydrological cycle. Although movement is mainly one-way (anticlockwise in this case), there are mechanisms which act in the reverse direction, of which the most important are shown here as dashed lines. Major storage compartments are boxed. P = precipitation (rain and snow); E = evaporation; T = transpiration.

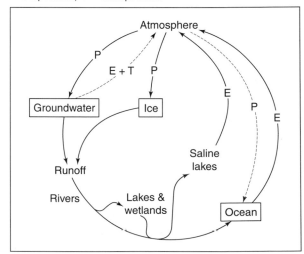

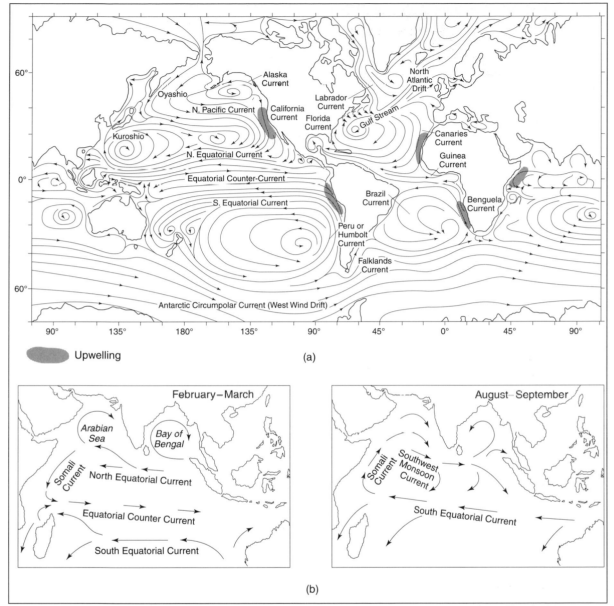

Figure 1.3 Surface ocean circulation patterns, showing zones of upwelling from deep ocean circulation. (a) The global system during February–March. (b) The monsoon (Box 1.1): an example of seasonal changes to oceanic circulation. During February–March, the northeast monsoon drives a small clockwise gyre circulation in the Arabian Sea, a clockwise gyre in the Bay of Bengal, and westerly flows throughout the remainder of the northern Indian Ocean. During August–September, the southwest monsoon creates a clockwise gyre circulation in the northern Indian Ocean and Arabian Sea with an anticlockwise gyre in the Bay of Bengal. The result is a reversal of the Somali Current between the two seasons and the presence of an Equatorial Counter Current in the northeast monsoon period.

atmosphere–surface link is lateral and vertical movement within aquatic systems themselves, dominated by terrestrial runoff and oceanic circulation. An important feature of the hydrological cycle, therefore, is that water moves both between its various components, as evaporation and precipitation, and within each component. The oceans and atmosphere are dominated by circulatory currents, and even apparently immobile ice sheets are in a state of flux, albeit more slowly than liquid water. The mobile nature of water is nowhere more apparent than in places where it is moving relative to the land: rivers as linear, one-way channels, and wave and tidal action against the seashore.

Within this cycle, biological habitats are rather unevenly distributed. The oceans are inhabited by living organisms which recognise, and have created, a wide variety of different habitats in what is effectively a single body of water. Habitat diversity of inland waters is augmented by their fragmented nature, but the vast majority of non-marine aquatic organisms live in the rivers, lakes and wetlands which, in terms of the volume of water they contain, are very minor components of the hydrological cycle. Ice is a virtually sterile environment, whose inhabitants are limited to a few specialist forms living on the surface, and groundwater, equally, supports a very low diversity and biomass of organisms, except where it occurs close to surface water features.

1.2b OCEANS

The oceans are clearly the most widely distributed aquatic habitats, containing almost all the world's water (Table 1.1). By far the largest component of the oceanic system is the water column itself, the pelagic zone. Geographically separate parts of the pelagic zone interact through the processes of ocean circulation, although different mechanisms, operating in shallow and deep waters, respectively, ensure that ocean basins contain two relatively discrete environments, separated by depth.

Surface ocean circulation

Surface ocean currents are generated by wind friction on the sea surface, and the global pattern of currents (Figure 1.3) therefore resembles that of atmospheric movement (**Box 1.1**). Coriolis force influences the movement of surface waters – the surface layer moves at $45°$ to the wind direction (deflected to the right in the Northern Hemisphere and to the left in the Southern Hemisphere) and this deflection increases with depth, as succeeding layers of water are deflected relative to those

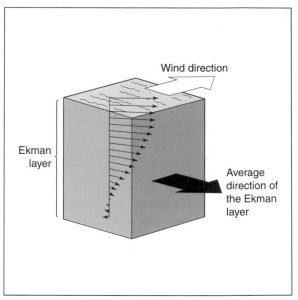

Figure 1.4 The Ekman spiral of water movement generated by wind on the sea surface. Each arrow indicates the direction of movement of that layer, the length of the arrow being proportional to the magnitude of flow. Net movement of the Ekman layer as a whole is $90°$ to the direction of the wind, the displacement being to the right in the Northern Hemisphere and to the left in the Southern Hemisphere.

above them, creating a spiral current pattern (Figure 1.4). The net motion of the wind-influenced layer, or Ekman layer, is at $90°$ to the wind direction.

Land masses interfere with the free movement of water, which tends to pile up against down-current coasts, creating a slope in the sea surface. The North Atlantic, for example, slopes up from America towards Europe and North Africa. Therefore, a true horizontal surface across the ocean will have more water above it, and therefore greater water pressure, on the European side than the American. Water, like wind, attempts to equalise pressure by flowing from high pressure to low pressure areas, generating a horizontal pressure gradient force, and therefore creating currents which are deflected, by Coriolis force, $90°$ to the right in the Northern Hemisphere (left in the Southern Hemisphere). Currents driven by this pressure gradient are known as geostrophic currents; in the North Atlantic, for example, the east–west pressure gradient force generates a geostrophic flow to the north.

BOX 1.1   THE GLOBAL WIND SYSTEM

Heat which arrives at the Earth from the Sun is lost through radiation into space. Heat loss is fairly constant with latitude, whereas input of heat is much greater at low latitudes than at high latitudes. Therefore, there is a net gain of energy in the low and mid latitudes and a net loss at the poles.

Assuming that the Earth's temperature is constant, then there must be a mechanism for redistributing this heat, primarily through the circulation of the atmosphere. Hot air rises, creating low pressure at low elevations, while cool air falls, creating high pressure. Air heated at the Equator rises and moves polewards; as it does so, it receives less solar energy, so cools and descends at about 30° latitude, spreading north and south at low altitude. Air at the poles, being cool, descends and moves towards the Equator at low altitude; when it reaches temperate latitudes, it meets air moving polewards from the subtropics and this converging air rises.

The movement of air from high to low pressure areas at low altitude and in the opposite direction at high altitude sets up a series of cells of air, the Hadley cells. Air movement is, however, not directly to the north or south, because the rotation of the Earth creates Coriolis force, deflecting air mass fluids to the right in the Northern Hemisphere and to the left in the Southern Hemisphere and creating the prevailing wind systems observed on the Earth's surface.

The strength of the Coriolis force increases at high latitudes so that, in mid–high latitudes, Hadley cells break down and vortices are produced, creating depressions and anticyclones. Winds circulating around a low pressure system are known as cyclonic (of which true cyclones are extremely low pressure examples), and rotate anticlockwise in the Northern Hemisphere, clockwise in the Southern. High pressure systems are known as anticyclones, their winds rotating clockwise in the Northern Hemisphere and

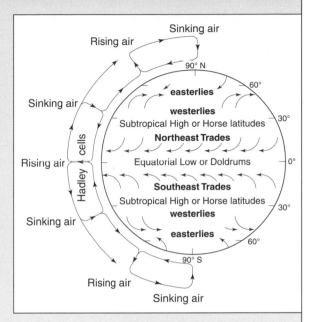

anticlockwise in the Southern.

This theoretical pattern of wind movement is close to that observed over the open oceans, but is broken by the effect of land masses, particularly in the Northern Hemisphere. The most spectacular example of this is the monsoon winds of the Indian Ocean, created by the presence of the Eurasian land mass. During the summer, air over the land mass heats up and rises, creating a low pressure area. Normally, this would draw in air from all sides, including cooler air from the north which would reduce overall temperatures and raise the pressure. In India, however, the passage of air from the north is blocked by the Himalayan massif, so only warm air from the south is drawn in, which rapidly rises, maintaining low pressure. This sucks in moisture-laden air from the Indian Ocean, the monsoon winds.

Deep ocean circulation

Deep currents, which flow independently of the wind-driven surface currents, are initiated by surface waters being cooled at high latitudes, which increases their density and causes them to sink to the ocean depths, a process described as down-welling. In most of the world's oceans, the water mass in contact with the abyssal sea floor is Antarctic Bottom Water (AABW), which down-wells in the Ross and Weddell Seas off Antarctica, although in the northern North Atlantic this is replaced by North Atlantic Deep Water (NADW), composed of Norwegian Sea Deep Water (entering over the Faroes Sill) and Arctic Intermediate Water (entering from the Denmark Strait). The continual sinking of these waters drives a slow circulation of water throughout the deep ocean: it is estimated that a water molecule, once moved into the deep ocean, would spend, on average, 510, 250 and 275 years below 1500 m in the Pacific, Indian and Atlantic oceans, respectively.

Upwelling

Continual downwelling of water into the deep ocean requires that, eventually, the deep water rises to the surface, rejoining surface circulation in regions of upwelling. These occur in areas where surface water circulation patterns diverge in equatorial regions, leaving a gap which is filled from beneath, and where surface water is forced away from the edge of continents which, in the absence of an extensive continental shelf (as occurs off the western coasts of North and South America and central Africa), forces deep water to rise (Figure 1.3).

Gyres

Localised upwellings or downwellings can be created by gyres, the circular currents produced by cyclonic and anticyclonic winds (**Box 1.1**). A cyclonic wind pushes surface water out of the gyre, generating upwelling (Figure 1.5a), whereas an anticyclonic wind forces water into the centre of the gyre, creating an area of downwelling (Figure 1.5b). Gyres also occur in large lakes, in which the entire water body slowly rotates around a relatively stagnant centre.

1.2c THE OCEAN BED

The ocean bed, or benthic zone, is a relatively small component of the marine environment, but highly diverse. It may be divided into a series of structures (Table 1.2).

The coastal zone

The coastal zone is where the sea meets the land,

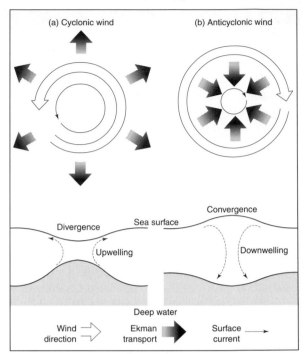

Figure 1.5 Ekman currents associated with the circulating patterns of winds around (a) a cyclonic and (b) an anticyclonic atmospheric pressure system, showing how each affects the sea surface shape, and localised up- and downwelling. This is the pattern in the Northern Hemisphere; in the Southern Hemisphere the directions of circulation are reversed.

and its area and diversity are, therefore, determined by the topography of the coast. Despite its small size relative to the rest of the marine environment, the coastal zone supports the highest diversity of marine habitats, including the intertidal (**Section 4.2a**), coral reefs (**Section 4.5e**), estuaries (**Chapter 3**) and coastal wetlands (**Chapter 7**).

The continental shelf and slope

At the edge of continents are continental shelves, shallow seas associated with the continental plates (**Section 5.7e**). When the continent and the adjacent ocean are part of the same plate, the continental shelf may be very wide, extending hundreds of kilometres out to sea. In many places, however, particularly around the Pacific Ocean, it is very narrow and deep water is encountered a few kilometres from the shore (Figure 1.6). The

Table 1.2 Main features of the principal ocean basins

	Pacific	Atlantic	Indian	World ocean
Ocean area ($km^2 \times 10^6$)	180	107	74	361
Land area drained ($km^2 \times 10^6$)	19	69	13	101
Ocean area ÷ drainage area	9.5	1.6	5.7	3.6
Average depth (m)	3940	3310	3840	3730
Area as % of total:				
shelf and slope	13.1	19.4	9.1	15.3
continental rise	2.7	8.5	5.7	5.3
deep ocean floor	42.9	38.1	49.3	41.9
volcanoes and volcanic ridges[a]	2.5	2.1	5.4	3.1
ridges[b]	35.9	31.2	30.2	32.7
trenches	2.9	0.7	0.3	1.7

[a] Volcanic ridges are those related to volcanic island chains that are not part of constructive plate margins, e.g. the Walvis Ridge in the South Atlantic. They do not include island arcs.
[b] These are the ridges that correspond to constructive plate margins, e.g. the mid-Atlantic ridge.

continental shelf is a zone of deposition for terrigenous sediments, produced by weathering of continental crust and therefore originating from land via coastal erosion or input from rivers. They consist of boulders, cobbles, pebbles, sands or muds, and dominate coastal regions and the continental shelf, slope and rise, where they may form deposits 10 km or more thick.

Much of the material that accumulates on the upper continental slope is in an unstable condition and likely to move down slope. These movements are classified according to the degree of deformation of the mass of sediment that has moved. Slides, slumps and debris flows contribute to the formation of the continental rise, the region of increased angle of slope at the base of the continental slope. Slides and slumps result from mechanical failure along inclined planes. Large volumes of sediment move in a way analogous to a landslip, giving rise to a hummocky topography, although there is relatively little deformation of the original mass and the sedimentary layers can still be traced. They can occur on slopes as little as 2° and may be triggered by earthquakes or simply after the rapid accumulation of sediments. Debris flows are caused in the same way, but are the sluggish movement of a mixture of sediments, down slopes as little as 0.1°, which obliterate the original layering of the deposit.

Turbidity currents are triggered by the same mechanisms as slides and debris flows, but can travel at up to 90 km h⁻¹ and transport 300 kg

Figure 1.6 Profiles of continental shelf margins. A wide shelf occurs at a seismically passive shelf margin, where deep ocean and continent are part of the same plate. A narrow shelf and trench occur at a seismically active margin, where the oceanic plate is descending beneath the continental margin. Note that the topography of the land mass approximates to that of the adjacent ocean, because the active margin generates uplift of mountain ranges.

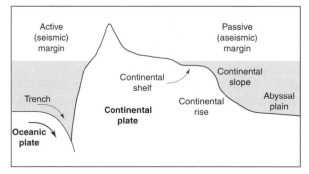

m^{-3} of sediment in suspension. They can move material up to 1000 km and are probably responsible for scouring out submarine canyons and the deposition of sand layers on the abyssal plain (see below). Some canyon systems were probably cut by river flows when sea levels were lower, and the deposition of sediments from major estuaries at their head means that turbidity currents are fairly frequent events.

Ocean ridges

Ocean ridges, which currently occupy about 33% of the ocean floor, are the site of production of new sea floor (**Section 5.7e**). Basaltic magma is extruded from the centre of the ridge as the plates separate, so seafloor spreading tends to be symmetrical about, and perpendicular to, the ridge. The mid-Atlantic ridge is a slow-spreading ridge (each plate is moving away from the ridge at $1-2$ cm yr^{-1}, widening the ocean by $2-4$ cm yr^{-1}), producing a well defined valley $25-30$ km wide and $1-2$ km deep, with the sea floor sloping away from the ridge at an angle of about $1°$. The East Pacific Rise, in contrast, is a rapidly-spreading ridge ($6-8$ cm yr^{-1}), so the median valley is poorly developed, and even absent in places, while the slope is typically $0.2°$.

The deep sea floor

Between the continental margins and the mid-ocean ridges lies the abyssal plain, with a slope of less than $0.05°$, accounting for 42% of the Earth's surface. This is covered by pelagic sediments, which settle from suspension in the open ocean, and are often biological in origin (**Section 5.2c**). These were formerly known as oozes, which gives some idea of their properties. They aggregate very slowly, so dominate only where terrigenous inputs are low. Rising rapidly from the surface of the abyssal plain, suggesting their bases are buried in sediment, are abyssal hills (rising less than 1 km above the plain) and seamounts (rising more than 1 km). Abyssal hills are most common near ridge systems, where there has been little time for pelagic sediment to build up and mask topographic relief produced by the spreading centre. Most seamounts, which are most abundant in the Pacific, arise as

sub-sea volcanoes, forming islands if they reach the surface. Guyots are seamounts with a flat top, created by wave erosion of the seamount when it broke the sea surface prior to sea level rise, subsidence of the mount, or a combination of the two.

Deep trenches are formed where an oceanic plate is being subsumed beneath a continental plate and so occur relatively close to land (Figure 1.6). They are steep-sided and can reach great depths (Figure 1.1).

1.2d INLAND WATERS

Inland waters are patchily distributed across the Earth's land surface. Glacial ice is confined to high latitudes and, in relatively small amounts, high altitudes, by its requirement for low temperatures. The very highest latitudes are cold deserts, with very little precipitation, and ice persists not because it is continually replenished, but because what little snow falls is unlikely to melt. Groundwater can be found under most of the Earth's surface; but only where it is close to the surface, usually in association with rivers, is it a significant biological habitat.

Rivers, lakes and wetlands are dynamic systems with a high turnover of water, their distribution and abundance being determined by precipitation and morphology of the landscape. Lakes and wetlands occur most abundantly where precipitation is high; rivers originate in these areas but can flow through much more arid areas.

Rivers

Rivers are drainage channels for the excess of precipitation over evaporation and, as such, are the main conduit for the return of water from land to the sea. Their formation requires enough of a slope to enable water to flow downhill easily, but inputs from steep headwaters can maintain flow in the lower reaches of a river even over low gradient terrain. Furthermore, the constant mobility of water, along with the sediments it carries, will rapidly create a discrete channel within which water is normally confined.

River systems originate most abundantly where rainfall is high, but their nature as channels for the transport of water means that they extend beyond the source region, normally into areas whose rainfall is inadequate to maintain the flow without inputs from upstream. In arid zones, river channels may be common but water flows only rarely, as runoff from occasional storms. Rivers rising in uplands or adjacent arid regions may flow perennially in their upper reaches but evaporate away, or be lost to groundwater, when they reach lower lying areas. Most of the rain which falls or flows into arid regions never reaches the sea, only the largest rivers, such as the Nile and the Euphrates, having enough volume to withstand the high rates of desiccation.

Lakes

Lakes, like rivers, are unevenly distributed, but their distribution correlates less clearly with precipitation than do the headwaters of river systems because they require a basin within which to form (**Box 6.1**) and, in high mountain ranges, such basins may be rare. Most of the world's lakes are in the recently deglaciated areas of northern North America and northern Europe. Equatorial regions, despite their precipitation, support few large permanent lakes, because they are generally low-lying and flat, although temporary ponds, oxbow lakes, etc. (**Box 6.1**) are very common; an exception is in East Africa, where tectonic activity has created a number of large basins now occupied by lakes.

Arid zones support saline lakes, either temporary or permanent (**Section 6.2a**). The importance of saline lakes is often overlooked, despite the large volume of water they contain (Table 1.1). Admittedly, over 70% of the entire volume of inland saline water is in the Caspian Sea (itself a remnant of a former marine system), but fresh waters, too, are concentrated: about half of all fresh water occurs in just seven lakes: Baikal, Tanganyika and the Great Lakes of North America.

Wetlands

Wetlands occur where inputs of water exceed evaporation, but outflow is impeded by flat topography. Their distribution is discussed in **Section 7.7a**. The vast majority of the world's wetlands occur in areas with the highest precipitation, but some of the largest individual wetlands, including the Okavango and Inner Niger Delta in Africa and the mouths of the Euphrates and Tigris in southwest Asia, occur in arid zones with very little direct rainfall, and are entirely dependent for water upon the large rivers which feed them. Coastal saline wetlands are maintained by the sea so they, too, require little or no direct precipitation.

1.3   Chemistry of water

Naturally occurring water is never pure, but contains a range of components, both suspended and in solution. The composition and concentrations of these substances, particularly those in solution, determine the quality of water.

1.3a   DISSOLVED INORGANIC MATTER

Salinity

Dissolved ions in water are expressed as units of mass ($mg\ l^{-1}$), parts per million (ppm), or sometimes as chemical equivalents ($meq\ l^{-1}$), while the total amount of dissolved material in a sample is referred to as its salinity. Salinity may be determined by evaporating off the water and weighing the residual salts. This gives rise to problems, however, as the drying process may alter some salts; examples are loss of hydrogen chloride (HCl) from hydrous magnesium chloride ($MgCl$), or combustion of carbonates. The constancy of seawater composition (see below) allows determination of salinity by measuring the concentration of a single constituent, for example chlorinity (the concentration of chloride [Cl^-]), where salinity = 1.806 55 [Cl^-]. Salinity is then expressed as parts per thousand (ppt) or ‰. Chlorinity can easily be determined by titration, and this was the routine method for estimating seawater salinity until the 1960s, when it was superseded by electrical measurement. Salinity is now defined and measured according to an internationally agreed Practical Salinity Scale, which specifies it as a dimensionless (and therefore unitless) property which is measured electronically, by determining the conductivity of water.

Conductivity

Conductivity is a measure of the ability of water to conduct electricity, as it is dissolved ions, rather than water molecules themselves, which are the conductors. Conductivity is expressed in siemens per centimetre ($S cm^{-1}$) or, for fresh waters, $mS cm^{-1}$ or $\mu S cm^{-1}$, measured at $25\ ^{\circ}C$. An increasing conductivity reading signifies increasing concentration of dissolved ions. Distilled water has a conductivity of $2-4\ \mu S cm^{-1}$, clean tap water is normally in the range $60-100\ \mu S cm^{-1}$, a clean upland river or lake will give a reading of less than $300\ \mu S cm^{-1}$, whereas an organically enriched river's conductivity is usually in excess of $500\ \mu S cm^{-1}$. Increasing conductivity in fresh waters is often used as an indicator of pollution, although there are many natural sources of ions, and rivers become naturally more enriched with distance from source (**Section 2.2f**), while ponds may have very high conductivities. As an extreme example of natural enrichment, of course, the conductivity of the sea is $35\,000\ \mu S cm^{-1}$!

A useful feature of conductivity is that it approximates to ion concentration; a conductivity of $60\ \mu S cm^{-1}$ will be more or less equivalent to a total dissolved ion concentration of $60\ mg\ l^{-1}$.

Dissolved matter in the sea

Sea water contains a high proportion of dissolved components, generally around $35\ g\ kg^{-1}$, giving a salinity of 35. This concentration varies little, except in estuaries or semi-enclosed seas with a high volume of freshwater inputs (**Section 3.2b**) or inlets in arid zones where evaporation rates are very high.

Components of sea water can be divided into major constituents, present at concentrations of 1 ppm or more, which account for 99.9% of the salt in the oceans, and minor or trace constituents, the remaining, non-biologically active salts, which are often used as chemical tracers of the source of waters. Most of the 92 naturally occurring elements have been isolated from sea water (Table 1.3), and those which are missing will probably be identified once appropriate analytical techniques have been developed. The chemical composition of the dissolved components is remarkably constant, so while the total salinity may vary in response to local evaporation, precipitation and mixing, this has no effect on the relative proportions of the main constituents. Exceptions to this occur in enclosed seas and estuaries (**Section 3.2**), where input processes may affect the composition, and in geologically or biologically active areas, including shallow tropical seas where extensive reefs may be removing calcium carbonate (**Section 4.5e**), or oceanic hydrothermal vent systems whose outflows are chemically very different from normal sea water (**Box 5.2**).

Sources and sinks of ocean salt

The most obvious source of salts for the sea is the weathering of rocks by rainwater and hence additions from river water to the sea (Table 1.4). However, some salts abundant in river water are relatively uncommon in crustal rocks. An important example is chloride (Cl^-), the dominant ion in oceanic waters, which is common in rock only where evaporites have been deposited by the sea. The Cl^- in rivers, therefore, originates mainly from the sea. It leaves the ocean as an aerosol and is carried in the atmosphere to fall as rain and return to the sea via rivers. Volcanoes produce large quantities of hydrogen chloride (HCl) gas, and the high level of volcanic activity early in the Earth's history is probably the source of the majority of the chloride present in today's oceans.

The time that the average molecule spends in the ocean, its residence time (RT), may be estimated by dividing the total mass of a given substance dissolved in the oceans by its rate of supply. As weathering of rocks is continuing but the composition of sea water remains relatively constant, there must be sinks for the material brought into the ocean by rivers. Much of it is precipitated out as sediment, particularly bicarbonate (HCO_3^-), calcium (Ca^{2+}) and silicate (SiO_2), which are proportionally less common in sea water than in river water. Removal mechanisms for these salts include inorganic precipitation, reaction of dissolved substances with particles, and biological processes such as reef building and construction of silicate and carbonate skeletons (**Section 5.2c**).

Calcium carbonate in oceans

Calcium carbonate ($CaCO_3$) is used by many

Table 1.3   The composition of sea water

Element		Concentration (mg l^{-1}) (i.e. parts per million, ppm)	Some probable dissolved species	Total amount in the ocean (tonnes)
Chlorine	Cl	1.95×10^4	Cl$^-$	2.57×10^{16}
Sodium	Na	1.077×10^4	Na$^+$	1.42×10^{16}
Magnesium	Mg	1.290×10^3	Mg^{2+}	1.71×10^{15}
Sulphur	S	9.05×10^2	SO_4^{2-}, $NaSO_4^-$	1.2×10^{15}
Calcium	Ca	4.12×10^2	Ca^{2+}	5.45×10^{14}
Potassium	K	3.80×10^2	K$^+$	5.02×10^{14}
Bromine	Br	67	Br$^-$	8.86×10^{13}
Carbon	C	28	HCO_3^-, CO_3^{2-}, CO_2	3.7×10^{13}
Nitrogen	N	11.5	N_2 gas, NO_3^-, NH_4^+	1.5×10^{13}
Strontium	Sr	8	Sr^{2+}	1.06×10^{13}
Oxygen	O	6	O_2 gas	7.93×10^{12}
Boron	B	4.4	$B(OH)_3$, $B(OH)_4^-$, $H_2BO_3^-$	5.82×10^{12}
Silicon	Si	2	$Si(OH)_4$	2.64×10^{12}
Fluorine	F	1.3	F$^-$, MgF$^+$	1.72×10^{12}
Argon	Ar	0.43	Ar gas	5.68×10^{11}
Lithium	Li	0.18	Li$^+$	2.38×10^{11}
Rubidium	Rb	0.12	Rb$^+$	1.59×10^{11}
Phosphorus	P	6×10^{-2}	HPO_4^{2-}, PO_4^{3-}, H_2PO_4	7.93×10^{10}
Iodine	I	6×10^{-2}	IO_3^-, I$^-$	7.93×10^{10}
Barium	Ba	2×10^{-2}	Ba^{2+}	2.64×10^{10}
Molybdenum	Mo	1×10^{-2}	MoO_4^{2-}	1.32×10^{10}
Arsenic	As	3.7×10^{-3}	$HAsO_4^{2-}$, $H_2AsO_4^-$	4.89×10^9
Uranium	U	3.2×10^{-3}	$UO_2(CO_3)_2^{4-}$	4.23×10^9
Vanadium	V	2.5×10^{-3}	$H_2VO_4^-$, HVO_4^{2-}	3.31×10^9
Aluminium	Al	2×10^{-3}	$Al(OH)_4^-$	2.64×10^9
Iron	Fe	2×10^{-3}	$Fe(OH)_2^+$, $Fe(OH)_4^-$	2.64×10^9
Nickel	Ni	1.7×10^{-3}	Ni^{2+}	2.25×10^9
Titanium	Ti	1×10^{-3}	$Ti(OH)_4$	1.32×10^9
Zinc	Zn	5×10^{-4}	ZnOH$^+$, Zn^{2+}, $ZnCO_3$	6.61×10^8
Caesium	Cs	4×10^{-4}	Cs$^+$	5.29×10^8
Chromium	Cr	3×10^{-4}	$Cr(OH)_3$, CrO_4^{2-}	3.97×10^8
Antimony	Sb	2.4×10^{-4}	$Sb(OH)_6^-$	3.17×10^8
Manganese	Mn	2×10^{-4}	Mn^{2+}, MnCl$^+$	2.64×10^8
Krypton	Kr	2×10^{-4}	Kr gas	2.64×10^8
Selenium	Se	2×10^{-4}	SeO_3^{2-}	2.64×10^8

Element		Concentration $(mg\ l^{-1})$ (i.e. parts per million, ppm)	Some probable dissolved species	Total amount in the ocean (tonnes)
Neon	Ne	1.2×10^{-4}	Ne gas	1.59×10^8
Cadmium	Cd	1×10^{-4}	$CdCl_2$	1.32×10^8
Copper	Cu	1×10^{-4}	$CuCO_3$, $CuOH^+$	1.32×10^8
Tungsten	W	1×10^{-4}	WO_4^{2-}	1.32×10^8
Germanium	Ge	5×10^{-5}	$Ge(OH)_4$	6.61×10^7
Xenon	Xe	5×10^{-5}	Xe gas	6.61×10^7
Mercury	Hg	3×10^{-5}	$HgCl_4^2$, $HgCl_2$	3.97×10^7
Zirconium	Zr	3×10^{-5}	$Zr(OH)_4$	3.97×10^7
Bismuth	Bi	2×10^{-5}	BiO^+, $Bi(OH)_2^+$	2.64×10^7
Niobium	Nb	1×10^{-5}	not known	1.32×10^7
Tin	Sn	1×10^{-5}	$SnO(OH)_3^-$	1.32×10^7
Thallium	Tl	1×10^{-5}	Tl^+	1.32×10^7
Thorium	Th	1×10^{-5}	$Th(OH)_4$	1.32×10^7
Hafnium	Hf	7×10^{-6}	not known	9.25×10^6
Helium	He	6.8×10^{-6}	He gas	8.99×10^6
Beryllium	Be	5.6×10^{-6}	$BeOH^+$	7.40×10^6
Gold	Au	4×10^{-6}	$AuCl_2^-$	5.29×10^6
Rhenium	Re	4×10^{-6}	ReO_4^-	5.29×10^6
Cobalt	Co	3×10^{-6}	Co^{2+}	3.97×10^6
Lanthanum	La	3×10^{-6}	$La(OH)_2$	3.97×10^6
Neodymium	Nd	3×10^{-6}	$Nd(OH)_3$	3.97×10^6
Silver	Ag	2×10^{-6}	$AgCl_2^-$	2.64×10^6
Tantalum	Ta	2×10^{-6}	not known	2.64×10^6
Gallium	Ga	2×10^{-6}	$Ga(OH)_4^-$	2.64×10^6
Yttrium	Y	1.3×10^{-6}	$Y(OH)_3$	1.73×10^6
Cerium	Ce	1×10^{-6}	$Ce(OH)_3$	1.32×10^6
Dysprosium	Dy	9×10^{-7}	$Dy(OH)_3$	1.19×10^6
Erbium	Er	8×10^{-7}	$Er(OH)_3$	1.06×10^6
Ytterbium	Yb	8×10^{-7}	$Yb(OH)_3$	1.06×10^6
Gadolinium	Gd	7×10^{-7}	$Gd(OH)_3$	9.25×10^5
Praseodymium	Pr	6×10^{-7}	$Pr(OH)_3$	7.93×10^5
Scandium	Sc	6×10^{-7}	$Sc(OH)_3$	7.93×10^5
Lead	Pb	5×10^{-7}	$PbCO_3$, $Pb(CO_3)_2^{2-}$	6.61×10^5
Holmium	Ho	2×10^{-7}	$Ho(OH)_3$	2.64×10^5
Lutetium	Lu	2×10^{-7}	$Lu(OH)$	2.64×10^5
Thulium	Tm	2×10^{-7}	$Tm(OH)_3$	2.64×10^5

Element		Concentration $(mg\ l^{-1})$ (i.e. parts per million, ppm)	Some probable dissolved species	Total amount in the ocean (tonnes)
Indium	In	1×10^{-7}	$In(OH)_2$	1.32×10^5
Terbium	Tb	1×10^{-7}	$Tb(OH)_3$	1.32×10^5
Tellurium	Te	1×10^{-7}	$Te(OH)_6$	1.32×10^5
Samarium	Sm	5×10^{-8}	$Sm(OH)_3$	6.61×10^4
Europium	Eu	1×10^{-8}	$Eu(OH)_3$	1.32×10^4
Radium	Ra	7×10^{-11}	Ra^{2+}	92.5
Protactinium	Pa	5×10^{-11}	not known	66.1
Radon	Rn	6×10^{-16}	Rn gas	7.93×10^{-4}
Polonium	Po	?	PoO_3^2, $Po(OH)_2$?	?

Note: The above table does not represent the last word on sea water composition. Even for the more abundant constituents, compilations from different sources differ in detail. For the rarer elements, many of the entries in the table will be subject to revision, as analytical methods improve. Moreover, most constituents behave non-conservatively, making averages less meaningful.

Table 1.4 Chemical constituents of rainwater and rivers

	Rainfall (continental) $(mg\ l^{-1})$	Rainfall (marine and coastal) $(mg\ l^{-1})$	Rivers[a] $(mg\ l^{-1})$
Ca^{2+}	0.2–4.0	0.2–1.4	5.3–24.2 (13.4)
Mg^{2+}	0.05–0.5	0.4–1.5	1.4–5.2 (3.4)
Na^+	0.2–1.0	1.0–5.0	3.2–7.0 (5.2)
K^+	0.1–0.5	0.2–0.6	1.0–1.6 (1.3)
Cl^-	0.2–2.0	1.0–10.0	3.4–7.0 (5.8)
SO_4^{2-}	1.0–3.0	1.0–3.0	3.5–15.1 (8.3)
HCO_3^-	0	0	26.7–80.1 (52.0)
SiO_2	0	0	6.8–16.3 (10.4)

[a] Range of mean values for different continents, with the world average in parentheses. All figures are estimates of natural values, from which anthropogenic pollutants have been excluded.
Source: adapted from Allan (1995) after Berner and Berner (1987).

marine organisms as a skeletal material. Upon death, these organisms sink and release the calcium and carbonate ions back into solution:

$$Ca^{2+}\ (aq) + CO_3^{2-}\ (aq) \leftrightarrow CaCO_3\ (s)$$

Surface ocean waters are supersaturated with $CaCO_3$, but spontaneous precipitation is rare, as most of the carbonate ions are weakly bound to magnesium ions, forming magnesium carbonate $(MgCO_3)$.

$CaCO_3$ solubility increases as depth (pressure) increases and as temperature drops. As skeletal material sinks, therefore, it enters the region in which $CaCO_3$ will begin to dissolve, the lysocline region. The depth below which all $CaCO_3$ has entered solution is the carbonate compensation depth (CCD), which is typically at 4–5 km deep. Variations in the depth of the lysocline are controlled by the chemistry of the sea water, while variations in the CCD are the result of both water chemistry and the rate of supply of carbonate debris; it is, for example, normally shallower near the continental margins as the higher biological activity in the sediment aids its dissolution.

Dissolved matter in inland waters

Inland waters, in contrast to the sea, show a wide variation in chemical constituents. While most are classed as fresh water, which, by definition means a salinity lower than 3 (W.D. Williams, 1996), there is a large number of lakes, classed as saline, in which salinity may be many times higher than that in the sea and very different in composition. Furthermore, chemical composition can vary greatly even within a single water body. The concentration of solutes generally increases in rivers with distance from the source and can vary in response to discharge (**Section 2.2f**), while fresh-water lakes become more solute-enriched with time (**Section 6.6**) and saline lakes may experience rapid fluctuations in salinity, determined by rainfall and volume of water (**Section 6.2d**).

The chemical composition of inland waters is determined particularly by the catchment. Rain brings some inputs but, except in areas with very hard rocks and thin soils, or adjacent to the coast, is relatively unimportant. On average, about 40% of rain becomes runoff and enters watercourses, the rest evaporating, so chemical constituents of rainwater, which will not evaporate, will be concentrated 2.5 times in runoff water. Many constituents of fresh water are, however, at much higher concentrations than these (Table 1.4), demonstrating the importance of catchment weathering.

1.3b DISSOLVED GASES

The most important gases in water are oxygen, for respiration, and carbon dioxide, for photosynthesis. Both originate mainly from the atmosphere, but diffusion mixes gases very slowly and physical mixing is required to ensure that they penetrate beyond the surface layers. Physical mixing in wave-swept water bodies and turbulent rivers will maintain high concentrations, but in less turbulent water bodies, concentrations will be determined to a large extent by biological activity. A large biomass of photosynthesisers can raise oxygen levels and lower carbon dioxide levels by day and, through respiration, produce the opposite effect at night.

Oxygen

Table 1.5 shows oxygen (O_2) concentrations at saturation, in which the amount in solution in pure water, at the given temperature and pressure, is in equilibrium with that in the air. High rates of photosynthesis create conditions of supersaturation (saturation in excess of 100%), in which oxygen concentrations are so high that bubbles of undissolved gas may be produced on plant surfaces. In contrast, high rates of respiration reduce concentrations well below saturation.

The concentration of oxygen in solution, even in pure water, is determined by temperature

Table 1.5 Oxygen concentrations in water at saturation. Figures given are for pure water at sea level; contaminants and changes in pressure will reduce these (see text). Concentrations are normally expressed as mg l^{-1}; volumetric concentrations (ml l^{-1}) are also given here, to allow easy comparison with the atmospheric concentration: 210 ml l^{-1}

Temperature (°C)	Concentration (mg l^{-1})	Concentration (ml l^{-1})
0	14.63	10.45
5	12.77	9.12
10	11.28	8.06
15	10.07	7.20
20	9.08	6.49
25	8.26	5.90
30	7.57	5.41
35	6.98	4.99
40	6.47	4.62

(Table 1.5) and pressure, a 100 m increase in altitude reducing solubility by about 1.4%. Solubility is also reduced by salinity because the more solutes it contains, the less oxygen water can hold. Sea water, therefore, contains approximately 20% less oxygen than fresh water at an equivalent temperature and pressure.

Carbon dioxide

Carbon dioxide (CO_2) is subject to the same effects of temperature, pressure and salinity as oxygen, but is considerably more soluble in water because it combines with alkali metals to form bicarbonates and carbonates according to the reaction:

$$CO_2 + H_2O \leftrightarrow H_2CO_3 \leftrightarrow H^+ + HCO_3^- \leftrightarrow 2H^+ + CO_3^{2-}$$

Therefore, very little CO_2 gas is present in water. Total dissolved carbon in the oceans decreases with depth to about 1000 m and then is fairly constant to the bottom. This is the result of carbon uptake in the surface zone by biological activity (photosynthesis and skeletal production) while, in deep waters, lower rates of carbon uptake are balanced by regeneration from decomposition of organic particles.

1.3C   ACIDITY AND ALKALINITY

Acidity

Acidity, the ability of water to neutralise alkalinity, is normally determined by the pH (which has no units), a measure of the concentration of hydrogen ions in solution ($[H^+]$):

$$pH = -\log_{10} [H^+]$$

All water contains some hydrogen ions, because a small number of water molecules will dissociate:

$$H_2O \leftrightarrow H^+ + OH^-$$

Pure water at 24 °C has a $[H^+]$ of 10^{-7} mol l^{-1}, giving a pH of 7. This is, therefore, classed as neutral, a greater pH signifying alkaline water while a lower pH is acid. Note that, as it is a logarithmic scale, a change of one pH unit is equivalent to a ten-fold change in $[H^+]$, and that increasing $[H^+]$ is signified by lower pH values.

Alkalinity and buffering capacity

Rainwater is slightly acid (pH around 5.6), because it dissolves CO_2 from the atmosphere to produce carbonic acid:

$$H_2O + CO_2 \leftrightarrow H_2CO_3$$

Carbonic acid, in turn, dissolves carbonates, particularly $CaCO_3$ and $MgCO_3$, which act as a buffer, neutralising excess acidity. The alkalinity of a solution is a measure of this buffering capacity, and is effectively the measure of the concentration of carbonate and bicarbonate in solution, although, in some lakes, borate (BO_4^-) may be important. Note that alkalinity is misleadingly titled, because it does not refer to how alkaline a solution is; even water with a low pH (i.e. acid) can have a high alkalinity.

Acid waters

For aquatic organisms, the pH range 5.5–8.5, within which most natural water bodies fall, is effectively neutral (and often referred to as circum-neutral). Acidification as a pollution problem occurs where two criteria are met. First, rain is acidified by anthropogenic release of sulphates and nitrogen oxides, which form sulphuric acid and nitric acid in the atmosphere, reducing rainfall pH below 5.0 or even 4.0 (10–100 times more acid than natural rainfall). Second, hard geology, with little weathering of buffering agents, limits the buffering capacity, so the excess acidity is not neutralised. It is important to remember, however, that many water bodies are naturally acidic. Volcanic activity contributes to acidification of rainfall by emitting sulphates. Lakes in active volcanic craters can be very acid, with a pH of 2.0 or even less. Very slow decomposition of plant material in peat-producing wetlands (**Section 7.1**) produces humic acids, acidifying pools and water bodies in such environments. *Sphagnum* moss (**Chapter 7**), which is well adapted to such environments, contributes to acidification of water by stripping Ca^{2+} ions from water and replacing them with H^+.

Alkaline waters

Highly alkaline water bodies are relatively uncommon, but include soda lakes, whose pH can be in excess of 11.0, which contain high concentrations of sodium carbonate (Na_2CO_3) and sodium bicarbonate ($NaHCO_3$) derived from lava.

Sea water

Sea water, in contrast to inland waters, has a pH typically 8.0 ± 0.2, with very little variation, because it is extremely well buffered with a high alkalinity generated by the high concentration of carbonates (**Section 1.3a**). It is difficult to measure the pH of sea water accurately, so in practice it is usual to measure the alkalinity and total dissolved carbon. It is then possible to use empirical chemical relationships to determine concentrations of CO_3^{2-} and HCO_3^{-} and hence calculate the pH.

1.4 Energy inputs in aquatic systems

1.4a PHOTOSYNTHESIS

Primary production is the creation of organic molecules from inorganic components, using an external energy source. By far the most common mechanism is photosynthesis, using sunlight to synthesise sugars from CO_2:

$$6H_2O + 6CO_2 \rightarrow C_6H_{12}O_6 + 6O_2$$

This mechanism is used by plants, algae and Cyanobacteria ('blue-green algae', formerly known as Cyanophyta). Other requirements include nitrogen, normally as nitrate (NO_3^{-}), and phosphate (PO_4^{-}) for protein synthesis. Of these, CO_2 is rarely limiting but the others, along with biotic processes, can have a major effect upon rates of production.

Light penetration

Light intensity in water is always very much lower than that in the atmosphere immediately overhead. Much light never manages to penetrate water, being reflected from the surface, while light which does enter the water column is absorbed or scattered (reflected) by water itself, as well as by dissolved organic molecules, phytoplankton and suspended particulate matter. Obviously the more turbid the water, the more light is scattered and absorbed.

The decrease in light intensity with depth is called attenuation (**Box 1.2**). Many aquatic macrophytes grow on the water surface or have emergent components extending into the air, and intertidal algae can photosynthesise during low tide, so light attenuation is not a problem, but submerged photosynthesisers will be light limited.

Compensation point and critical depth

Phytoplankton (**Section 1.6a**) are floating photosynthesisers which are mixed vertically by water movements. Figure 1.7 illustrates the relationship between photosynthesis, respiration and depth in a water column. Rate of photosynthesis is dependent upon the intensity of light and so, apart from a small amount of photo-inhibition near the surface, it declines with increasing depth, whereas respiration rate remains relatively constant, so that eventually a depth is reached where the energy assimilated by photosynthesis is exactly matched by the energy requirements for photosynthesis, a point known as the compensation point or depth. Above this point, net production can occur, while below it, there is an excess of respiration over production. The point at which total photosynthesis matches total respiration (i.e. the two shaded components in Figure 1.7 cover the same area) is the critical depth.

Sverdrup's model

Obviously, a phytoplankter which remains beneath the compensation point will be unable to sustain itself but, in practice, vertical mixing moves phytoplankton through different depths in the water column. The mixing depth is the depth to which phytoplankton are mixed, and is generally the depth of the thermocline (**Box 1.3**). If the mixing depth is greater than the critical depth, then there can be no net production, but if it is less than the critical depth, then net production occurs. This is known as Sverdrup's model and links primary production to the critical depth versus mixing depth relationship.

BOX 1.2   LIGHT ATTENUATION

Light attenuation can be estimated according to the following formula:

$$I_d = I_0 \, e^{-kd}$$

where I_d is the light at depth d, I_0 is the light at the surface (depth 0) and k is the extinction coefficient. We can measure k directly with a light meter or it can be estimated as:

$$k = 1.7D_s$$

where D_s is the Secchi depth (see **Box 6.2**).

Attenuation varies according to the wavelength of light. In clear waters, blue-green light (wavelength around 480 nm) penetrates to the greatest depth, while in turbid waters blue light is selectively scattered and the wavelength of maximum penetration moves towards the red, ending up in the green part of the spectrum at about 550 nm.

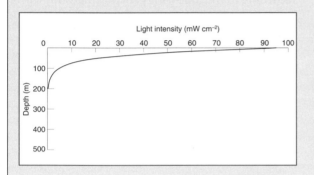

The model makes some important assumptions:

1   There is a uniform depth distribution of phytoplankton in the mixed layer.
2   The extinction coefficient of light (**Box 1.2**) is a constant (this is rarely true as a result of self-shading by the phytoplankton).
3   Nutrients are not limiting.
4   Phytoplankton production is proportional to radiation.
5   Respiration is constant with depth.

The layer of water from the surface to the compensation depth is often referred to as the photic (or euphotic) zone; in practice, this is very difficult to measure accurately and is generally considered to be down to a depth where the light value is about 1% of surface light.

Measuring primary production

Primary production by phytoplankton is generally measured by following either CO_2 uptake or O_2 production. The former uses radio-labelled $^{14}CO_2$ (the most widely used technique) while the latter measures change in O_2 either by electrode, by titration or using 'heavy water': $H_2^{18}O$.

As respiration occurs simultaneously, an adjustment for the respiration rate is applied by making measurements in the dark. In order to gain realistic estimates, samples are incubated under conditions which are as natural as possible in both the light and the dark for 4–12 h. This is done either in the controlled environment of an incubator or *in situ*, by suspending sample bottles from a buoy. This technique assumes that, excepting photosynthesis, the processes occurring in the light and the dark are the same, which may not always be the case. These techniques also tend to underestimate photosynthesis, as the soluble products exuded by phytoplankton (**Section 1.6c**) are not readily measured. Therefore, some care must be taken in interpreting the results.

Nutrient limitation

Although light is clearly limiting at great depths, there are many environments where light intensi-

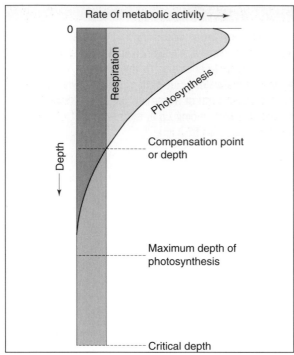

Figure 1.7 Change in photosynthetic rate by phytoplankton with depth. Photosynthesis declines with increasing light attenuation (**Box 1.2**) whereas respiration remains relatively constant. The depth at which production exactly matches consumption is the compensation point. The critical depth marks the point above which total respiration and total production are equal; note that this point is below the maximum depth at which photosynthesis occurs. The actual depths will vary according to species, water clarity, temperature, season and, of course, time of day.

ties are high and yet primary production is low, even close to the surface. This is normally because one or more nutrients are limiting. As in terrestrial systems, limiting nutrients in aquatic systems are normally nitrates and phosphates, although nitrate is the most common limiting nutrient in marine systems, whereas phosphate is most commonly limiting in fresh waters (Elser & Hassett, 1994). Silicate commonly limits production by diatoms (**Sections 5.4a, 6.4b**), while iron has recently been identified as a limiting nutrient in some parts of the ocean (**Section 5.4a**).

Nutrient limitation in open waters is often a result of water stratification (**Box 1.3**); nutrients are depleted in the upper, illuminated layers while concentrations remain high in the depths, beneath the photic zone (**Sections 4.4a, 5.3c, 6.3b**).

Biotic limitation

Primary production may be limited by the activities of grazers consuming the photosynthetic organisms. This is considered in detail in **Sections 4.4b, 5.5b** and **6.4c**.

1.4B   CHEMOSYNTHESIS

In the absence of light, certain bacteria can generate organic matter using the chemical energy in reduced compounds to drive their metabolism according to the following general equation, where X signifies one of a number of reduced substances:

$$XH_2 + H_2O \rightarrow XO + 4[H^+ + e^-]$$

reduced   oxidised reducing
substances   form   power

The reducing power is used to generate energy via the cytochrome system, a process which is most efficient if free oxygen is available.

$$4[H^+ + e^-] + mADP + mPi + O_2 \rightarrow 2H_2O + mATP$$

and:

$$2[H^+ + e^-] + NAD \rightarrow NADH_2$$

These can then be used to assimilate sugars using carbon dioxide:

$$12NADH_2 + 18ATP + 6CO_2 \rightarrow C_6H_{12}O_6 + 6H_2O + 18ADP + 18Pi + 12NAD$$

Chemoautotrophic bacteria include nitrogen-fixing species (**Box 7.1**), which derive their energy from ammonia (NH_3) or nitrite (NO_2^-), while others use sulphur compounds, such as sulphides (S^{2-}) or methane (CH_4).

The most celebrated sites for the occurrence of chemoautotrophy are deep ocean vents (**Section 5.7b; Box 5.2**). Reduced compounds are normally oxygenated in the presence of oxygen, and the interface between vent waters and oxygenated deep ocean waters is one of the few situations where reduced compounds and oxygen occur together.

1.4C DETRITUS

Detritus is of fundamental importance to aquatic systems and the dominant source of energy for many (**Sections 2.4b, 3.4b, 5.4b**). Even in environ-

BOX 1.3 STRATIFICATION AND THE THERMOCLINE

Increasing the temperature of water reduces its density, so warm water floats on top of cool water. Solar energy heats up the surface of a water body, and this warm surface water is mixed, by wave action, with deeper water. If, however, there is little wave action, the depth of mixing will be shallow and heated water will remain close to the surface, as it is of a lower density than deeper water. Therefore, it receives yet more solar energy and becomes even warmer.

This leads to stratification of the water column into distinct horizontal layers: warm, low density water on top and cooler, higher density water beneath. Within each layer there is free mixing and little temperature variation, but between layers there is little mixing and therefore a clear temperature difference.

Three vertical layers are created in this way: the warm upper layer (epilimnion to limnologists; mixed layer to oceanographers), the cool lower layer (hypolimnion or deep ocean) and, between the two, the zone of rapid temperature change, called the thermocline (occasionally referred to as the metalimnion by limnologists).

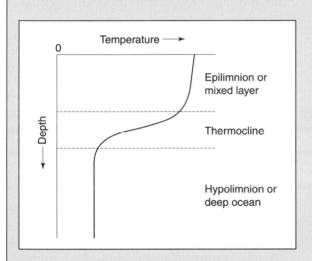

ments where primary production occurs, certain primary producers are rarely grazed as living organisms, but are consumed after death, as detritus. Therefore, the terms autochthonous and allochthonous detritus are often applied, the former referring to detritus derived from primary production *in situ*, the latter to detritus imported from elsewhere, including the terrestrial environment. A range of different types can be identified, the main distinction being between particulate and dissolved components.

Particulate organic matter

The terms particulate organic matter (POM) and particulate organic carbon (POC) refer to dead particulate matter in water bodies, the detritus. These terms are sometimes used interchangeably, although the distinction should be what was measured, the entire mass of organic material or just the estimated carbon content. Freshwater biologists generally distinguish between coarse particulate organic matter (CPOM) and fine particulate organic matter (FPOM). CPOM has a diameter of a least 1 mm, and will include recognisable plant fragments, including coarse woody debris (CWD), up to the size of entire trees, along with carcasses of macrofauna; it is often relatively heavy and will sink to the bed unless resuspended by turbulence or a strong current. FPOM, with a diameter of less than 1 mm, will settle out only in sheltered waters and much may remain in suspension. While plankton (**Section 1.6a**) are living particles of organic matter, they are not normally classed as POM, although the distinction is artificial for some filter-feeding organisms which consume both living and non-living particles. The non-living POM suspended in association with plankton is occasionally referred to as tripton; tripton and plankton together constitute the seston.

Dissolved organic carbon

Dissolved organic matter (DOM) or dissolved organic carbon (DOC) is defined as that which passes through a 0.45 μm mesh, although it is now known that some colloidal organic matter and even very small bacteria and viruses will pass through this mesh size.

1.5 The diversity of aquatic life

1.5a WATER AS A MEDIUM FOR LIFE

Sea water versus fresh water

The conditions under which life originally evolved are the subject of much debate, but what is beyond reasonable doubt is that the sea was the cradle for multicellular development. The development and radiation of marine forms was well advanced before the land, or even fresh waters, were colonised at all. All water provides buoyancy and protection from desiccation and extremes of temperature. The fundamental difference between marine and freshwater systems is salinity: sea water, unlike fresh water, provides a ready supply of dissolved salts, essential for aquatic organisms, which need to maintain high ionic concentrations in their tissues and internal fluids. The high concentration of salts in the sea and, crucially, its constancy, allow marine organisms to have an internal salt concentration equal to external concentrations. If they are transferred to fresh water, and they lack effective osmoregulatory abilities, salts will diffuse from their bodies and be lost through excretion, without being replaced, while excess water may be absorbed by osmosis, leading to cell damage. Therefore, to colonise fresh water, these problems must be overcome by developing an efficient excretory mechanism to remove excess water or by sealing tissues and internal fluids from the water outside, and by active maintenance of internal salt concentrations. A third option – reducing internal salt concentrations – is not normally possible, because these salts are essential in metabolism.

Freshwater species have significantly higher metabolic rates than closely related marine forms. Freshwater shrimps of the genus *Gammarus*, for example, have a rate of oxygen uptake up to 65% higher than marine species, and at least 11% of the total metabolism of the freshwater species *G. pulex* is devoted to active ion transport to maintain internal concentrations (Sutcliffe, 1984). Acidification exacerbates the problem of ion exchange: not only does the low buffering capacity of acid water ensure reduced concentrations of ions such as sodium (Na^+), but high concentrations of H^+ ions compete with Na^+ for active transport sites across gill membranes. Therefore, rather than absorbing Na^+, animals which are not adapted to acid waters absorb H^+ and become ion stressed (Mason, 1990).

Maintaining the correct ionic concentration is the fundamental stumbling block that has led to the reduced diversity of animal life in fresh waters relative to marine environments. Not only is overall diversity different, but the dominant groups in each case are, in the main, taxonomically different.

Diversity of marine life

Of 33 phyla in the animal kingdom, 30 occur in the sea, and 16 of these are confined to marine environments (Margulis & Schwarz, 1988). Among other kingdoms, marine diversity is less extensive, so that, for example, only 14 of the 27 phyla in the kingdom Protoctista (algae and single-celled eukaryotes) occur in the sea, although three of these – Phaeophyta (brown seaweeds), Rhodophyta (red seaweeds) and Foraminifera – are among the most familiar of non-animal marine organisms.

Major groups of marine animals include Echinodermata (starfish, sea urchins, etc.), which are confined to sea water, and Porifera (sponges) and Cnidaria (jellyfish, corals, sea anemones, etc.), which are almost exclusively marine, while Mollusca (bivalves, snails, octopus, etc.) and Nematoda are at their most diverse in the sea. Arthropods are represented almost exclusively by crustaceans, including crabs, shrimps and barnacles, and arachnids. Where light penetrates to the sea bed, or in the intertidal zone (**Section 4.2a**), macrophytes (multicellular photosynthesisers) are dominated by algae, generally described as seaweeds: Rhodophyta and Phaeophyta, which are both almost exclusively marine, along with some multicellular Chlorophyta (green algae). Single-celled algae are dominated by the mainly marine Dinoflagellata, Haptophyta (coccolithophores) and Actinopoda, along with the exclusively marine Foraminifera. The only abundant algae which are common in both marine and fresh waters are diatoms (Bacillariophyta).

Diversity of freshwater life

Fresh waters, in contrast to the sea, support only 14 animal phyla, several of which are mainly marine groups for which the freshwater environment is peripheral, but 20 protoctist phyla (Margulis & Schwarz, 1988). The other two multicellular kingdoms, the fungi and the true plants, are largely terrestrial, but the latter clearly originated in fresh waters, and includes the Bryophyta (mosses and liverworts) and spherophytes (horsetails) which, although not truly aquatic, live in very damp environments. One group of true plants, the Angiosperms (flowering plants), has successfully re-invaded fresh waters to the extent that it dominates aquatic marginal habitats, and even includes several marine representatives in coastal areas.

The freshwater macrofauna is dominated by insects, particularly orders such as Ephemeroptera (mayflies), Plecoptera (stoneflies), Odonata (dragonflies), Trichoptera (caddisflies) and Diptera (true flies), whose adult phase is a terrestrial winged form; excepting Diptera, these orders are almost exclusively fresh water as larvae. Insects with aquatic adult stages include Hemiptera (waterboatmen, pond skaters, etc.) and Coleoptera (beetles). Annelids (true worms and leeches), bivalve molluscs and crustaceans may be locally abundant, although their diversity rarely matches that in the sea; among the smaller fauna, however, the crustacean class Branchiopoda, including copepods and cladocerans (water fleas), achieves similar diversity in both the sea and fresh waters. Macrophytes are dominated by vascular plants, although filamentous Chlorophyta (e.g. *Cladophora*) can be locally abundant, while single-celled algae, apart from diatoms, are dominated by unicellular Chlorophyta and a series of phyla which are mainly or exclusively fresh water, including Chrysophyta, Euglenophyta (e.g. *Euglena*) and Gamophyta (e.g. *Spirogyra*).

1.5B COLONISATION OF FRESH WATERS

Direct colonisation

Representatives of predominantly marine groups entered fresh waters directly from the sea, without an intermediate terrestrial stage. Freshwater bivalve molluscs clearly originated in this way, as their filter-feeding habits require immersion in water. Similarly, hydroids, the only freshwater cnidarians, and the relatively few freshwater sponges, are obligate aquatic species. Of the three classes of Annelida, Polychaeta have a poor system of osmoregulation and are mainly confined to marine environments, whereas Oligochaeta (true worms) and Hirudinea (leeches) possess an effective osmoregulatory system and have successfully colonised fresh waters and beyond, into terrestrial habitats.

Fish are very good examples of direct colonisation. They are fully aquatic and the origin of this group in the sea is beyond doubt, even though they demonstrate the full range of tolerance, from truly marine species to those confined to fresh waters ('primary' species). Nevertheless, fresh water and marine forms are generally closely related and many species ('diadromous' fish) actively move from one to the other, including salmon, eels and lampreys (**Section 3.3a**). A few species, including trout (*Salmo trutta*), have both fully freshwater forms and migratory forms within the same species.

Secondary colonisation

Many organisms colonised fresh waters secondarily, via terrestrial ancestors. Insects exploded across the land after development of their waterproof cuticle; the same development allowed colonisation of fresh waters, as it effectively sealed body fluids from the outside world, so ion exchange ceased to be a problem. Fungi are almost exclusively terrestrial, with few species in aquatic environments, but they include specialist freshwater forms, the aquatic hyphomycetes (phylum Deuteromycota), which play a crucial role in aquatic decomposition processes (**Section 2.4b**).

Among freshwater snails, prosobranchs (e.g. limpets) have gills and colonised directly from the sea, while pulmonates (e.g. pond snails) have lungs, and include terrestrial land snails, suggesting recolonisation from the land. Crustacea probably colonised from the sea; there are shrimps today in estuaries which have a wide salinity tolerance (Figure 3.11), but equally some crustaceans, such as woodlice, have colonised damp terrestrial habitats.

Ironically, the conditions in saline lakes are so variable, and salinity is often so much greater than in the sea, that they are inhospitable to marine species and were probably colonised via freshwater habitats. The main exceptions to this are the Caspian and Aral Seas in central Asia, which are the remnants of an arm of the Tethys Ocean, cut off from what is now the Mediterranean Sea by tectonic movement (**Section 5.7e**).

Recolonising the sea

Although there are many examples of organisms colonising fresh waters from the sea, there are relatively few cases where freshwater organisms have successfully invaded the sea. Even whales, which include a handful of freshwater species, such as the Ganges river dolphin (*Platanista gangetica*), almost certainly colonised the sea directly from land and have secondarily entered river systems.

Insects are easily the most diverse group of animals, accounting for the vast majority of all known species, and dominate terrestrial and freshwater environments alike, and yet only a few hundred species are known from marine systems, almost all of them being confined to the intertidal or to saline wetlands (Cheng, 1976). The only truly oceanic species are hemipterans of the genus *Halobates*, wingless species which live on the surface of the sea and lay their eggs on floating debris and which can, therefore, persist many hundreds of kilometres from land.

Many theories have been proposed for the general absence of insects from marine environments, including an inability to overcome the physiological constraints of respiration and osmoregulation or the problems associated with physical barriers, such as wave action and surface tension (Williams & Feltmate, 1992). Clearly, these are inadequate explanations because most of them apply also to fresh waters, while the problem of osmoregulation has been overcome by saltmarsh and rock pool species, as well as by those species occurring in saline lakes. More compelling is the competition theory of Usinger (1957): insects attempting to colonise the sea would have faced competition from established groups, particularly crustaceans.

The enormous success of insects is due, in no small part, to their ability to fly, which gives them effective powers of dispersal. Insects' wings do not, however, work in water and aquatic species require a terrestrial environment in which to emerge. A possible reason, therefore, for the absence of insects beyond the sea coast is the lack of land or exposed surface on which to metamorphose into the adult phase. Recently, van der Hage (1996) has proposed an alternative explanation: insects coevolved with angiosperm plants, themselves almost absent from the sea because their pollination mechanisms, whether passive or through the activity of pollinating animals, do not work under water. Therefore, angiosperms dominated the land and, secondarily, fresh waters, providing resources for insects. Had angiosperms invaded the sea, then insects would have followed. This theory is compelling but, as van der Hage (1996) concedes, does not explain the absence of predatory and detritivorous insects in the marine environment.

1.6 Ecological groupings of aquatic organisms

Taxonomically, denizens of marine and freshwater environments are very different. Ecologically, however, there are clear similarities. Ecological classifications group organisms according to common functions and, within the aquatic environment, there are two basic ways in which this is normally done: classification according to habitat or according to functional feeding mechanism.

1.6a CLASSIFICATION BY HABITAT

Aquatic organisms can be categorised into four major groups – pelagic, benthic, neuston and fringing – according to the part of the water body which they inhabit.

Pelagic organisms

Pelagic organisms are those which live within the water column, and can be further subdivided into plankton and nekton. Plankton, which include algae, bacteria and a variety of animals, are either completely passive, or with powers of locomotion too weak to swim against horizontal currents, and therefore drift in the water column. Traditionally, plankton have been divided into phytoplankton ('algae') and zooplankton ('animals'), terms which reflect their perceived ecological function, rather than any rigid taxonomic divisions (**see Section 1.6c**). The nekton, in contrast, are active swimmers capable of independent motion; all are animals, particularly fish, but including also whales, turtles, squid, and, as temporary members, aquatic birds such as penguins, gannets and grebes.

Plankton may be further subdivided. Holoplankton are permanent members, rep-resented by many taxa in the sea but dominated in lakes by branchiopod crustaceans, including *Daphnia* (Figure 6.9) and copepods. Meroplankton are temporary members, spending only part of their life cycle in the plankton. They include larvae of anemones, barnacles, crabs and even fish, which, later in life, will join the nekton. Meroplankton are very much a feature of the sea, particularly coastal waters, as the often sedentary adult forms of coastal species use their planktonic stage for dispersal. They are less diverse in fresh waters, but can be individually very abundant, including certain dipteran (midge) larvae.

Benthic organisms

The benthic community, or benthos, comprises organisms on the bed of the water body. Animals attached to or living on the bottom are referred to as epifauna, while those which burrow into soft sediments or live in spaces between sediment particles are described as infauna. Hyporheos are those species which inhabit sediments where surface waters and groundwaters interact (the hyporheic zone - **Sections 2.3f, 2.7d**). Attached multicellular plants and algae are referred to as macrophytes, while single-celled or filamentous algae are called periphyton, benthic microphytes, or microphytobenthos. Epiphytic algae are those which grow on macrophytes.

Benthic consumers can be divided by size into macrofauna (>500 µm [0.5 mm] in length), meiofauna (10–500 µm) and microorganisms (<10 µm). This is not simply a classification of convenience, because most benthic species do fall clearly into one of these size categories (Figure 1.8).

Neuston

Neuston are those organisms associated with the water surface, where they are supported by surface tension. They include small Acari (mites) and Collembola (springtails), along with some larger insects. Most neuston require a very still water surface and this component of the fauna is, therefore, taxonomically very restricted in rivers and the sea, although by no means absent (e.g. *Halobates*: **Section 1.5b**).

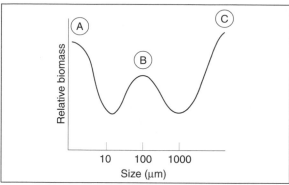

Figure 1.8 Biomass-size spectra for benthic organisms occurring in soft coastal and estuarine sediments, showing the peaks in frequency associated with the microbial component (A), the meiofauna (B) and the macrofauna (C).

Fringing communities

Fringing communities are floral communities that occur where the water is shallow enough for plentiful light to reach the bottom, allowing the growth of attached photosynthesisers, which may be entirely submerged or emergent into the air. Freshwater fringing communities are dominated by higher plants such as water lilies and reeds, though usually with a high biomass of small attached algae, while marine communities are composed almost entirely of algal seaweeds. These communities will merge in space with local plankton and also are doubtfully distinct from benthic communities, as the majority of macrophytes are attached to the substrate. Wetlands (**Chapter 7**) are composed of this type of vegetation, often supporting significant terrestrial as well as aquatic components.

1.6b CLASSIFICATION BY FUNCTIONAL GROUP – BENTHOS

The differentiation of organisms into guilds or functional groups, based upon what they eat and how they eat it, has been pursued particularly with respect to benthic assemblages. Cummins (1974) proposed a classification which differentiated five groups of benthic invertebrates, based upon their trophic role in fresh waters. Grazer-scrapers, in this classification, feed upon attached algae; shredders eat CPOM, whereas collectors feed upon FPOM, collector-filterers removing particles from the water column while collector-

gatherers pick them off the river bed. Finally, there are predators which, like predators in every system, consume other living animals.

In practice, this distinction, often considered to be into clear-cut groups, is imprecise. Periphyton, for example, normally occur as part of a biofilm (the *aufwuchs* of river ecologists), also containing fine particulate detritus and bacteria, held together by bacterial secretions, and most grazer-scrapers will scrape and consume the entire film, whether or not it contains algal cells. Shredders and collector-gatherers are often the same species at different stages in their life cycles and some species, normally considered to be detritivores, will become predators under certain circumstances. These include larvae of limnephilid caddis flies, which, if the opportunity arises, will become predatory (Giller & Sangpradub, 1993) and even cannibalistic. The freshwater shrimp *Gammarus pulex* is normally classed as a shredder, but following its introduction into Northern Ireland during 1958–59, it has gradually replaced the native *G. duebeni*, apparently by predating upon recently moulted females of the native species (Dick *et al.*, 1990).

These are just a few examples of the difficulty of applying a feeding classification based upon exclusive categories; in real life, it would appear that most benthic invertebrates will eat a wide range of foods, if given the opportunity. Despite these problems, however, the classification of macroinvertebrates into functional feeding groups is useful, so long as it is understood that they should not be too rigidly applied.

Precise classifications such as this, though devised for fresh waters, can be applied to marine systems, although the terminology is normally different. Thus suspension or filter feeders and deposit feeders of marine and coastal systems are equivalent to collector-filterers and collector-gatherers, respectively, in freshwater systems, while scavengers are the marine equivalents of freshwater shredders.

1.6c CLASSIFICATION BY FUNCTIONAL GROUP – PELAGIC COMMUNITIES

In pelagic communities, attempts to classify on the basis of type of food eaten are less successful because, typically, consumers are opportunistic

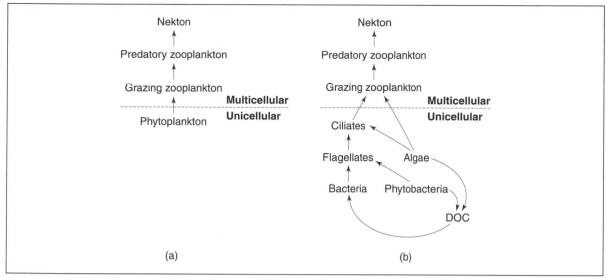

Figure 1.9 (a) The traditional food web in pelagic systems. (b) Incorporation of recently discovered microbial components makes this food web more complex. All unicellular organisms would formerly have been lumped together as 'phytoplankton'. Curved arrows show the direction of the microbial loop.

and will eat anything that is the correct size for their mouthparts to deal with.

The pelagic food web

Traditionally, pelagic food webs were considered to be straightforward: small phytoplankton carried out primary production, and this energy was consumed by progressively larger classes of organisms (Figure 1.9a). Phytoplankton were considered to be dominated by algae, mainly because sampling was done by nets of a mesh size which only caught these relatively large cells (Figure 1.10). It is now recognised that, in addition to this 'net-phytoplankton', there is also a range of very small phytoplankton, consisting of photosynthetic bacteria and microflagellates, which may be responsible for more of the primary production than the net-phytoplankton. More modern views of pelagic food webs, therefore, still acknowledge the importance of basal primary production, but put it into a more complex setting (Figure 1.9b).

Large pelagic species, particularly the nekton, are almost exclusively predatory but, among smaller species, there is much overlap in size between the various photosynthetic groups and

zooplankters, such that consumers at these levels are both predators and grazers. The traditional distinction between phytoplankton (algae) and zooplankton (animals) is upset by the role of phagocytic (literally: cell-eating) protists, which act as grazers and predators at very small scales, and the distinction between grazers and predators is also untenable. Plankton are, therefore, classified by size, although again there is overlap as many species will change to a larger size class as they grow older. Their classification is as follows:

1 Picoplankton (0.2–2 μm). Mainly bacteria.
2 Nanoplankton (2–20 μm). Microflagellates.
3 Microplankton (20–200 μm). The 'classical' phytoplankton (algae) and grazing zooplankton.
4 Mesoplankton (200–2000 μm [0.2–2 mm]). Predatory zooplankton and some large grazers.
5 Macroplankton (>2 mm). Includes cnidarians – jellyfish – which are among the largest planktonic organisms. Jellyfish were virtually ignored in the 'traditional' food web, because sampling techniques missed them: their gelatinous nature ensured that nets would shred

them rather than sample them. The importance of these organisms is still unclear.

The microbial loop

Many of the bacteria in pelagic systems are photosynthetic, but others specialise in feeding upon DOC, derived from much larger algal cells. Up to 15% of sugars synthesised by algae diffuse into the surrounding water, while much more is added by the messy feeding of zooplankton, which rip algal cells apart, shedding yet more DOM into the water column. Estimates of the loss of DOC vary from 20 to 60% of total primary production.

This DOC is consumed by bacteria, which, in turn, are eaten by microflagellates. Ciliates, which are small enough to eat microflagellates but large enough to be eaten by 'traditional' zooplankton, complete the link (Figure 1.9b). Azam *et al.* (1983) proposed the term 'microbial loop' for this bacterial portion of the food web; it is by this microbial activity that DOC, which would otherwise be lost to the pelagic system, re-enters the food web (Sherr & Sherr, 1991).

1.7 The organisation of aquatic communities

1.7a THE ROLE OF PHYSIOLOGICAL CONSTRAINTS

The fundamental determinant of the distribution of an organism is its physiological tolerance of the abiotic environment. Every species has a range of physicochemical conditions under which it can live, and these tolerances ultimately control where a species can be found, although it requires conditions close to its optimum before it can breed successfully. The most obvious facet of the aquatic environment is salinity (**Section 1.5a**), to which every species will have its own tolerance limitations, although many other factors, such as temperature, pH and light intensity, will also have effects and all will, of course, interact with each other. The actual distribution of a species, however, rarely matches that which would be predicted from laboratory measurements of its physiological requirements, due to the modifying effect of biotic interactions with co-occurring species and the consequences of the spatial and temporal variability of the physical environment.

1.7b THE ROLE OF PHYSICAL DISTURBANCE

Water in almost all aquatic systems is moving. Movement is most obvious when it is relative to a solid substrate, as in rivers and coastal seas, and we can identify current and wave action, respectively, as the main physical processes. These are apparently harsh environments, structured entirely by the extreme physical forces, but this is not necessarily the case. Aquatic organisms in

Figure 1.10 Retrieval of a plankton net from a research vessel. The size of the net and the way it is deployed influence the species captured, and whenever such samples are analysed these constraints must be borne in mind. (*Photo by C. Frid*)

mobile environments are adapted to, or even dependent upon, regular or continuous movement of this sort, because levels of variation in the physical environment which occur within the average life span of an organism will provide an evolutionary drive to which the species will respond. When the environment fluctuates outside this range – examples being strong currents associated with a 50-year flood event, waves associated with a severe storm or unusually high summer temperatures – this will result in removal or mortality of individuals and can be classed as disturbance. It is important to recognise that an event which is a disturbance to one community will not be for another; for example, ice scour on the shore of a warm temperate lake is a major disturbance event, but in polar regions it is a common occurrence to which the local biota are well adapted. The crucial parameter is the frequency with which a particular level of the factor occurs.

At intermediate frequencies of disturbance, the community becomes a series of patches forming a mosaic. Some patches are recently disturbed and support a pioneer community, others are occupied by the competitive dominant, and others are at some point in between. So, depending on our scale of observation, we see, in the community as a whole, an increase in diversity, as the disturbance frequency allows species from all stages in the successional process to coexist (Connell, 1978). The size of the patch is determined by the scale of the disturbance, and patch size will tend to increase with decreasing frequency of disturbance. For example, a storm of the scale which occurs, on average, every year may overturn a relatively small proportion of the stones on the bed of a river or coastal sea, creating patchiness on stone surfaces the size of individual stones, while a storm of the scale encountered every 20 years overturns all the stones, creating disturbance patches as large as the entire stretch of river or shoreline affected.

The most widely studied disturbances are generated by the vagaries of the physical environment (Sousa, 1984), but it is also possible to consider various biological factors as disturbance events. Predation not only removes individuals, depressing the population below the carrying capacity of the environment, but effectively acts as a small scale disturbance, in that resources are freed in a patch where the predator was foraging. Similarly outbreaks of parasitism, disease, etc., can be viewed in this patch dynamics way.

1.7c THE ROLE OF BIOTIC INTERACTIONS

Hairston et al. (1960) identified biotic interactions as the primary determinants of gross community structure in ecological systems. Observing that the Earth's terrestrial surface is dominated by plants, they reasoned that these organisms, the primary producers, must be limited by competition for space, water or light. As herbivores were unable to limit the growth of green plants to any great extent, this suggested that they, in turn, were kept below their theoretical carrying capacity by predation. Therefore, if herbivores are limited by predation, it follows that predators are limited by competition for a limited food resource (Figure 1.11a). This model has been criticised, most notably on the grounds that plants persist not through predator control of grazers, but because they possess physical and chemical defences (Murdoch, 1966), but the basic premise, that communities are biotically structured, holds.

The model of Hairston et al. (1960) is, by their own admission, applicable only to terrestrial systems, where physical disturbance is of only local importance. Aquatic systems are, however, affected by disturbance and physical heterogeneity, both spatial and temporal, to the extent that it cannot be overlooked in describing their community structure. Menge and Sutherland (1987), therefore, developed a model of community organisation which takes into account physical as well as biological factors (Figure 1.11b). This acknowledges that, although predation and competition are important components of most aquatic systems, their effects are tempered by the underlying abiotic (and, particularly, physical) environment and that, furthermore, the physical environment in aquatic systems continually creates heterogeneity and disturbance, across the entire range of spatial and temporal scales. Biotic interactions are, therefore, less likely to be the primary determinants of community structure than they are in terrestrial systems.

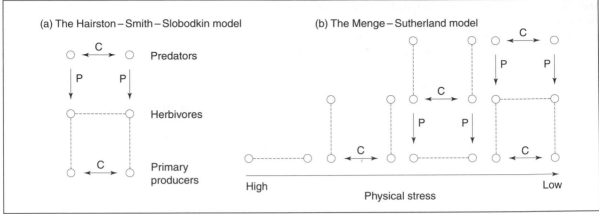

Figure 1.11 Alternative models of community structure. (a) The Hairston–Smith–Slobodkin model, showing competition operating at top and bottom levels, while predation structures the intermediate level.(b) The Menge–Sutherland model, in which the relative importance of competition and predation are modified by physical stress. At the highest stress levels, it acts as a continual disturbance, allowing no species the opportunity to establish but, as physical stress is reduced, the community becomes more complex until, at low stress levels, it is equivalent to that envisaged by Hairston *et al*. (1960). C = competition; P = predation; solid arrow = strong effect; dashed line = weak or no effect.

1.8 Summary

The Earth's aquatic habitats are part of a single hydrological cycle. The vast majority of water is contained in the open ocean, but coasts and inland waters, despite their very small relative volume, are structurally diverse.

Within the open oceans there are two separate water circulation systems: surface water circulation, driven by the wind, and deep water circulation, driven by cool water sinking at high latitudes. The two are connected only in regions of downwelling and upwelling.

Salinity and proportions of dissolved constituents are very constant in the sea, in contrast to the wide variation encountered in inland waters, and even within a single water body at different times or places.

Photosynthesis is limited to shallow waters and, additionally, is often nutrient limited. Chemosynthesis can be locally important but the dominant energy source for many aquatic systems is detritus, mainly from external sources.

Sea water is the optimum medium for life, which achieves a high taxonomic diversity in marine environments. The low salinity of fresh waters is the main reason for their restricted diver-sity, relative to the sea. Most higher taxa now found in fresh waters originally colonised directly from the sea, although some, most notably insects and higher plants, entered via the land.

Aquatic organisms can be classified into ecological groups, either on the basis of habitat or by functional group. Habitat-based classifications differentiate between pelagic organisms, floating or swimming in the water column, and benthic species, living on or in the bed of the water body. Neuston, occupying the surface film, and fringing communities can also be distinguished. Functional classifications differentiate organisms on the basis of what they eat and how they eat it. Most consumers are, however, opportunistic and consume particles according to size, without distinguishing between living and non-living components. These classifications work equally well in marine and freshwater systems.

Aquatic food webs can be complex at the microbial scale. The microbial loop is important in transferring dissolved organic carbon (DOC) into a particulate form, that is then available for larger consumers.

The distribution and relative abundance of aquatic organisms are determined, to a large extent, by disturbance which, at a low frequency, can enhance species diversity by inducing patchiness. Whereas terrestrial communities are structured primarily by biotic processes, the fundamental determinant of aquatic community structure is frequency and intensity of physical disturbance.

2

Rivers

2.1 Introduction

The tiny fraction of the world's water that is contained in rivers (Table 1.1) belies their enormous significance as geomorphological processes on the Earth's terrestrial surface. At any one time, there are approximately 2000 km³ of water contained in river channels worldwide, but the volume of water discharged annually into the sea by rivers is around 41 000 km³ (World Resources Institute, 1992), demonstrating that the average river, even discounting evaporation, replaces its water about 20 times per year. A river is a channel of flowing water, whose movement is determined by gravity and is therefore downhill. Some rivers may cease to flow, and may even dry up completely, if inputs of water are low; indeed, rivers in limestone areas may be seasonal and in arid zones they can be unpredictably intermittent. The vast majority of rivers are, however, continuously flowing, though discharge and rate of flow will be variable. Their linearity and unidirectional flow are of fundamental importance in determining their structural and biological features, as are the volume of water present and its quality.

The nature of a river is determined by its catchment. Geology and topography, in association with the hydrological activity of the river itself, determine the physical form of the channel and the nature of the substrate, while water chemistry is determined principally by the terrestrial system from which the river's water originates.

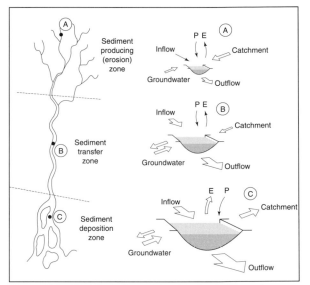

Figure 2.1 The three stages of an idealised river system, showing the relative importance of different inputs and outputs of water along its length. Precipitation refers to direct precipitation into the channel; evaporation refers to direct losses from the channel. Inflow and outflow refer to channel flow. The width of each arrow is proportional to the volume of water in each case. P = precipitation; E = evaporation.

2.2 The abiotic environment

2.2a INPUTS AND OUTPUTS

Inputs of water to a river at any given point are from four sources: direct precipitation, catchment runoff, groundwater and flow from upstream. Proceeding from source to mouth, the primary input changes from catchment runoff – just about the only source of water in the headwaters – to flow from upstream, itself ultimately from the catchment, which dominates in the lower reaches (Figure 2.1). Outputs are generally three-fold: evaporation, which is important in hot climates and dominant in arid zones; lateral flow onto the floodplain, most of which will eventually return to the river, albeit downstream; and downstream flow (Figure 2.1). Additionally, if the water table is low, there is a net vertical loss of water from the river into groundwater (**Section 2.2c**).

2.2b RIVER ZONATION

A river system can be divided into three zones (Figure 2.1). The erosion zone, comprising drainage basins and headwater streams, is the major source of water and of sediment. Channel slope is relatively steep and deposition of sediment, if it occurs, is localised or ephemeral. The eroding nature of the channel ensures that substrate particle size is large (cobbles and boulders) and, occasionally, the river may have eroded to the bedrock. The steep channel slope and coarse substrate may produce turbulent flow, in which riffles (**Section 2.2c**), rapids and even waterfalls will be present. The sediment transfer zone is a region in which river gradient is reduced so that water and sediment are transported with little net loss or gain. Any deposition of sediment is balanced by erosion elsewhere as the river cuts a new channel. Substrate particle size is dominated by sand and gravel and flow is relatively smooth and unbroken. The deposition zone is where the river deposits its sediment load, typically as it approaches the sea and develops a delta or an estuary. The substrate is dominated by fine silt.

This idealised river structure can be modified by local geology. For example, the river may be divided into distinct floodplain reaches by bands of hard or less eroded bedrock (Figure 2.2). Even large rivers can pass through stages where they are constricted by topography. The River Danube has a zone of deposition downstream of Vienna (Austria), beyond which it passes through a relatively constricted gorge in what is effectively a sediment carrying zone once more; the process is repeated further downstream in Romania, as the now very large river passes through the Carpathian Mountains. The River Nile passes

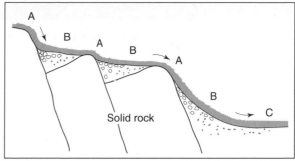

Figure 2.2 An example of how underlying geology can modify the idealised river system. The letters A, B and C refer to the three stages defined in Figure 2.1; in this case, a series of hard bands of rock has created a repeating alternation of stages A and B.

over cataracts in southern Egypt, well below the stretch in which such rapids would occur in an idealised river, while the River Niger in Mali has a very large delta (**Sections 2.7c, 7.6e**; Figure 7.12), below which it becomes a relatively constrained river channel once more.

River classification

The way that a river changes along its length has inspired many attempts to classify the various stretches in a way that allows direct comparison between river systems. River classifications based upon purely biological parameters, such as the presence of particular species, are of only limited value, mainly because they are restricted to geographical regions in which those species occur. European rivers, for example, have been divided, moving in a downstream direction, into trout zone, grayling zone, barbel zone and bream zone, determined in each case by the presence of typical fish species; this system, devised for central Europe, fails even in Britain, where the grayling is a rare species. Nowadays, therefore, river ecologists, particularly those working in the upper reaches of river systems, use the stream ordering system, borrowed from hydrologists (**Box 2.1**).

2.2c RIVER CHANNEL FORM

Rivers normally run in clearly defined channels, particularly in the erosion and sediment transfer zones. The size of the channel is determined by

BOX 2.1 STREAM ORDER

Stream ordering is a method of assigning a number to each river stretch, this number being an indication of its relative size within a drainage basin. There are several ways in which ordering can be applied, full details of which may be found in Gordon *et al.* (1992); only two are considered here.

The system most widely used by river ecologists in the Strahler Method. All headwaters without tributaries are assigned to 1st order. When two 1st order streams converge, they form a 2nd order stream, two 2nd order streams form a 3rd order stream, and so on.

(a)   (b)

A lower order tributary does not change the order of the main stream so that, for example, a 4th order stream can be joined by 1st, 2nd and 3rd order tributaries without changing its order; only merging with a 4th order stream will create a 5th order channel.

In this method, the smaller, headwater streams rapidly change their order as they merge with each other, but the rate of change slows down as channels become larger. Large rivers such as the Garonne or the Rhône in France are only 9th order at their mouths, and even the Amazon barely gets into double figures. The disadvantage of this system, therefore, is that stream order can bear no relation to discharge as smaller tributaries, however many of them, will not affect stream ordering. Note that the two outlet streams in the illustration above are both 4th order but, assuming the same initial discharge for all the 1st

order streams, point Y in system (b) will have twice the discharge of point X in system (a).

An alternative, the Shreve Method, overcomes this problem by being additive: the order numbers are summed whenever two branches meet. The problem with this system is that the numbers can quickly become very large.

In principle, whenever stream order is quoted, the system by which it has been calculated should be given. In practice, this is not normally a problem, because the vast majority of research into river ecology is on smaller streams, whose order rarely exceeds three, and is often one or two, in both of these classifications. Indeed, many publications refer simply to 'low order' streams, which can be taken to mean three or less.

Stream order is quoted to give the reader an opportunity to visualise the size of the river being studied. This works because there is consistency within a geographical area: a reference to a 2nd order stream in eastern North America will be meaningful to anybody who has experience of streams in that part of the world. Unfortunately, it might not be meaningful to those unfamiliar with eastern North America and, worse, those with experience of rivers in very different places, such as the humid tropics or the Australian outback, may get the wrong impression of the type of stream being discussed. Stream ordering, despite its value, suffers the same limitations as ecological classifications, and should be interpreted accordingly.

Figure 2.3 (a) During periods of low discharge, a large river will flow at well below its channel capacity, and in extreme cases, bed sediments may be exposed in certain parts of the channel. Note that the banks of this river have been artificially increased in height to control flooding (River Loire, northern France). (*Photo by M. Dobson*). (b) Very high discharge may exceed the capacity of the river channel, causing flooding in the adjacent area (Guadeloupe River, Texas). (*Photo by M. Dobson*).

discharge, but as this can fluctuate widely in response to precipitation or inputs from upstream, rivers generally flow at somewhat less than full channel capacity (Figure 2.3a). In contrast, occasional high discharge events will cause the river to overflow, flooding the adjacent land (Figure 2.3b). In the deposition zone, a river may

exceed its channel capacity on a regular, seasonal basis, producing a predictable flood cycle which supports associated wetlands (**Section 2.7c; Chapter 7**); such a river may have a poorly defined channel, constantly changing its form, and may become braided into a series of interconnected channels.

Natural river channels are never homogeneous in form, but contain a variety of structural features, producing a range of current velocities even within a short stretch. These may be conveniently divided into whole channel features and partial channel features.

Whole channel features

A low order stream (**Box 2.1**) displays an approximately regular alternation between riffles and pools (Figure 2.4). Riffles are relatively shallow, high gradient stretches, where high velocity water passes over a substrate of large cobbles or boulders, many of which break the surface and cause turbulence. Pools are relatively deep, low gradient stretches, with slow-flowing water and relatively fine substrate. Between the two may occur glides (or runs), where water flows rapidly but smoothly, as the substrate does not break the surface.

Partial channel features

Within the main riffle-pool sequence, a range of other features may be present. Some, such as gravel bars, undercut banks, and slow-flowing sections on the inside of a meander, are associated with the riffle-pool sequence or with the sinuosity of the river channel. Others are more unpredictable in their occurrence, and include features such as clumps of aquatic vegetation, trailing bankside vegetation, tree stumps and large boulders. At a smaller scale, minor variations in conditions can be found in different areas of a single riffle, upstream or downstream of channel features such as clumps of vegetation, or even on different sides of stones.

2.2d GROUNDWATER

When river water enters a deposition zone, it percolates into the sediments, creating a store of fluvial groundwater which flows, albeit much more slowly than the river itself, in a downstream direction. This groundwater can be important in regulating the flow of a river. Groundwater inputs are low in upstream sections, where there is little alluvium, although groundwater may be the source if the river is spring fed. Further downstream, groundwater will enter the river if the water table is high, and will be responsible for ensuring continual flow during periods of low precipitation.

2.2e FLOODPLAINS

A river in a sediment transfer or deposition zone generally has a floodplain, a flat valley bottom constructed of loose or unconsolidated alluvial sediment deposited when the river floods or shifts its channel. Geomorphologically, a floodplain is an area flooded by the river with a predictable – though by no means regular – frequency; a five-year floodplain, for example, is that part of the valley which will be inundated by a flood of a magnitude occurring, on average, once every five years. Ecologically, however, the floodplain is better restricted to the zone close to the river which receives regular, seasonal flooding. All rivers experience floods but whereas low order streams, which are strongly influenced by local precipitation, have an irregular flood pattern with numerous peaks, larger rivers, fed mainly by their tributaries, are affected by seasonal weather patterns rather than single rainfall events. This difference is of fundamental ecological importance, as organisms in low order streams are adapted to surviving the rigours of flood events,

whereas those in higher order rivers may be adapted to benefit from the predictable inundation of adjacent floodplains (**Sections 2.3e, 2.3f; 2.7c**).

Alluvial terraces

Beyond the floodplain there may be an alluvial terrace. This is a former floodplain, consisting of sediment laid down when the river was flowing at a higher elevation, or was larger, and is generally no longer flooded, except at intervals of tens or even hundreds of years. An idealised river will create its own floodplain by depositing sediment but, particularly in the case of large rivers, this may take hundreds of thousands or even millions of years, and the possibility of being overtaken by geological events cannot be discounted. Thus most rivers in north temperate regions are flowing over alluvial beds laid down by glacial activity, or when the rivers themselves were significantly larger than they are today, as they transported glacial meltwater at the end of the Pleistocene. Despite no longer being flooded, however, the alluvial terrace will contain groundwater, and some interaction between fluvial and alluvial groundwater may occur.

2.2f CHANGES IN WATER QUALITY

Rainwater contains relatively few impurities (Table 1.4) but, as it flows through or over the ground, it picks up solutes and suspended matter. Once these enter the river channel, they normally remain there, becoming concentrated by further inputs and by evaporation. Therefore, proceeding from its source towards its mouth, the concentration of solutes and suspended particles in a river gradually increases, although rapid changes over a short distance can occur when a river channel passes through areas of contrasting catchment geology, vegetation or land use.

Major fluctuations in the concentration of impurities result from high discharge, which resuspends sediment from the bed and, if it causes flooding, will input matter from the floodplain. During heavy rain, excess water from the catchment passes rapidly into the river channel, bringing with it a pulse of sediment, detritus and solutes. As an example, much of a heavy fall of

---

Figure 2.4 The riffle–pool sequence of a river channel, showing variations in substrate composition and surface turbulence that it generates.

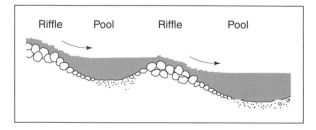

acid rain may pass straight into watercourses via overland flow without interacting with the soil. Therefore, even if the buffering capacity of the catchment soil is high, a pulse of acid water reaches the river without being neutralised, and can lower its pH considerably for a short period of time.

2.3 Ecological effects of the abiotic environment

2.3a PELAGIC AND BENTHIC ASSEMBLAGES

The primary feature of a river system is the physical environment of the water itself. The current, in particular, is the defining characteristic of running waters, whose most obvious effect is to carry downstream any organisms living within the water column. For this reason, pelagic communities in running waters are normally poorly developed, or even absent, and fish are among the few permanent residents of the water column in rapidly flowing waters. The benthos is, therefore, the dominant ecological group in most rivers.

Adaptation to microhabitats

Most benthic species are able to swim very weakly, if at all, and endeavour to remain on or in the substrate. Epibenthos have adopted a range of morphological strategies to withstand dislodgement by the current, including hooks, claws and suckers, while behavioural strategies include orientation of the body parallel to the direction of flow to reduce the surface area impacted by the current (Hynes, 1970). Although there is a viscous sublayer at the interface of the solid substrate and the moving water, this is normally so thin that only the very smallest organisms (microorganisms and the smaller meiofauna) are unaffected by current. The boundary layer is, in fact, a very turbulent environment with a complex flow regime – see Allan (1995) for a review.

Each species has specific habitat requirements and will inhabit only those patches of river bed to which it is best suited. For example, species which need high concentrations of oxygen, or feed directly from the water column, live in exposed, fast-flowing riffles. Other groups are more abundant in pools, backwaters and other patches of reduced flow, either because they require the relatively fine sediments or organic matter which aggregate in such environments or because they are intolerant of flow, including, for example, active predators requiring pond-like habitats in which to swim.

Patchiness and species diversity

The diversity of the biota of rivers is enhanced by the structural diversity of the channel, which leads, in turn, to a diversity of flow regimes even within a short stretch of river. Obviously, the greater the number of microhabitats represented, the greater the overall diversity of the river. The most diverse of all are those beds containing a mosaic of habitats, comprising a series of discrete entities, or 'patches'. These include the major channel types and whole channel features, but also partial channel features, which act as specialist microhabitats (**Section 2.2c**). Any single patch may support very few species, but a variety of patches within a single stretch of river will ensure that overall species diversity is high (see **Section 1.7b**).

As a river becomes larger, the bed becomes more homogeneous and much of the structural diversity is lost, but pelagic species assemblages may become more varied and marginal wetland habitats add diversity. Channelisation drastically reduces the range of microhabitats present, both by removing channel features and by cutting the river off from its marginal habitats, with a consequent reduction in species diversity.

2.3b LONGITUDINAL DISTRIBUTION PATTERNS

The abiotic components of a river change along its course, as it moves from a relatively steep, eroding channel with turbulent flow and nutrient-poor water, to a more gentle, depositing channel, with smoother flow and a higher concentration of dissolved and suspended components. The biota, in turn, respond to these changes, the precise physicochemical requirements of the majority of benthic species resulting in a downstream zonation. This is well illustrated by net-spinning caddisflies of the family Hydropsychidae (Figure 2.5), which are among the dominant benthic invertebrates of many European rivers. Hydropsychids in the Welsh River Usk show a clear zonation of species from headwaters to lower reaches (Figure 2.5a): *Hydropsyche siltalai* frequents rapidly flowing, turbulent conditions, whereas *H. pellucidula* becomes dominant as flow is reduced, so these two species can coexist along much of the river by virtue of the complex nature of its physical environment, each showing a microdistribution related to the patchiness of its preferred current regime. The other species are not, however, responding simply to current: *H. contubernalis*, for example, is tolerant of low oxygen saturation and moderate organic enrichment (which rarely occur separately in rivers); *Diplectrona felix* and *H. instabilis*, on the other hand, each require relatively cool water and have precise, but slightly different, temperature tolerances (Hildrew & Edington, 1979). On a larger scale, a zonation of five species of *Hydropsyche* occurs in the French River Rhône, downstream of Lake Geneva (Bravard *et al.*, 1992). Here, *H. siltalai* and *H. pellucidula* are confined to the upper reaches, several species overlap in the middle reaches of the river, but only one, *H. modesta*, occurs in the Lower Rhône (Figure 2.5b).

2.3c EFFECT OF WATER CHEMISTRY

Changes in water chemistry can have a profound effect on river species assemblages. Most freshwater organisms require at least some dissolved impurities, without which they are unable to maintain the correct internal ionic balance for survival (**Section 1.5a**). Generally, however, as the concentration of solutes in fresh water increases and, in human terms, the water becomes dirtier, the diversity of species present will decline.

This is well illustrated by organic inputs to water. Benthic macroinvertebrates show large differences in their tolerance to organic matter loading, such that the species assemblage in a given river can be used to predict the water quality, and vice versa, with reasonable accuracy. Indeed, there are many taxa which are known to be good biological indicators of the quality of water and whose absence may be used as evidence

for organic pollution. Where organic loading is very high, macroinvertebrates are limited to the few most tolerant species, particularly oligochaete worms and certain chironomid larvae, although these may be present in very large numbers. A slightly lower organic loading allows pollution-tolerant molluscs and leeches to persist, along with baetid mayflies and crustaceans such as hoglouse (*Asellus* sp.). As water quality improves, so species diversity increases, but only the cleanest water will support stoneflies and the majority of mayfly and caddisfly taxa.

Abrupt changes in water quality can cause marked discontinuities in species distributions, for which the River Goyt, a major tributary of the River Mersey in northwest England, provides a well documented example. A single point source of organically rich effluent changes the water quality of the river substantially, with an immediate loss of stoneflies, mayflies and other pollution-sensitive species. The more hardy of these groups return to the river in smaller numbers downstream of a tributary, the River Sett, which dilutes the effluent in the River Goyt (Holland & Harding, 1984).

Biological patterns such as these are widely exploited in the development of biotic indices of water quality, in which the differential sensitivity of organisms is taken into account. Each species present is given a score, reflecting its sensitivity to organic pollution, so that the more sensitive taxa, such as stoneflies, are allocated high scores, while very tolerant species have low scores. Summing the scores from a site produces an index number: the higher this number, the cleaner the water. Most biotic index systems are based upon macroinvertebrate species, for reasons of practicality, but other taxa, including bacteria, can be used (Mason, 1996).

Similar trends have been observed with increasing acidification, as sensitivity to low pH is a common feature among freshwater organisms. Thus, spatial studies of a range of sites will generally show species richness declining as pH falls (e.g. Townsend *et al.*, 1983) and, within a single site, acidification of water can drastically reduce the number of species present (Hall *et al.*, 1980; Stoner *et al.*, 1984). Ironically, stoneflies, which are among the species most sensitive to organic

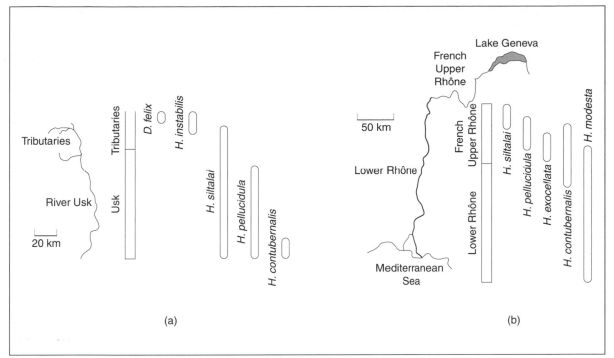

Figure 2.5 Longitudinal distribution patterns of hydropsychid caddis larvae in (a) the Welsh River Usk (after Hildrew & Edington, 1979), and (b) the French River Rhône (from Bravard *et al.*, 1992). The species present change in response to different physicochemical conditions along the rivers' lengths. *D, Diplectrona; H, Hydropsyche.*

loading, are, in many cases, tolerant of very acid waters and may be among the few macroinvertebrates present in highly acidified streams.

2.3d DRIFT

The water column of any river will contain large numbers of 'drift': individuals of normally benthic species suspended in the water column and being carried downstream by the current (Brittain & Eikeland, 1988). Drifting invertebrates may enter the water column after accidental dislodgement, but also as a deliberate behavioural tactic, to find new food resources or to avoid inclement conditions, including predation (Lancaster, 1990). Actively entering the water column in this way can be a dangerous strategy, because once part of the drift, most benthic invertebrates have little or no control over where the current will carry and deposit them, and they are generally inactive, at the mercy of predators such as salmonid fish and net-spinning caddisflies (Brittain & Eikeland, 1988). It is possibly for this reason that drift rates

are generally higher at night than during daylight, as darkness reduces the chance of being caught by a visual predator. The nocturnal increase in drift, which is triggered by light intensity, is probably a mixture of active dispersal and increased levels of accidental dislodgement, as individuals which spend the day under stones emerge at night to forage on upper surfaces and thus become susceptible to dislodgement at greater densities (Allan, 1995).

Catastrophic drift

The number of individuals drifting at any one time, even during the night, is normally only a small proportion of the total population of benthic invertebrates. Accidental drift on a large scale may, however, be triggered by floods or other adverse events, including inputs of a pollutant. This 'catastrophic drift' can occur at such high densities that it significantly lowers benthic densities; if in response to pollution, it may be either an active attempt to avoid the undesirable conditions or a passive response, drifting organisms having been disabled by the pollutant and therefore no longer able to resist the current.

Hall *et al.* (1980) provide a very clear example of the effect of a pollution episode upon both drift rates and benthic densities. Following artificial acidification of a small stream in the Hubbard Brook Experimental Forest, New Hampshire, there was a major increase in drift densities over a four-day period (Figure 2.6). The organisms drifting could be divided into three groups: (a) acid-tolerant species, whose drift rates remained constant despite acidification; (b) species which, prior to acidification, had not been recorded in the drift, and which, therefore, drift only in extreme circumstances; (c) species whose drift rates increased enormously in response to acidification. After the first pulse, drift rates settled down (Figure 2.6), despite continual addition of acid for a further five months, but remained high relative to the control stretch because benthic densities in the acidified zone had been reduced to around one-quarter of those in the control.

2.3e   FLOODING AND FLOOD REFUGIA

A continually flowing environment requires adaptations to avoid accidental dislodgement (**Section 2.3a**) but, in addition, most rivers show variation, often major, in their flow regime. Organisms are adapted to the typical flow regime of their environment, but may have difficulty if the flow changes markedly over a short period of time. Periods of relatively high or low flow may be predictable and regular if, for example, they relate to snow melt, but most small rivers suffer irregular spates, which can have major effects upon organisms living on the river bed, or even upon the river channel structure itself (Dobson *et al.*, 1997). Giller *et al.* (1991) provide an example of a flood at a scale expected once every hundred years, appreciably longer than the generation time of even the longest-lived inhabitants of the system. This flood, in the Glenfinnish River in southern Ireland, reduced populations of benthic invertebrates so severely that, even several years later, there was little sign of recovery (Figure 2.7). Most spates are rather less disruptive than this example, however, and what is remarkable is the speed at which most communities will recover, frequently more rapidly than an enhanced level of reproduction would allow. Clearly, therefore, these organisms are able to persist through all but the most severe floods in appreciable numbers, by exploiting flood refugia, places within the river system where disturbance is reduced relative to that in surrounding areas. There are three types of refugia available during high discharge events: the floodplain, the hyporheic zone and the channel itself (Hildrew & Giller, 1994).

Figure 2.6   Catastrophic drift in response to acidification of a stream. The numbers drifting per day in the acidified stretch (dashed line) were, for several days, many times those drifting in the reference stretch (solid line) (from Hall *et al.*, 1980).

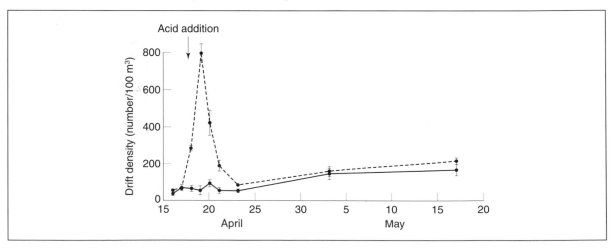

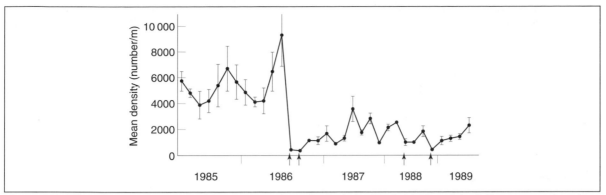

Figure 2.7 Effect of a major flood on benthic macroinvertebrate density in the Glenfinnish River, Ireland. The mean number of individuals recorded per square metre is plotted. Arrows along the horizontal axis indicate major (1986) and minor (1988) floods (from Giller *et al.*, 1991).

The floodplain

If a river overtops its banks, water spills out over the floodplain, carrying large numbers of dislodged organisms. As the water enters the floodplain, however, its velocity is reduced and the organisms will be deposited. That this process occurs is evidenced by pools left on floodplains after flood water has receded: these contain river organisms, which, now trapped, will perish. Its importance as an area from which recolonisation can occur is less clear, although Badri *et al.* (1987) demonstrated that very large numbers of many species of benthic invertebrates were deposited onto the floodplain of the Rdat in northern Morocco during a spate, and that the recovery of populations within the river channel coincided with large numbers drifting out of the floodplain while it was still inundated.

The hyporheic zone

The hyporheic zone is a layer of saturated sediments and subsurface water beneath the river channel, within which invertebrates can occur in substantial numbers (Danielopol, 1989). Spates, other than very severe ones which scour the sediment deeply, have little impact upon this zone, which has, therefore, been proposed as a refugium into which river organisms can migrate during high flow. Against this, Palmer *et al.* (1992) demonstrated that, in their study site at least, the hyporheic zone was not enough. They showed that the meiofauna in Goose Creek, Virginia, suf-

fered severe losses in even moderate floods, as they were concentrated in the upper layers of sediment. Furthermore, they were unable to migrate vertically rapidly enough, in response to raised flow, to protect them from being washed away with the sediment.

The river channel

The river channel itself may, at first, seem to be an odd place to look for flow refugia during a flood. The very heterogeneity of the channel, however, ensures that there will be dead zones where flow remains low, even during spates, allowing otherwise vulnerable benthic or swimming species to persist (Hildrew *et al.*, 1991). Dead zones occur wherever physical features, such as backwaters or boulders, provide patches where the flow of the river is interrupted. They may experience some flow, but this will fluctuate little relative to the rest of the channel. Evidence from Broadstone Stream in southeast England suggests that some macroinvertebrates do, indeed, aggregate in such flow refugia during high flows, though whether they move into them actively or are accidentally dislodged and then deposited is unclear (Lancaster & Hildrew, 1993).

2.3f EFFECTS OF FLOODS

Four possible effects of a flood upon biota are illustrated in Figure 2.8. Before a flood, individuals are evenly distributed across the river bed.

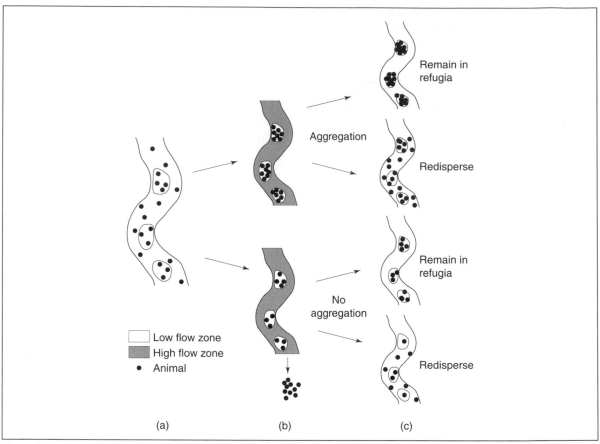

Figure 2.8 Potential responses of benthic invertebrates to floods: (a) before the flood, (b) during the flood, (c) after the flood. Each dot represents one individual; shading represents areas of high flow during a flood event; outlined areas are dead zones in which flow will remain low. See text for explanation.

During high flow, only those that are in refugia will persist; if the entire population aggregates in refugia, there will be no mortality, but otherwise only those that were in refugia anyway will persist, the rest being washed away. After the flood, surviving individuals will either disperse or remain within the flow refugia. If the aggregated population disperses, a second flood will result in further aggregation. The non-aggregated population may remain in refugia, ensuring little further likelihood of flood-induced mortality, or disperse, in which case another high flow event will cause further mortality. Several high flow events within one generation time will ensure that aggregating or remaining within refugia is the best strategy. If a species adopts the strategy of remaining in dead zones then, over generations, these can

be considered not as refugia but as source areas: individuals in dead zones are the ones which will survive long enough to reproduce. Individuals which leave source areas are unlikely to reproduce unless they are washed into other dead zones, and may be considered to be a 'doomed surplus' (Robertson *et al.*, 1995).

2.3g REFUGIA THROUGH COMPLEX LIFE CYCLES

Refugia from disturbance are generally considered only at the microhabitat scale within a river stretch, but Lancaster and Belyea (1997) suggest that between-habitat refugia must also be considered. Species with complex life cycles, in which different stages occupy different habitats, can use one habitat as a refugium if other habitats are disturbed. For example, aquatic insects with terrestrial adult stages may persist in the terrestrial habitat during a flood which destroys the larval population within the river, the adults then being able to facilitate recolonisation of the larval habitat. In order to function, however, the two life stages must be present at the same time, so that there are adults which persist after the loss of larvae, and each life stage must be relatively long-lasting, whereas most adult aquatic insects are short-lived and have little temporal overlap with larval stages. A more likely use of different habitats as refugia is shown by cased caddis of the genus *Sericostoma* in Oberer Seebach, Austria, which, in addition to an adult stage, has a spatial separation of larvae: young larvae live in the hyporheic zone, up to 1 m deep (Waringer, 1987), and are more likely to persist during spates than older larvae, which live close to the sediment surface.

A second large-scale refugium described by Lancaster and Belyea (1997) is the same habitat at a different site, so that, if a population is devastated by disturbance, recolonisation is from a different river. This is related to the complex life cycle mechanism in that organisms require a means to move between rivers. Again, aquatic insects, with their flying adult stage, are good examples, although their dispersal abilities as adults are limited (**Section 2.6a**), hence the slow recovery of streams such as that illustrated in Figure 2.7.

Note that, unlike refugia in the floodplain, hyporheic zone or river channel, described in **Section 2.3e**, survival of individuals affected by disturbance is not required in these cases, as recolonisation is by individuals from unaffected sites. Between-habitat refugia are probably most important in facilitating recovery following water quality change, such as a pollution event affecting an entire river, from which there will be no instream refugia.

2.4 Energy inputs

2.4a PRIMARY PRODUCTION

Phytoplankton

Primary production in rivers can be very low. Phytoplankton, in particular, face the problems associated with continually being carried downstream and, in larger rivers, with insufficient light as a result of being mixed through water of increasing turbidity. There are, however, phytoplankton species which are true river specialists – the 'potamoplankton', which occur most commonly in large rivers. Phytoplankton can become abundant in small or turbulent rivers if there are dead zones, such as backwaters, where the turnover time of water is less than the life cycle of algal species, allowing a continual replenishment into the water column (Reynolds, 1988). The River Orinoco and its tributaries in Venezuela show a clear seasonal pattern of planktonic primary production, its maximum coinciding with low discharge during the dry season. The dead zones in this case are secondary channels which, as they stagnate, quickly develop large populations of phytoplankton; minor increases in river discharge will then flush these out into the main channel (Lewis, 1988). There is, therefore, little true potamoplankton, despite the size of the river. The River Meuse in Belgium, in contrast, has few natural dead zones as a consequence of heavy channelisation, but supports a high biomass of diatoms with a clear longitudinal zonation. Descy *et al.* (1994) suggest that their source is the middle reaches of the river itself, where high nutrient levels, originating from partially treated sewage inputs, and relatively shallow water contribute to high productivity of a genuine potamoplankton. This, in turn, is exported downstream, where reduced growth and dilution contribute to a gradual reduction in biomass.

Attached photosynthesisers

Attached photosynthesisers, including macrophytes and microphytes, are limited as abundant components of the biota to small streams and the shallower edges of larger rivers; light is typically the limiting factor in deep stretches because of the turbidity caused by transport of suspended sediments and solutes. Vascular plants are susceptible to damage by flowing water and occur only where current is reduced. They are, therefore, only of local importance but, where conditions are good, can become very abundant. In England, some of the most productive rivers for macrophyte growth are chalk streams, where a combination of clear water, high nutrient levels and stable flow allow very high densities to develop. The dominant species is usually stream water crowfoot (*Ranunculus penicillatus* var. *calcareus*), an annual which will typically achieve a biomass of around 200 g m^{-2} within one growing season (Berrie, 1992). Attached algae, the periphyton, are important primary producers, particularly in smaller streams. Single-celled algae growing on stone surfaces are unaffected by current and can become very abundant in clear streams, but their biomass will necessarily remain low. They can, however, be a major energy input to shallow, stony-bedded streams, where they support a specialist guild of grazer-scraper invertebrates. Macrophytic algae can become seasonally abundant in such streams, as they can withstand buffeting by moving water without suffering structural damage.

2.4b Detritus

Where primary producers are rare, in river stretches with low light intensity due to turbidity or shading, the primary energy inputs will be in the form of detritus, such as dead leaves from the surrounding catchment, which either fall directly into the water from riparian trees, are blown in laterally off the ground, or are transported from upstream. A river system can be considered a parasite of its catchment, relying on excess primary production on its bank or in the riparian zone to support its detritus-based communities. Therefore, the productivity of a stream will be determined by the productivity of its catchment and the dominant primary consumers will be detritivores. Even in highly productive chalk streams, most of the energy inputs are from external sources (Berrie, 1992). Indeed, even where macrophytes are present, they are rarely grazed as living matter, and are consumed mainly as detritus (Allan, 1995). Species which live on macrophytes and apparently feed on them may simply be consuming the epiphytic algae and small particulate detritus which aggregates on their leaves (Berrie, 1976).

Underground rivers, which are common in karstic limestone, are, of course, completely dark,

and their food webs are entirely heterotrophic. Their energy derives from transport of organic matter from the surface and they are dependent, therefore, upon the productivity of a system from which they may be spatially very distant. Most unpolluted groundwaters, including karstic systems, are characterised by scarce trophic resources, to which subterranean faunas respond by adopting low metabolic rates (Gibert *et al.*, 1994).

Composition and flux of detritus

Organic matter comes in a variety of forms, from large leaves or pieces of wood to dissolved components. The main inputs to rivers are in the form of coarse fragments of vegetation from the surrounding catchment, including leaves and twigs and, if leaf-fall is seasonal, litter inputs will show a similar seasonality. Chauvet and Jean-Louis (1988) estimated that the shaded edges of the River Garonne near Toulouse in southwest France receive around 3.3 kg of litter from riparian trees per metre of bank per year, mainly as direct inputs from overhanging trees. Of this, around two-thirds is leaf litter, of which more than half enters the river during two months of autumn leaf-fall. Conversely, inputs of flowers and fruits (360 g m^{-1} yr^{-1}) from riparian trees are concentrated into the spring and summer while inputs of twigs and bark (670 g m^{-1} yr^{-1}) are evenly distributed throughout the year. Most detritivores in temperate areas respond to the strongly seasonal autumn pulse of leaf litter inputs, by synchronising their life cycles to take advantage of the resource when it is abundant, their larvae hatching in early autumn and then achieving rapid growth rates when the detritus arrives.

Leaf litter cannot be consumed by detritivores, or even colonised effectively by decomposers, while moving in the water column; it needs to be retained on the river bed. A river's detritus standing stock is, therefore, determined by how much falls in, but equally by the presence of barriers that hold it (Dobson & Hildrew, 1992). In this respect, woody debris can be of great importance as a retention agent – it decomposes and is consumed very slowly, but acts as a trap, holding large quantities of detritus (Figure 2.9). Removal of such debris dams will result in a major increase in export of particulate organic matter (Bilby & Likens, 1980).

Conditioning and detritus transformation

The quality of most plant detritus as a food source for invertebrates is relatively poor. It is low in nitrogenous compounds and much of the carbon is in forms such as cellulose, which macroorganisms are unable to digest. It is, however, readily colonised by microorganisms, particularly hyphomycete fungi, whose filamentous mycelia can attain a biomass in excess of 10% of the mass of detritus itself. The breakdown rate of leaf litter is strongly correlated with fungal activity, which is, in turn, determined by the initial lignin content of leaves: species with a low lignin content, such as alder (*Alnus glutinosus*) and ash (*Fraxinus excelsior*), decompose rapidly, whereas evergreen oak (*Quercus ilex*) and beech (*Fagus sylvatica*), whose initial lignin content is high, degrade slowly (Gessner & Chauvet, 1994). Fungal degradation facilitates leaf litter breakdown through assimilation into fungal biomass, but also, in weakening its structure, makes detritus susceptible to fragmentation and leaching. In addition, microbial activity increases the nutritional quality and palatability of detritus for detritivores, a process referred to as conditioning. Invertebrates will selectively feed upon detritus that has been conditioned, gaining nutrition either from the partially decomposed detrital material or from the fungal biomass itself (Graça *et al.*, 1993).

The action of shredding invertebrates, microbial decomposition and physical attrition together transform coarse detrital fragments into smaller particulate fragments and dissolved components. In a highly retentive river, CPOM is processed *in situ* and a higher proportion of FPOM will therefore be exported than is imported. Iversen *et al.* (1982) produced an energy budget for Rold Kilde, a small spring-fed river in a beech wood in Denmark. They demonstrated that input of CPOM amounted to around 716 g m^{-2} yr^{-1}, of which 71% was leaves and 11% was other identifiable plant fragments. Outputs over the same time totalled 535 g m^{-2} yr^{-1}, of which all identifiable plant fragments together contributed 7%,

and FPOM made up 92%. Moreover, both inputs and outputs of coarse fragments were strongly seasonal, occurring mainly during the autumn leaf-fall period, whereas fine fragment export was more evenly distributed throughout the year. The role of shredding invertebrates in these transformations was demonstrated by Cuffney *et al.* (1990), who showed that addition of insecticide to an experimental stream in Coweeta, North Carolina, reduced leaf litter processing rates by at least 50%, and caused export

Figure 2.9 Two examples of wood in streams acting as a dam: (a) a single large branch has dammed the stream creating a pool (Oaken Clough, northern England). (*Photo by M. Dobson*) (b) An aggregation of small branches, twigs and leaves (Broadstone Stream, southern England). (*Photo by M. Dobson*)

of FPOM to decline from over 60 kg yr^{-1} to less than 20 kg yr^{-1}. Clearly, therefore, shredding insects have an important role in the transformation process and in providing food for other feeding groups, as FPOM is important as food for collectors, which are unable to process the coarser fractions and are thus dependent upon these transformations.

2.4c ALLOCHTHONOUS INPUTS AND WATER QUALITY

The ability of river organisms to process and consume organic inputs is not simply important as a way of supporting a diversity of feeding groups through biological activity; it also works as a self-cleansing mechanism: by transforming and consuming organic inputs, organisms remove them from the system. The response of river organisms to organic sewage inputs is simply an extreme example of this same process. Sewage often contains a large proportion of suspended solids, which cloud the water and clog external organs, such as gills, but its main effect upon river biota is rather more simple: it causes depletion of dissolved oxygen concentrations. Sewage is a very rich source of organic carbon and, by its very nature, breaks into tiny particles with a vast surface area. Onto these particles settle bacteria, which begin to decompose the organic components and, in doing so, respire, using up the available oxygen in the water (Mason, 1996). Although this bacterially mediated deoxygenation appears to be completely detrimental, there are two points to bear in mind. First, in respiring oxygen, bacteria are contributing to decomposition and therefore removal of organic pollutants. Second, all stages of deoxygenation and contamination with organic matter have their equivalents in natural situations. Therefore, for any state of organic pollution, there are aquatic species adapted to the conditions, each of which, through consumption, will contribute to the cleansing process.

Modern sewage treatment processes include the use of filter beds, in which the contaminated water percolates through gravel upon which grow bacteria, whose effect is to mineralise and remove organic contaminants. Vervier *et al.* (1993) dem-

onstrated an equivalent process in a gravel bar in the River Garonne, and suggested that these structures are important cleansers of river water, because, as it percolates through the gravel, bacteria extract and remove DOC.

2.5 Community structure in rivers

Traditionally, the physical environment of rivers has been viewed as the overwhelming determinant of community structure, such that biotic interactions were thought to be of little importance. In recent years, however, many specific examples have been identified which demonstrate the role of biotic interactions, at least at a local scale.

2.5a COMPETITION AND PREDATION

Interspecific competition has been identified in a number of situations, particularly among sedentary species which require an area of stream bed in which to forage. The North American caddis larva *Leucotrichia*, for example, is an algal grazer which attaches its retreat to stone surfaces and uses it as a base from which it aggressively defends its foraging area from all intruders, thereby affecting distribution and numbers of other grazers, both sedentary and mobile (McAuliffe, 1984; Hart, 1985). The European net-spinning caddis *Plectrocnemia conspersa* will compete intraspecifically for a similar resource: a space in which to construct its net. If two individuals occupy a vacant site at the same time, an aggressive encounter will ensue and will continue until the loser concedes defeat by launching itself into the water column and drifting away (Hildrew & Townsend, 1980).

Predation may be inferred from negative correlation between numbers of predators and of particularly vulnerable prey, but is difficult to demonstrate unequivocally. Schofield *et al.* (1988), however, demonstrated in a series of field manipulations that predation pressure by acid-sensitive trout (*Salmo trutta*) was responsible for effectively confining *P. conspersa* in southern England to acid streams.

2.5b RIVER COMMUNITY TYPES

Examples of biotic interactions exerting a strong influence on community structure have led Hildrew and Giller (1994) to propose three types of river community: disturbance-dominated, competitive and predation-structured.

Disturbance-dominated communities are composed of species among whom there are no influential interactions. Physical disturbance in such systems is so intense and frequent that communities never become stable enough for biotic interactions to become important, and species dynamics are essentially independent. A predator living in such a situation will, obviously, have a major detrimental effect upon an individual that it eats, but consumption by the predator species will have an insignificant effect on abundance of the prey species as a whole.

Competitive communities are those governed by a resource which is both limiting and patchily distributed, such as detritus occurring in the form of discrete leaf packs. In some ('shuffled competitive communities'), competing species are very similar in their requirements for the limiting resource, and within a patch, competition will be intense. Whichever species colonises a patch first will dominate it ('founder control' – see **Section 4.6c**), but coexistence is possible because it is a matter of chance which species will arrive first. In other communities ('partitioning competitive communities'), competitors have slightly different requirements and partition the resource accordingly. In both cases, a high degree of mobility is required to facilitate colonisation or to enable an individual to find a patch that provides its specific requirements.

In predation-structured communities, the activity of predators has a significant effect on numbers of their prey. In some, predators may aggregate on certain patches of prey – those where prey density is highest or the habitat is preferable, for example – leaving other areas as refugia from predation. In others, spates may increase predator pressure by concentrating both predators and their prey into restricted flow refugia.

Which of the three community types – disturbance-controlled, competition-controlled or predation-controlled – will prevail in a given area is determined by a complex mix of interacting forces, but the intensity of disturbance will be the overriding feature (see **Section 1.7c**, Figure 1.11b). If environmental stress, such as discharge or frequency of floods, is high, then this disturbance will structure the community. As environmental stress is reduced, however, competition will start to occur, but even relatively low levels of disturbance will maintain the system in a non-equilibrium state, by removing patches of competitively superior species, thus ensuring that they do not dominate the entire system. Predation will only be a major determinant at low levels of environmental stress, as most predators need to be mobile to seek their prey and are therefore more susceptible to dislodgement. It must be emphasised, however, that the communities are not mutually exclusive: extreme disturbance to epilithic algae may be tolerable perturbation to an otter.

Neither are they fixed. McAuliffe (1984) demonstrated that the competitive dominance of *Leucotrichia* over larvae of the moth *Parargyractis* was tempered by physical disturbance. The moth constructs a net which, upon emergence of the adult, is destroyed, creating space for a new coloniser of either species, whereas *Leucotrichia* larvae construct stone cases which persist after emergence of the adults and, in the majority of cases, are reoccupied by the subsequent generation. The expectation, therefore, is that, over time, *Leucotrichia* would take over completely. This does not occur because occasional spates overturn stones, destroying the caddis retreats and, temporarily, giving equal advantage to both species on the newly exposed stone surfaces. A second type of physical disturbance, reduced summer discharge, allows a third species, the chironomid *Eukiefferiella*, to coexist. During low summer flow the upper surface of many stones will be exposed, causing *Parargyractis* to abandon its net but killing *Leucotrichia*. These species, with a single generation per year, must wait for the following summer and a new cohort before recolonisation can take place. *Eukiefferiella*, however, has several generations per year, so can take advantage of the temporary absence of the competitively superior species.

2.5c DISTURBANCE AND SPECIES DIVERSITY

The example above demonstrates that continual disturbance at a very small scale contributes to the patchiness of the river bed environment and therefore to overall species diversity of the benthos. Without physical disturbance, *Leucotrichia* would be the only grazing species present, but localised events allow two other species to coexist, each in different patches. Thus, for benthic communities, moderate disturbance results in the highest species diversity (**Section 1.7b**).

At a geographical scale, however, even seasonally predictable disturbance can serve to reduce diversity. A fluctuating physical environment ensures that long-lived species such as fish need to be adapted to a range of conditions. Swimming species, as opposed to those able to live on the river bed or in the sediment, show little habitat specialisation because no habitat is predictably long-lived. The effect of this on species diversity is well illustrated by the larger rivers of tropical Africa. The River Zaire (= Congo) catchment is a low gradient basin with rich habitat diversity but, more significantly, is unique in Africa in that it straddles the Equator, with tributaries in both the Northern and Southern Hemispheres. The equatorial basin experiences little seasonal variation in rainfall; seasonal rainfall patterns occur in its tributaries, but peaks on one side of the Equator are countered by dry conditions on the other. Therefore, fluctuations in water level and discharge are small in the main basin. In contrast, the other main rivers in Africa are each confined to a single hemisphere, so the entire catchment experiences the same seasonal variation in rainfall, resulting in discharge and water levels being high during the wet season and low during the dry season. A consequence of this is that, whereas the Rivers Niger, Nile and Zambezi support, respectively, 134, 115 and 110 species of fish, the Zaire has nearly 700 (Ribbink, 1994).

2.6 Succession and change

2.6a COLONISATION AND SUCCESSION

Primary succession

Longitudinal distribution patterns illustrate spatial succession in running waters in relation to changing physicochemical conditions, but primary succession over time is more difficult to study, because formation of new streams is rare. Among the few new streams that have been studied are those formed by retreating glacial ice in Glacier Bay in southeast Alaska, which show an interesting pattern of development. Newly exposed meltwater streams are quickly colonised by a small but distinctive biota of algae and cold-tolerant chironomid larvae. The insect fauna at this stage is very specific, and will be present only so long as the low temperature and bed instability impede colonisation by other species (Milner, 1994). The second stage of colonisation of these streams is closely related to improvement in the physical conditions, and involves the gradual colonisation of species which will then persist in the community.

Rate of stabilisation is a key determinant of rate of succession. Unstable streams, characterised by rapid fluctuations in discharge and consequent redistribution of sediment, remain low in species diversity and overall productivity. The presence of a lake in a catchment adds an element of stability, buffering discharge fluctuations and acting as a sediment trap, which allows a more diverse, productive community to develop. Milner (1987) suggests that a long-term factor of importance in stream development in Alaska is riparian vegetation, which will structurally modify the river channel and banks. Development of such vegetation depends upon terrestrial successional processes, but will also require a dampening of discharge fluctuations, as frequent spates will retard growth of riparian plants.

Colonisation abilities

Once the physical conditions are acceptable, rates of colonisation by aquatic organisms will be the limiting factor in stream community development. Despite often very severe seasonal fluctuations in discharge, almost all river systems have at least some stretches of perennially flowing water and can persist for many millions of years, providing evolutionary stability. As a consequence, river specialists rarely require a capacity to move between river systems and their powers of dispersal between catchments are limited. Some fish species, including many salmonids, are tolerant of salt water (see **Section 3.3a**) and can disperse through the sea to different river systems, but most river taxa are confined to the freshwater habitat. Insects have the ability to fly, but river specialists – including caddisflies, stoneflies and mayflies – have adult stages which are typically short-lived or weak flying. Therefore, their aerial dispersal abilities, apart from accidental displacement, are limited to flights which rarely exceed several hundred metres and are normally, therefore, confined to the catchment from which they emerged.

Wolf Point Creek in Glacier Bay runs directly into the sea. Thus, 25 years after its formation, it supported a fauna containing only a handful of insect species, which flew as adults from an adjacent catchment, and salmonid fish, which entered from the sea (Milner, 1994). If a stream is formed in an area containing plenty of established streams, however, colonisation can be rapid. Flugströmmen, an artificial stream adjacent to other watercourses in southern Sweden, supported a faunal assemblage similar to that of adjacent natural streams after one year (Malmqvist *et al.*, 1991). Colonisation of Flugströmmen continued throughout the 18 months of the study, with new species being recorded on every sampling occasion. In contrast, Morrison (1990) showed that recolonisation of four small streams in central Scotland that had ceased flowing during a dry summer was very rapid, with most of the expected species being present within a month of flow returning. In the former case, it appears that colonisation was determined by the rate at which new species could reach the site by drifting from upstream or in the flying stage, whereas in the latter, recolonisation was probably precipitated by the presence of eggs *in situ*, which hatched at the time that conditions improved.

Drift and upstream colonisation

Active drift and passive dislodgement both result in downstream movement of organisms (**Section 2.3d**), and one of the most enduring conundrums in river ecology is why this does not result in depletion of upstream populations. Müller (1954) proposed that this could be explained, for aquatic insects, by a colonisation cycle: larval movement is essentially downstream, so adults will fly upstream to compensate for this. Unfortunately, the evidence available provides little support for this hypothesis. Some studies (e.g. Elliott, 1967) have found no evidence for a tendency to fly upstream and even those which do find support for the idea, such as Flecker and Allan's (1988) study of mayflies in Colorado, are not as clear as may be expected. These authors showed a significant tendency for *Baetis* spp. to fly upstream, although, in several of their samples, more were flying downstream, whereas *Rhithrogena hageni* tended to fly downstream. A further problem with the colonisation cycle hypothesis is that it does not explain how species without a flying stage, such as crustaceans, can persist in upstream stretches. Upstream movements by benthos moving over or within sediment (positive rheotaxis) have been recorded – see Allan (1995) for a review – but, again, are inadequate to compensate for downstream drift.

Allan (1995) suggests that upstream movement is unnecessary to replace losses, as drift from headwaters is loss of surplus individuals and enough will remain to replenish the population. The evidence is, however, equivocal and, for the moment, the phenomenon remains unexplained.

2.6b SECONDARY CHANGES

Temporal change of physical conditions in established river systems is mainly at a local scale – redistribution of the features present, such as erosion and redeposition of gravel bars or severance of meanders to form oxbow lakes. From the point of view of organisms, these processes simply shift the microhabitats that they occupy spatially. Recolonisation after disturbance events, such as spates, can be very rapid, but, although a predictable sequence of species colonising a disturbed patch may occur, this is caused by different rates of dispersal among species, and is not a true succession (Hildrew & Giller, 1994). Continual spates, moreover, act as a reset mechanism, ensuring that the pattern is continually repeated, rather than reaching an end point. Only major spates, such as that illustrated in Figure 2.7, will have

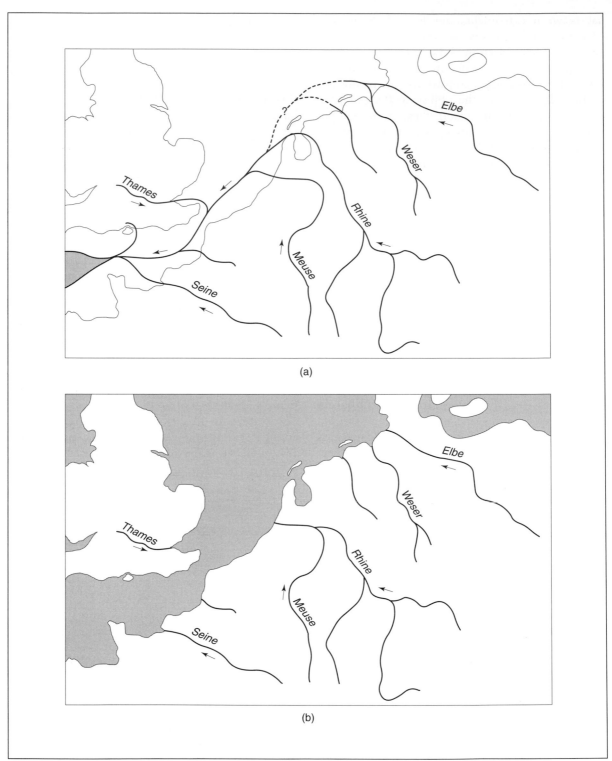

Figure 2.10 The relative positions of major rivers of northwest Europe (a) during the last glacial, around 20 000 BP; (b) today (after Gibbard, 1988). Arrows indicate the direction of flow.

long-term effects upon the entire channel. Changes in water quality are, however, more likely to affect the entire community. A pulse of organic pollution into an otherwise clean river will eliminate sensitive species, and its effects may be measurable for a long period of time afterwards, even if the pollution event itself was only of a few hours' duration. This will be the case particularly if the pollution event occurs close to the source of a river, so that there is no opportunity for recovery through drift, and restoration of the eliminated species requires recruitment from the next generation (**Section 2.3g**). One of the advantages of using living organisms as indicators of aquatic pollution is that they not only show water quality at the time of sampling, but also may provide evidence for any previous, short-lived, pollution events.

Abrupt changes in water quality do not occur simply as a result of human activity. DeWalt and Olive (1988) provide an example of Silver Creek, a small river in Ohio, which occasionally erodes into beds of silt laid down during the last glaciation. This results in a sudden influx of fine sediment, turning the water milky in colour and eliminating silt-sensitive invertebrates over a distance of several kilometres. Within a few months, however, the river erodes through the silt deposit and the sedimentation ceases, allowing the affected area to recover.

Recolonisation by organisms drifting from upstream can take a matter of days or weeks, once the perturbation has ceased, but if the entire river is affected, so that there is no upstream reservoir from which to drift, then recovery can take rather longer. Even insects with flying adult stages will disperse across catchment boundaries very slowly, and natural restoration may take years or even decades. Species confined to upstream reaches and with no terrestrial stage in their life cycle may never recolonise the upper reaches of a river impacted from its source. Poor dispersal between catchments can, however, be countered by geological or climatic events which cause separate river systems to merge. In eastern England, for example, the River Thames is separated from rivers elsewhere in Europe by sea, but during glacial periods, when sea levels fell, it became part of the River Rhine system which drained much of the area now covered by the North Sea (Figure 2.10), allowing an exchange of flora and fauna. For this reason, the rivers in eastern England are in many ways faunistically more similar to those in central Europe than to those elsewhere in the British Isles (Wheeler, 1977).

2.6c EFFECT OF HUMAN ACTIVITY

Long-term or permanent changes to the physical or chemical attributes of a river will occur if it erodes through different geological strata, or even in response to climate changes, particularly changes in amount or seasonality of precipitation. Human modifications, too, are often of long duration or permanent, and can give insights into the ecological response to perturbations. Structural modifications to the river channel, such as the construction of dams or barrages, have clear, and effectively permanent, effects upon a river system. Construction of barrages along the River Danube in Austria illustrate well the effects of flow reduction and altered patterns of sedimentation (Humpesch, 1992). The Austrian stretch of the Danube is 351 km in length, along which it descends in altitude by 156 m. Until the early 1950s it was free-flowing, but since then 10 barrages have been constructed, converting the river into a series of impoundments, with only two free-flowing stretches remaining (Figure 2.11a). The effect of the barrages has been to reduce flow and increase sedimentation in the impounded stretches, so that a bed dominated by rocks and gravel in free-flowing stretches changes into one of fine silt immediately upstream of a barrage (Figure 2.11b).

Biological changes are equally profound (Humpesch, 1992). Free-flowing stretches of the Danube, such as that above the Altenwörth Dam, have a low density but high taxonomic diversity of benthic macroinvertebrates, whereas the fine silt in the impoundment immediately above the dam supports very high densities of a few silt-tolerant species – 98% of individuals are oligochaetes, the remaining 2% are almost entirely chironomids and the freshwater polychaete *Hypania invalida*. Towards the upstream end of the impoundment, physical conditions and therefore the invertebrate fauna more closely resemble those of the free-

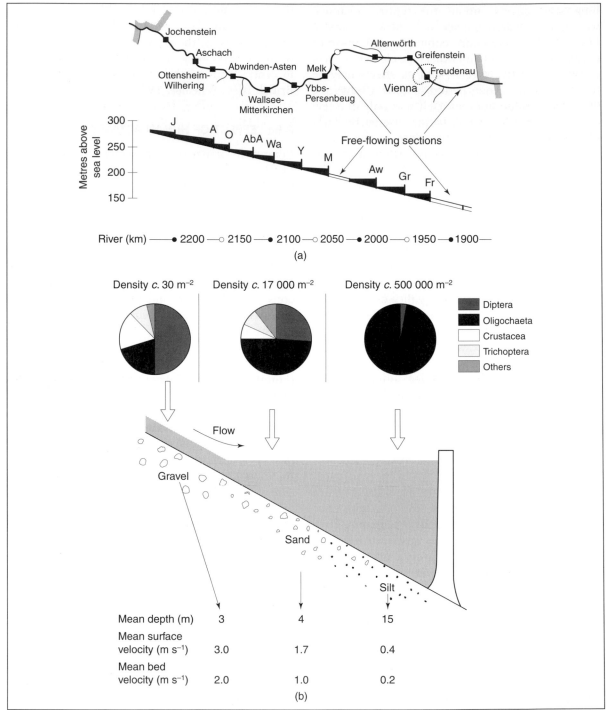

Figure 2.11 Effects of impoundment upon a river. (a) The River Danube in Austria, showing impounded and free-flowing sections. (b) Diagrammatic representation of physical and biological changes that occur moving from a free-flowing to an impounded stretch of the River Danube above the Altenwörth Dam. Pie charts show changes in relative numbers of different macroinvertebrate groups at each of three points; note the major increase in total density. Depth and mean flow at each of the three points are also given (after Humpesch, 1992).

flowing stretch, though total numbers of individuals are much greater, mainly due to the presence of numerous small Oligochaeta and Diptera (Figure 2.11b).

The impoundments have more subtle effects upon fish assemblages. Free-flowing stretches are dominated by running water species, particularly nase (*Chondrostoma nasus*), whereas the impoundments offer conditions more suitable for species more typical of lakes, such as roach (*Rutilus rutilus*). Impoundments have not developed a true lake fish fauna, however, because of the lack of shoreline diversity and low densities of plankton. The Altenwörth impoundment is still dominated by the original running water fish assemblage, capitalising on the rich macroinvertebrate food resource, but these species do not breed in the impoundment because suitable spawning grounds are lacking, and rely upon juvenile recruitment from the free-flowing stretch upstream. Impounded stretches that are bordered by impoundments at both ends, which is the situation along most of the length of the Danube in Austria, may, therefore, have undergone rather more profound changes in faunal assemblages (Humpesch, 1992).

2.7 Longitudinal and lateral linkages

2.7a UPSTREAM–DOWNSTREAM LINKS

The changing conditions that can be expected as one moves downstream along a river channel are integrated, in that upstream processes, by virtue of the unidirectional nature of the current, have a knock-on effect downstream. Thus, the eroding nature of high gradient streams provides the sediment which is then deposited in the low gradient river further downstream (Figure 2.1). Equally, build-up of sediment and other particulate or dissolved matter modifies light penetration and oxygen concentration. Just as there are physicochemical links, so are biological processes connected in this way. Production of plankton in the middle reaches of the River Meuse (**Section 2.4a**), for example, supports its high biomass fur-

ther downstream and, in turn, the production of consumers in the lower reaches. Similarly, the export of fine particles of detritus from low order streams suggests that breakdown processes in the headwaters are not only supplying food to collectors *in situ*, but also to those that live further downstream, so upstream production and downstream consumption of FPOM are coupled.

A consequence of this continual movement is that nutrient cycling processes in rivers differ from those in other systems. Nutrient cycling is the transfer of an element from a dissolved inorganic form – during which it is available as a nutrient for an autotroph – through incorporation into living tissue and its subsequent transformation into the inorganic form, available as a nutrient once more, by decomposition processes. In most terrestrial systems, nutrient cycling takes place within the same geographical area, with relatively little input or output of elements, but in rivers a given element will be continually transported downstream, either in solution or as part of a living organism, and the cycle is broken, becoming more of a spiral. Losses of nutrients downstream are, therefore, high and must be matched by inputs from upstream.

2.7b THE RIVER CONTINUUM CONCEPT

The River Continuum Concept, or RCC (Vannote *et al.*, 1980; Cummins *et al.*, 1995), attempts to provide a simple mechanism for explaining biological connections between the various stages of a river system. It proposes that energy inputs will change in a longitudinal direction, in relation to channel size, degree of shading, light penetration, and so on, and relative importance of functional feeding groups will change in tandem (Figure 2.12). One major prediction of the RCC is that downstream stretches, with little primary production, support detritus-based communities which are heavily dependent upon breakdown of plant litter in upstream reaches, and therefore exploit the excess production of such upstream sites in the same way that the river as a whole exploits excess terrestrial production in its catchment.

For a model of upstream–downstream linkages to work effectively, it must take into account the range of different types of rivers, and particu-

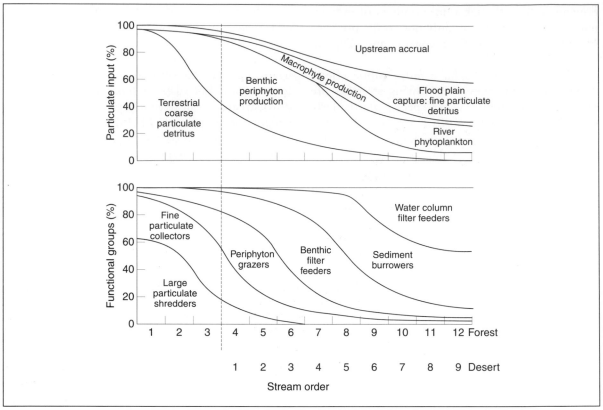

Figure 2.12 Expected longitudinal changes in particulate organic matter inputs and corresponding changes in the relative importance of functional feeding groups along a river system. Different streams enter the continuum at different points so that, in this example, the forest stream is shaded by trees and has a large initial input of terrestrially derived coarse particulate detritus, primarily leaf litter, whereas the desert stream, with fewer trees and less shading, is dominated initially by photosynthetic algae. Stream order is shown using the Shreve method (see **Box 2.1**) (from Minshall *et al.*, 1985).

larly variation in catchment vegetation and in channel stability. Riparian trees are a common feature, even in grassland biomes, but they can be absent in, for example, desert streams, in which case the dominant energy inputs in upper reaches will not be leaf litter, and shredders and collectors will be absent (Minshall *et al.*, 1985). Channel stability and retention are also key determinants of benthic invertebrate community structure: a river will support few shredders if leaf litter that enters the channel, however copious, is not retained. Upstream–downstream links ensure that organic inputs, primary production, retention and stability, particularly in the upper reaches, will have a knock-on effect throughout the length of the river.

2.7c THE FLOOD PULSE CONCEPT

Despite its value in conceptualising longitudinal linkages along a river system, the RCC fails to explain adequately processes in very large rivers, whose requirements for organic carbon are apparently not met by upstream production (Sedell *et al.*, 1989). It also treats floods as unpredictable or catastrophic, failing to recognise their predictable seasonality in larger rivers. The Flood Pulse Concept (Junk *et al.*, 1989) is an alternative model which overcomes these difficulties while remaining complementary to the RCC. Its basis is that the pulsing of river discharge – the flood pulse – is the major force controlling biota in river floodplains, and that lateral exchange between the river channel and its floodplains is more important in determining nutrient and carbon supply in lower reaches than longitudinal connections.

The key component of the Flood Pulse Concept is the 'aquatic–terrestrial transition zone' (ATTZ), which is the ecological floodplain as defined in **Section 2.2e**. Organisms use the floodplain for feeding and reproduction, and use the main channel to move to other parts of the floodplain or as a refugium during low flow. Such movements have been demonstrated from several floodplain systems in the tropics, including the Inner Delta of the River Niger in Mali, a system whose water surface area fluctuates from less than 1000 km² at the end of the dry season to more than 12 000 km² during flooding (**Section 7.6e**; **Figure 7.12**). Movements of fish between river and floodplain are closely related to the direction of water flow but, whereas some species migrate into floodplains during the entire three-month period of rising water level, others move in rapidly as the water begins to rise. The river is the main spawning site for most species, but eggs or fry are transported, presumably passively, into the floodplain, which acts as a nursery (Bénech and Peñáz, 1995).

The main limitation of the Flood Pulse Concept is that active movement between the channel and the floodplain has so far been identified only among fish and a few other vertebrates. It may, therefore, be limited in value to consideration of taxa which can actively move, whereas invertebrates and phytoplankton, which are less able to move independently of the current, will probably show different patterns. Extensive floodplains contain permanently flooded lakes and channels, which could act as a source for these smaller organisms to populate the floodplain during inundation, without requirement for immigration from the river channel. Certainly the inundated floodplain of the River Orinoco in Venezuela (**Section 2.4a**) supports a planktonic system independent of that in the river channel itself and exports relatively little phytoplankton biomass to the river, despite its high productivity (Lewis, 1988); zooplankton and benthos may show the same pattern, with the only inputs to the river being excess individuals.

2.7d GROUNDWATER CONNECTIONS

Lateral and vertical connections exist between the river and its associated groundwater in alluvial sediments. Many benthic invertebrates will enter the sediment on the river bed, even if for brief periods, but some species, known as amphibites, have a life cycle which involves both surface water and groundwater systems. The most celebrated amphibites are various species of stoneflies associated with the Flathead River, Montana: the nymphs spend one or two years in the sediments before migrating to the main river to emerge as flying adults; these then lay their eggs in the river and the newly hatched nymphs migrate back into the sediments. Movements in this system are generally lateral, and stonefly nymphs have been extracted from the broad alluvial terrace of the Flathead River up to 3 km from the river channel itself (Stanford & Ward, 1988). The Flathead River is perhaps exceptional in the extent of these movements, but such lateral connections probably occur wherever conditions are suitable, the degree to which organisms penetrate from the river being related to the strength of hydrological connection between the river and its alluvial sediments. A high turnover of water in the interstitial spaces enhances availability of food and oxygen and encourages lateral movements of river species, but will also lead to passive dispersal of organisms within the sediments, such as diatoms in the Flathead River floodplain which have been recorded in complete darkness up to 350 m from the river (Gibert *et al.*, 1994). A lower flushing rate by river water will reduce numbers of amphibites and of species which become part of the hyporheos only occasionally or accidentally. Groundwaters thus hydrologically separated from surface waters will, however, offer stable environmental conditions and will be typified by an increased importance of the permanent inhabitants of groundwater – the stygobites.

2.7e BREAKING LONGITUDINAL OR LATERAL CONNECTIONS

River system interactions are well illustrated by situations in which the natural upstream–downstream linkages are broken. The free-flowing stretch of the Danube downstream of Vienna and

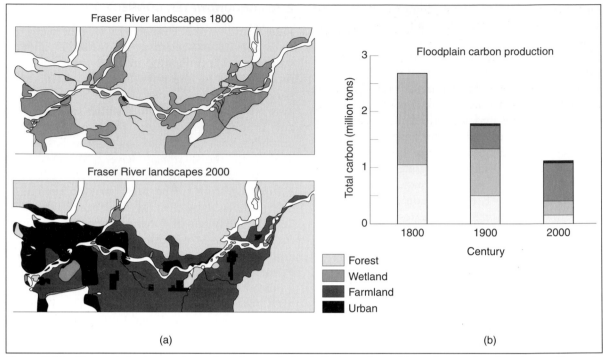

Figure 2.13 Changes in land use and organic carbon production in the lower Fraser River valley, western Canada, over the past 200 years. (a) Land use in 1800, dominated by forest and wetland, and in 2000, dominated by urban development and farmland, with forest confined to the edges of the valley. (b) Estimated total organic carbon production on the floodplain, showing the decline associated with forest and wetland loss. Total organic production has declined, and flood control strategies ensure that a lower proportion of this enters the river (from Healey & Richardson, 1996).

into Slovakia and Hungary was formerly a zone of deposition, creating an inland delta and associated wetlands, but the barrages constructed in Austria (**Section 2.6c**) now trap the sediment eroded from the Alps, and effectively starve this part of the river of an estimated 600 000 m³ of gravel per year. As a consequence, the channel is now eroding its bed, lowering the water table and threatening the wetlands (Pearce, 1994).

Reduction in organic matter inputs may be one of the most profound effects of anthropogenic catchment modification. Transformation of a formerly wooded catchment to agriculture or urbanisation will inevitably reduce the inputs of organic matter as numbers of trees or area of wetland are reduced. Healey and Richardson (1996) estimate that the total annual carbon production in the lower Fraser River valley in western Canada is now only 40% of that of 200 years ago, as productive forests and wetlands have been replaced by cultivated land and urbanisation (Figure 2.13).

Furthermore, dyking to prevent flooding has cut the river off from some of the remaining sources of carbon inputs. Clearly, land use modification on this scale will have more than a local effect upon the river, but will modify its productivity throughout the downstream reach and out into the estuary.

2.8 Summary

Rivers are characterised by unidirectional flow of water. The conditions at any one point on a river will, therefore, be determined not only by the surrounding catchment but also by discharge from upstream. Therefore, any process occurring upstream, in the river channel itself or in the catchment from which runoff originates, can potentially affect the ecology of the river further downstream.

Rivers are intimately coupled with their catchments, with which they interact through direct runoff, groundwater transfer and flooding. Rivers which flood regularly have a clearly defined floodplain.

The current is the primary determinant of community structure. It ensures that pelagic communities, if present, are poorly developed and that most species, particularly in eroding rivers, are benthic. The diversity of microhabitats on the river bed or in the lateral margins of the channel determines species diversity. Species assemblages change according to physical and chemical parameters. Longitudinal zonation is often present, mirroring abiotic changes that occur along a river.

A benthic organism entering the water column will drift downstream. This may be initiated as an active strategy if rapid movement is required, but will only be in a downstream direction. There is a variety of refugia employed by river benthos to avoid accidental dislodgement during periods of high flow, or to facilitate recolonisation following major disturbance.

Rates of primary production are generally low in rivers. The major source of energy is therefore detritus, from the catchment or from upstream.

Biotic interactions have a role to play in structuring the majority of river communities, but are continually tempered by disturbance. Unpredictable disturbance ensures that the most competitive species do not dominate to the exclusion of all others and, in this way, moderate disturbance can enhance the patchy nature of river beds and therefore their species diversity.

Colonisation of new streams can be slow, unless there is a direct freshwater connection to a potential source of colonists. Disturbance ensures a continuous turnover of species at a small spatial scale. Modification of physical conditions will profoundly affect community structure.

The River Continuum Concept integrates longitudinal biological connections, and the importance of the catchment and headwaters as energy sources, while the Flood Pulse Concept emphasises the role of lateral connections, particularly through floodplains. Additionally, many species utilise groundwater in alluvial sediments. Breaking these connections will severely reduce the potential productivity of a river system.

3

Estuaries

3.1 Introduction

An estuary may be defined as 'a semi-enclosed body of water having a free connection with the open sea and within which the sea water is measurably diluted with fresh water deriving from land drainage' (Cameron & Pritchard, 1963). Estuaries are not, however, simply zones where freshwater and marine ecosystems merge with each other. There is a gradation of chemical characteristics of estuarine water, particularly salinity, from the freshwater to the marine end but, of equal importance, estuaries are in a constant state of flux. River imports may vary seasonally or in response to local weather conditions, while marine inputs are determined by tidal movements. Zones of mixing, and the degree to which mixing occurs, can therefore vary on a daily or even more frequent basis.

In addition to water chemistry variations, estuaries are generally zones of deposition of sediment and are therefore structurally dynamic. The complex physical and chemical gradients in the estuary and the way they fluctuate impose physiological limits on the organisms able to exploit them. Estuaries therefore have an ecology that is very different from the adjacent freshwater or coastal systems.

3.2 The abiotic environment

3.2a TIDES IN RIVERS AND ESTUARIES

Tides are the periodic, normally twice daily,

Figure 3.1 At low tide, a drowned river valley type estuary typically has a low residual volume of water and extensive areas of intertidal sediment (Baie du Mont St Michel, northern France). (*Photo by M. Dobson*)

change in depth of the sea, resulting in an inflow (flood or rising tide) and outflow (ebb or falling tide) in coastal areas; they are described in detail in **Chapter 4** (**Section 4.2; Box 4.1**).

Estuaries are generally wide at the mouth and narrow at the head. As the tide moves into the estuary, it becomes constrained by the topography of the basin, being forced into a narrowing channel. Initially, this raises the height of the tidal wave, as a smaller estuary volume tries to accommodate the same volume of water, so that tides in the lower estuary are higher than those along adjacent open coasts. Indeed, some of the highest tidal ranges in the world, such as the Severn Estuary in southern England and the Baie du Mont St Michel in northern France (Figure 3.1), are in rapidly narrowing estuaries.

As one goes further up the estuary, the tidal range begins to decline as the bottom and the sides of the basin both exert a frictional drag on the advancing tidal wave, removing energy as it moves up the estuary. Waves of lower energy have lower amplitude for a given wavelength, so the tidal range is progressively reduced up the estuary, until at the tidal limit it is zero. The frictional force of the bed declines, however, with increasing depth. Therefore, as the tide rises and water depth increases, the incoming water experiences less friction and moves more rapidly. As the tide falls, however, depth is also reduced and friction slows the ebb of water. As a consequence, tides in estuaries are asymmetrical, with a rapid flood tide and a slow ebb tide (Figure 3.2).

In some estuaries, either as the result of sudden narrowing or a steepening of the river bed, a wall of water, or tidal bore, is produced when the rising tidal front forces the water to move more rapidly than a shallow water wave can freely propagate in water of that depth. It is analogous to the sonic boom, in which a pressure disturbance is forced to travel faster than the speed of sound. Most tidal bores are small, less than 0.5 m

high, but the Severn bore in southern England can be 1–2 m high, while the Amazon bore (the *pororoca*) can reach 5 m and move upstream at 12 knots (21.6 m s^{-1}).

3.2b ESTUARINE SALINITY

Estuaries may be classified according to their origin (**Box 3.1**). A more meaningful classification from an ecological perspective, however, is related to their salinity. An estuary will contain a gradient of salinity from fully saline (35–37) at the seaward end to fresh water (less than 3) at the landward end. This gradient is not a simple one, being influenced by the topography of the estuary, the tidal regime and the nature of the residual circulation. The position of the gradient also moves up and down the estuary with the tidal cycle.

Four fundamental types of estuaries can be differentiated on the basis of the relative distribution of salt water and fresh water and the degree to which they mix.

Salt wedge estuaries

Salt wedge estuaries develop where a river discharges into a virtually tideless sea. Fresh water is less dense than salt water and the river water spreads out over the surface of the sea water, which, if there is no tidal movement, can be regarded as a stationary salt wedge penetrating up the estuary (Figure 3.3a). Between the two water masses is a distinct halocline. However, as the fresh water is moving relative to the salt water, it exerts a shear stress across the interface, creating internal waves at the interface which, when they break, pull some salt water into the freshwater layer. Therefore a limited amount of mixing occurs. The water mixed up into the fresh water needs to be replaced so a weak flow up-estuary occurs in the saline waters.

The position of the salt wedge in the estuary is dependent on the freshwater flow. Under low flow conditions, the volume of freshwater input is small and salt water can penetrate much further inland than under higher flows. Open salt wedge estuaries only occur if sedimentation is low; high sedimentation produces a delta at the mouth of the estuary, such as those of the Nile and Mississippi.

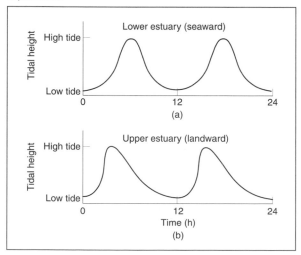

Figure 3.2 The effect of estuary topography on the tidal cycle. (a) In the lower estuary, as on the open coast, the flood tide and ebb tide occur at the same rate and a symmetrical tidal wave is produced. (b) In the upper estuary, where the channel is narrower and shallower, the flood is faster than the ebb and an asymmetrical pattern is produced (see text for explanation).

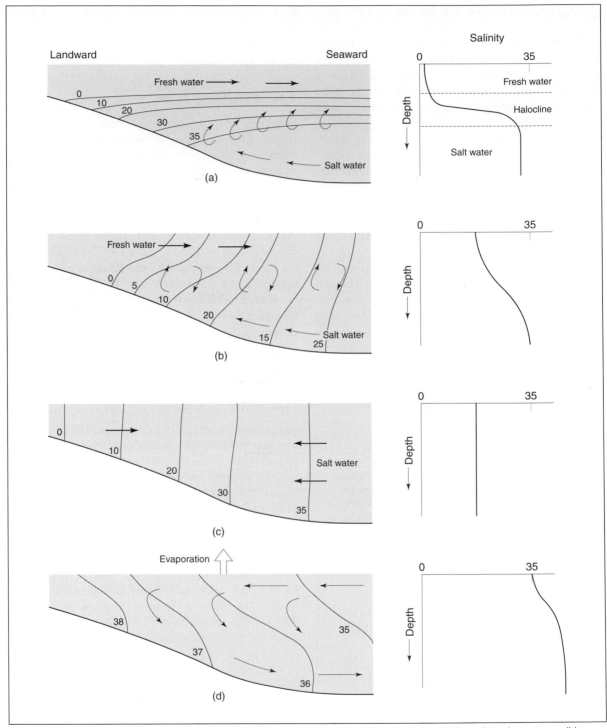

Figure 3.3 The idealised pattern of tidally averaged water circulation and salinity distribution in (a) a salt wedge estuary; (b) a partially mixed estuary; (c) a well mixed estuary; (d) a negative circulation estuary, showing salinity contour lines (see text for explanation). The graphs to the right show a salinity–depth profile from each estuary, illustrating how salinity changes along a vertical line from a single point on the surface.

BOX 3.1 TOPOGRAPHIC CLASSIFICATION OF ESTUARIES

Most of the world's river systems are in part tidal in their lower reaches, as a result of the rise in sea level during the last glacial recession, which ended 5000 years ago. During this period, sea level rose 100 m in 10 000 years, flooding low lying areas of what had been land during the glaciation, including river valleys and glacial channels.

Drowned river valley

This is the most common type of estuary in Europe, including, for example, all of the larger estuaries in the British Isles. Such estuaries are often V-shaped in section but are normally relatively wide and shallow, with a very high width : depth ratio (100 : 1 or more). At low water, extensive mudflats are revealed. They have low sedimentation rates and a low river flow.

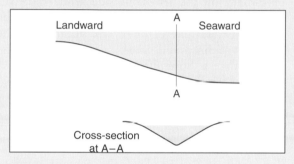

Fjord

Fjords are drowned glacial valleys and occur at high latitudes, including those in Norway (from which the name derives) and sea lochs of western Scotland. They tend to be U-shaped in section and are much deeper than drowned river valleys, with a width : depth ratio as small as 10 : 1.

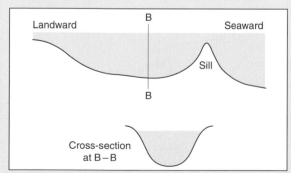

Fjords often have a sill at the mouth, a shallow lip created by the barrier-forming processes acting at the foot of the glacier which scoured out the depression (see **Box 6.1**). Therefore, the mouth of the fjord can be very shallow relative to the rest, restricting water circulation in the body of the fjord and, in some cases, leading to development of anoxia in the bottom waters. Some fjords have several sills, dividing the estuary into a number of distinct basins which vary in the level of exchange of water, so that, while some may always contain oxygenated water, others may be permanently anoxic. Intermediate basins may be periodically recharged with oxygenated water by storm surges pushing water over the sill. As the biota use the oxygen, and as organic matter builds up leading to more oxygen being used up by decomposition processes, so anoxia develops again. This persists until the next storm surge recharges the basin with oxygenated water.

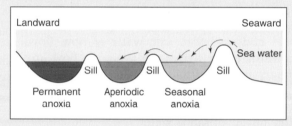

Fjords typically have very low freshwater inputs, which may be highly seasonal, for example most occurring in spring following the melting of winter snows. Sedimentation rates are low.

Bar-built estuary

Bar-built estuaries are predominantly tropical in distribution. They are drowned river valleys with high sedimentation rates, the sediment being deposited across the estuary mouth to form a partial barrier. The barrier, or bar, is formed of sediments which are not necessarily of river origin, but river sediments will be deposited behind it to generate extensive mudflats. Seasonal pulses of water such as floods associated with monsoons may periodically flush out the estuary, destroying all or part of the bar. This then gradually reforms after the monsoon when normal conditions prevail once more.

BOX 3.1 – CONTINUED

Tectonically formed estuary

A limited number of estuaries have been formed by the inundation of the land through land subsidence as a result of tectonic processes, usually at a geological fault. San Francisco Bay, in California, lying in the junction of two plates, is an example of an estuary formed by this mechanism.

Partially mixed estuaries

A partially mixed estuary is formed where rivers discharge into sea which has a moderate tidal range. Tidal currents are significant, so that the whole water body moves up and down the estuary with the tide. Therefore, in addition to the shear stress between the saline and fresh waters, there is a shear stress at the bed. This generates turbulence which is effective at mixing the two water masses, so that not only is salt mixed upwards, but fresh water is mixed downwards (Figure 3.3b). This two-way mixing leads to a less pronounced halocline and, as more salt water is now flowing seawards in the freshwater layer, the flow up the estuary in the bottom layer is also much larger. The total outflow at the mouth of the estuary is large and equals the inflow of fresh water plus the large inflow of saline water.

The currents produced by the mixing process are termed the residual currents, and are typically only 10% of the magnitude of the tidal currents which are superimposed on them. Residual currents are, however, important when considering transport processes in estuaries, of both sediments and pollutants.

Well mixed estuaries

In broad shallow estuaries where the tidal range is high and tidal currents are strong relative to the river flow, the water column becomes completely mixed. Such estuaries include the lower Thames and the Severn in southern England. In well mixed estuaries, salinity hardly changes with depth and there is no halocline (Figure 3.3c). As a result, although the estuary may have a large volume, the total outflow essentially equals the inflow of fresh water.

Although there is little vertical structure to a well mixed estuary, there may be horizontal vari-

ations in salinity. Most estuaries are funnel shaped, wide at the mouth and tapering inland. Coriolis force (**Box 1.1**) tends to generate circular movement of water within the relatively confined estuary basin, swinging both the inflowing sea water and the outflowing river water to the right in the Northern Hemisphere and to the left in the Southern Hemisphere. This means that, looking seaward from the river mouth, the sea water flows up-estuary on the left-hand side while the river water tends to flow on the right-hand side in the Northern Hemisphere, the reverse occurring in the Southern Hemisphere. Some mixing occurs laterally so that a horizontal residual circulation is produced (Figure 3.4).

Negative estuarine circulation

In areas such as the Arabian Gulf, high evaporation rates at the head of the estuary produce hypersaline waters which, being denser than

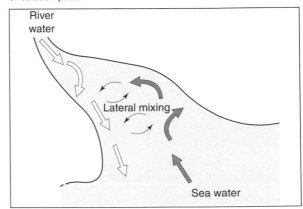

Figure 3.4 Lateral deflection of the riverine and seawater flows due to Coriolis force (deflected to the right in the Northern Hemisphere). This lateral mixing induces a horizontal circulation pattern.

normal sea water, sink and flow seaward, drawing in a surface flow of sea water. This results in a distortion of salinity gradients, or isohalines, to seaward in the bottom waters and is referred to as a negative estuarine circulation (Figure 3.3d).

3.2c SEDIMENTATION IN ESTUARIES

Estuaries are zones of sedimentation. River water emptying into the relatively large volume of an estuary and sea water entering its relative shelter both lose their momentum and are unable to retain the larger sediment particles that they are carrying. Aggregation of fine particles, described below, adds to sedimentation, so estuaries are typically dominated by soft sediment substrates, particularly fine muds.

Deposition of muds is encouraged by two processes which cause aggregation of very fine particles, increasing their weight and their tendency to be precipitated: biological aggregation and flocculation. Biological aggregation results from the ingestion of fine particles by filter-feeding animals and their subsequent egestion as components of faecal pellets, much larger than the original particles and therefore with higher settling velocities. Flocculation is aggregation of small clay particles into larger particles, resulting from molecular attractive charges. In fresh water, clay minerals tend to carry a negative charge and repel each other, whereas in saline waters these charges are swamped by free cations, allowing the natural molecular attractive forces to dominate. This is further enhanced by the absorption of clay particles on to the surface of organic molecules, which brings them into close proximity, allowing the molecular forces to take effect.

Muds are deposited only in areas of low flow, but as mud particles are cohesive once deposited, they resist resuspension by flows much stronger than those under which they were deposited. Muds are rich in organic matter, but the small particle size leads to small interstices – restricting opportunities for meiofauna and reducing oxygen penetration. The latter, combined with the high bacterial oxygen demand associated with decomposition of the organic matter, leads to anoxic conditions away from the surface. There are, therefore, two distinct ecological zones in the sediment, oxic and anoxic, separated by the Redox Discontinuity Layer (RDL), a zone of rapid change in oxygen levels and hence redox conditions (Figures 3.5 and 3.9).

Figure 3.5 Exposing a piece of sediment clearly shows the change from oxic (pale) to anoxic (dark) sediments at the RDL. It is also possible to see the local oxidation of sediment along the sides of macrofaunal burrows, in this case the amphipod *Corophium volutator* (Alnmouth, northern England). (*Photo by C. Frid*)

Sedimentation in salt wedge estuaries

Because the dominant flow in salt wedge estuaries is a seaward movement of fresh water at the surface, with only a weak inflow in the saline layer, virtually all suspended material in the estuary will be of river origin. Some of the coarser material settles through the halocline, but most is carried to sea, where flocculation and the reduced flow rates allow deposition. If flow rates are low and suspended load high, then deposition may occur immediately to seaward, forming a delta. Larger particles are carried by rivers as bedload, rolling along the river bed rather than being carried in the water column. At the head of the estuary, where the fresh water meets the salt wedge and flows over the saline water, the currents pushing this bedload along rise above the bed, and any material being transported as bedload will be deposited here, forming a shallow bar of coarse sediments immediately upstream of the salt wedge.

Sedimentation in partially mixed estuaries

In partially mixed estuaries, the potential to move sediment down-estuary by the freshwater flow is balanced by the up-estuary flow of the saline waters, ensuring that export of sediment from such estuaries is generally low. The landward flows adjacent to the seabed are, however, sufficiently strong to move material. A turbidity maximum is produced where the net landward transport ceases: this is essentially an area of extremely high concentration of suspended sediment, containing small particles up to 10 µm grain size, and is produced by the residual currents acting as a sediment trap.

In estuaries with low tidal ranges, suspended loads in the turbidity maximum are of the order of 100–200 mg l^{-1}, whereas in estuaries with high tidal ranges, such as the Severn, they may reach up to 100 times this concentration. The turbidity maximum does not remain stationary, but moves back and forth with each tide and with the spring–neap cycle (**Box 4.1**), while unusually high freshwater discharges may push it down and even out of the estuary.

Sedimentation in well mixed estuaries

The horizontal flow asymmetry in well mixed estuaries leads to the deposition, in the Northern Hemisphere, of marine sediments on the left bank (looking seaward) and river sediments on the right bank, the converse occurring in the Southern Hemisphere.

3.3 Ecological effects of the abiotic environment

The estuarine environment is rigorous and requires that its inhabitants possess adaptations to cope with a wide range of salinity concentrations, salinity fluctuations over short time periods and continual movement and deposition of sediment.

3.3a SALINITY

Estuarine organisms are divisible into three groups: those of marine origin, those of freshwater

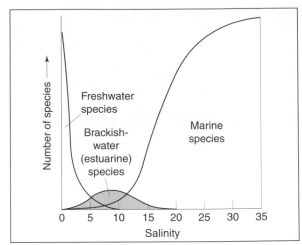

Figure 3.6 The pattern of species richness and the proportion of the biota comprising freshwater, brackish water and marine species along the estuarine salinity gradient.

origin and true estuarine species. The majority of organisms in an estuary are marine species, adapted to a fully saline environment, which are, however, euryhaline: able to tolerate the lowered and variable salinities of estuaries. Each species has its own salinity tolerance, but most can exist in salinities as low as 18, and some can cope with salinities as low as 5. Marine organisms which lack the ability to cope with the salinity regime in estuaries (stenohaline species) will occur at the mouth of estuaries but rarely penetrate into areas where the salinity falls below 25. Freshwater organisms (oligohaline species) are generally unable to tolerate salinities of more than 5 and so they, too, will not penetrate into the estuary proper. There is a range of salinity at around 7–10 in which there is a break in faunal distributions (Figure 3.6).

While freshwater species dominate in waters of lower salinity than this critical level and marine species become diverse at higher salinities, the number of species occurring within this range is very low. It would appear that it is difficult for marine organisms to osmoregulate down to such low concentrations, while freshwater organisms are unable to cope with the cell volume changes that these salinities induce.

The majority of truly estuarine species are able to cope with fully saline conditions, having evolved from marine lineages, but they are restricted to the estuaries by competition with stenohaline species or by a requirement for fine sediments on the bed. They are most common in the 5–18 salinity range where the number of potential competitors is limited (Figure 3.6), but require physiological adaptations to tolerate salinity fluctuations, often supplemented by behavioural responses which reduce the exposure to salinity stress.

Physiological adaptations

There has been considerable research into the physiological adaptations of estuarine organisms – see Remane & Schlieper (1971) and Rankin & Davenport (1981) for more detailed treatments. For most soft-bodied invertebrate species, the ability to osmoregulate is poorly developed. Many estuarine organisms, known as osmoconformers, are, however, able to tolerate wide fluctuations in their internal concentrations, by altering the concentration of amino acids within their cells to maintain cellular fluids at a similar concentration to the external medium (Figure 3.7). Such mechanisms are usually only possible down to salinities of 10–12, but some species are able to osmoregulate to maintain a constant concentration of ions in their body fluids, rather than allowing it to fluctuate according to external conditions (Figure 3.7). This ability occurs in polychaetes such as the lugworm (*Arenicola* sp.) and molluscs including mussels (*Mytilus edulis*), but is most developed in the crustaceans, where the presence of a shell reduces the permeability of the body, and there is evidence of the active uptake of ions and in some species the production of very dilute (hypotonic) urine. Intermediate between the osmoconformers and the regulators are those species which show partial regulation. This usually involves conforming to changes in environmental salinity over a certain range, but initiating active osmoregulation when environmental concentrations move outside this range.

Behavioural mechanisms

Most resident estuarine species employ behavioural mechanisms to reduce the exposure to

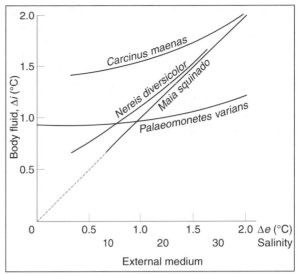

Figure 3.7 The varying concentration of body fluids of various animals in response to changing salt concentrations in the surrounding media, measured as depression of the freezing point (°C); approximate equivalent salinities are also shown. The spider crab (*Maia*) is unable to regulate its fluids. The ragworm (*Nereis*) is an osmoconformer: it is a poor regulator but has a high tolerance of reduced salinity. The shore crab (*Carcinus*) and prawn (*Palaemonetes*) will tolerate some dilution of their body fluids, but are good osmoregulators, holding their body fluid composition despite further changes in external concentrations (from Nelson-Smith, 1977).

salinity stress and hence obviate either physiological stress or the need to expend energy osmoregulating. Among molluscs, the most common behaviour is the closing of the shells, either by an operculum in the case of gastropods or by closing the valves in the case of bivalves, in which state the organism is unable to feed or respire. As intertidal species have adaptations to withstand aerial exposure, including sealing the valves and respiring either at low levels or anaerobically, these provide pre-adaptations to survival in estuaries.

Environmental fluctuations, including salinity, are much less marked within the sediment matrix than in the overlying waters (Figure 3.8). Thus species living in burrows are exposed to less salinity variation than epibenthic forms, some of which, including the mud snail (*Hydrobia*) and the brown shrimp (*Crangon*), will burrow during the ebb tide to avoid exposure to fresh water.

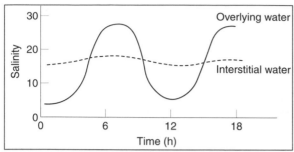

Figure 3.8 Comparison of salinity variation in interstitial water with the overlying water column through a tidal cycle. Salinity in the sedimentary environment varies much less than above the sediment surface, and is intermediate between the high and low tide values.

Anadromy and catadromy

The most dramatic changes in salinity are experienced by fish species which, at some stage in their life cycle, pass through the estuary on migration between the sea and fresh water.

Anadromy is the term given to life history patterns in which the adults migrate from the sea into fresh water to breed, salmon (Salmonidae) and sturgeon (*Accipiter* spp.) being the best known examples. All anadromous fish have well developed osmoregulatory capacity, but the pattern of movement from saline to fresh water varies between species, with some moving rapidly through the estuary while others, such as Atlantic salmon (*Salmo salar*), spend a period of several days resting and acclimatising in the estuary. Anadromy may be a mechanism for reducing competition between the adults and young by placing them in different environments, thus allowing exploitation of a different set of resources, or to avoid high levels of predation when the fish are young. It is much more common at high latitudes than in the tropics, possibly due to the greater diversity of the freshwater fish fauna in tropical regions filling all the available niches, so that the high levels of competition or the higher predation risk in these communities negate any advantage of moving out of the adult environment to breed. The importance of competitive exclusion is suggested by the observation that, in the absence of a typical freshwater fish fauna, marine species have invaded. This has been shown in the coastal

ponds of Hawaii (Brock, 1977) and the small estuaries of Newfoundland (Scott & Crossman, 1964).

Catadromy is the term given to the life history pattern of species such as the eel (*Anguilla* spp.) in which the adults live in fresh water but migrate to sea to spawn. It is much less common than anadromy. For these species, the need to return to the sea is probably related to an incomplete adaptation to the freshwater environment rather than the need to exploit a different habitat to the adults.

Seasonal changes in salinity

The strength of the tide varies over the tidal cycle, the spring–neap cycle (see **Box 4.1**) and over longer time periods, including an annual component. The amount of fresh water entering an estuary also follows a seasonal pattern, with certain times of year having a greater freshwater inflow than at other times. As the distribution of salt in the estuary and the mixing regime are determined, in part, by the balance between the inflow of fresh water and the mixing derived from tidal flows, so these patterns also vary seasonally. It is possible for a single estuary to display characteristics of a well mixed, a partially mixed and a salt wedge estuary at different times of the year, and mobile elements of the biota will move in response to these changes. Marine organisms often penetrate further up estuaries during drier seasons, when freshwater flows are lower than in wet seasons, and this is enhanced in north temperate regions by the fact that many species of marine zooplankton are able to tolerate lower salinities at higher temperatures (Soetaert & van Rijswijk, 1993), corresponding to the drier summer season. In the St Lawrence Estuary (Canada) the zooplankton can be divided into three groups, whose spatial distribution varies seasonally in response to the changing distribution of salinity, temperature, turbidity and circulation (Laprise & Dodson, 1994). It is, however, often difficult to separate a response to a seasonal change in the salinity distribution from a true seasonal behaviour. For example, movement of marine species into an estuary during the summer may be the result of dispersal as a response to increased population densities following reproduction, rather than simply following increases in estuarine salinity. Periodic events such as droughts can provide opportunities to separate these responses. During the period 1989–93, freshwater flows into the Thames Estuary were very low as a result of low rainfall and heavy extraction of water from the river upstream. During this period, salinity in the estuary remained high throughout the year and certain marine species, which had previously entered the estuary only during the summer months, persisted all year. Flow may also be an important component; the Chinese mitten crab (*Eriocheir sinensis*) successfully colonised the Thames Estuary during the drought period, after 60 years of occasional records, probably because winter flows, previously too rapid to allow establishment of young crabs, were significantly reduced (Attrill & Thomas, 1996).

3.3b SEDIMENTATION

Estuarine organisms must be adapted to sedimentation and, indeed, most have adopted a burrowing life style, which has the advantage that it offers a refuge from harsh abiotic conditions and from predation, particularly for those individuals which occupy the tidal flats, exposed at low tide. Burrowing species need to remain near the sediment–water interface in order to feed and respire, but remain buried whenever possible to reduce the risk of predation. A rapid burrowing ability allows any exposed individuals quickly to regain the safety of the sediment and any individual upon which sediment is deposited to return to the surface of the sediment.

While estuaries are regions of high sedimentation when assessed on geological time scales, the rates are rarely high enough to cause smothering of the fauna. Nevertheless, the high quantities of mobile sediment in certain turbid estuaries can exert an ecological pressure on the fauna, a problem compounded by the temporal variability in the quantity of sediment in suspension, which varies with both the ebb–flood and the spring–neap tidal cycles. Few species are able to tolerate the extreme conditions in the turbidity maximum. Those that do are either mobile epifauna such as the brown shrimp (*Crangon*

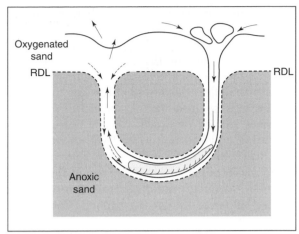

Figure 3.9 Effect of a lugworm (*Arenicola*) burrow on the position of the RDL, and hence the extent of oxygenated and deoxygenated sediments. The lugworm creates a respiratory current (solid arrows), drawing oxygenated surface water into its burrow, so that it may respire without surfacing; sediment upon which it feeds moves in the opposite direction (dashed arrows). Lugworms grow up to 15 cm in length.

crangon), or rapid burrowing infauna with heavy shells such as the cockle (*Cerastoderma edule*). The heavy shell lowers the chances of their being transported in the turbidity maximum and reduces predation pressure on individuals exposed by the scouring away of sediments.

Many of the larger infauna occupy anoxic zones, either to avoid predators or to exploit the undecomposed organic matter which aggregates; they construct burrows which they irrigate to obtain a flow of oxygenated water for respiration and, in doing so, generate localised RDLs along the length of the burrow (Figures 3.5 and 3.9). The majority of biological activity, however, occurs above the RDL where aerobic microbial communities develop on the particles and are available for exploitation by deposit-feeding macrofauna (**Section 3.4b**).

3.3c RESIDUAL FLOWS AND DISPERSAL

Irrespective of the type of estuary, all estuaries have a net seaward residual flow. This is not a problem for large mobile organisms, but organisms with limited mobility risk being flushed out of the estuary. Estuarine plankton overcome this by the use of behavioural mechanisms which utilise the residual circulation. Many estuarine zooplankters use a tidally synchronised vertical migration to maintain their position in the estuary (Hardy, 1956; Hill, 1991), travelling up-estuary in the near-bed flow during the ebb, rising to the surface waters to feed during the flood when the distance carried seaward will be least, before migrating down to be carried back up-estuary on the next ebb. Such cycles may also occur in response to seasonal changes. For example, the red-tide forming dinoflagellate *Prorocentrum mariae-lebouriae* is carried around Chesapeake Bay on the eastern coast of the USA in an annual migration cycle that covers 240 km. The centre of the *Prorocentrum* population is carried in out-flowing surface waters to the mouth of the bay by late winter, where it is mixed into the more dense coastal waters. Freshwater flow into the bay is low over winter because most of the precipitation into the catchment is retained as snow and ice. In early spring, however, melt water generates a large volume of freshwater runoff, establishing a strong density difference, or pycnocline, in the estuary, with salt water forced towards the bed as a salt wedge. The coastal water, containing *Prorocentrum*, flows up-estuary as a near-bed flow in the salt wedge. *Prorocentrum* accumulates just below the pycnocline and, in late spring, reaches the northern part of the bay, where the rapid shelving of the bottom forces the pycnocline upwards and increases turbulent mixing. This mixes nutrient-rich deep waters, containing the previously light-limited *Prorocentrum,* to the surface, allowing a red-tide bloom to occur in the upper part of the bay. The population is then carried seaward in the surface waters. Precipitation in summer is low and the seaward flow is therefore weak, so the centre of the *Prorocentrum* population is once again in surface waters at the mouth of the bay late in the following winter (Tyler & Seliger, 1978).

As the majority of estuarine benthos are of marine origin, broadcast breeding and a plank-tonic larval phase are the norm. Flushing of the larvae out of the estuary could result in the population being unable to replace itself, so estuarine benthos often show reduction of the larval phase, either by adoption of direct development (e.g. cer-tain strains of the polychaete worm *Capitella cap-itata*) or by reducing the length of time the larvae spend in the plankton (Grassle & Grassle, 1974; Giangrande *et al.*, 1994). Other species utilise a combination of active migration by the adults and the residual circulation to ensure that the popu-lation is maintained. For example, female blue crabs (*Callinectes sapidus*) in Chesapeake Bay migrate to the higher salinity waters near the entrance to the bay after mating. Spawning takes place on an ebb tide so that the larvae enter the coastal water mass (Epifano *et al.*, 1989). The young metamorphose approximately 40 days after hatching. For most of the year, the currents off the bay entrance sweep southward and would carry the larvae out of the system, but during June–August, which is the peak spawning time, wind stress consistently establishes a northward-flowing current inshore of the south-flowing mid-shelf current. So while larvae are initially ejected from the bay in a southeasterly direction, the strength of the ebb flow diminishes and they are entrained in the north-flowing nearshore cur-rent and returned northward. In September, the wind shifts towards the south-southwest and aids reinvasion of the Bay (Johnson & Hester, 1989).

3.4   Energy inputs

3.4a   PRIMARY PRODUCTION

The variety of primary producers is high in most estuarine systems, including phytoplankton, salt-marsh plants or mangroves growing at the margins, macroalgae and sea grasses growing in the intertidal, and microphytobenthos – dinofla-gellates and diatoms – inhabiting the spaces between the sediment particles. Estuarine environ-ments therefore rank among the most productive habitats on Earth, but primary production is unevenly divided among these groups, and is dominated by higher plants in adjacent wetlands, rather than within the water itself. Primary pro-duction by phytoplankton, although high compared with that in the open sea, is, therefore, relatively low (Table 3.1). Processes occurring in estuarine wetlands – saltmarshes and mangals

Table 3.1 Comparison of primary production by various components of the estuarine ecosystem and equivalent marine systems. Algal production is generally quoted as g C m^{-2} yr^{-1} (see **Box 6.2**), while macrophyte production is quoted as dry wt g m^{-2} yr^{-1}. Approximate conversions for algal production are given (in parentheses) to allow comparison: dry weight production is approximately twice C production

	Locality	g C m^{-2} yr^{-1}	dry wt g m^{-2} yr^{-1}
Estuarine			
Phytoplankton	Lynher, UK	82	(164)
	Grevelingen, Netherlands	130	(260)
	Barataria Bay, USA	210	(420)
Microphytobenthos	Lynher, UK	143	(286)
	Grevelingen, Netherlands	25–37	(50–74)
	Barataria Bay, USA	240	(480)
Sea grass (*Zostera*)	Range:		116–856
Saltmarsh	*Limonium*, UK		1050
	Salicornia, UK		867
	Spartina, UK		970
	Spartina, east coast USA		445–3990
	Spartina, west coast USA		1360–1900
Mangrove	*Rhizophora*, SE Asia		340–1580
	Sonneratia, SE Asia		790–1700
Marine			
Kelp (*Laminaria*)		1200–1800	(2400–3600)
Coastal plankton		100	(200)
Open sea plankton		50	(100)

Sources: from data summarised in Chapman (1997), McLusky (1989) and Wafar *et al*. (1997)

(mangrove swamps) – are considered further in **Chapter 7**; their contribution to energy budgets within the open water estuarine system is returned to in **Section 3.4e**.

The intertidal and subtidal zones (**Section 4.2**) support few macroalgae, as these require solid substrate on which to grow. Rooted flowering plants may, however, be present, including sea grasses, such as *Zostera* spp. and *Thalassia* spp., which can grow over extensive areas, creating what are known as sea grass meadows. The intertidal zone of estuaries along the Atlantic coast of North America is often dominated by *Spartina* *alterniflora*, a saltmarsh grass. Other *Spartina* species are, however, generally confined to the upper part of the shore, which is less frequently flooded, and therefore European saltmarshes, from which *S. alterniflora* is absent, do not extend far into the intertidal zone.

The rate of primary production within the estuary itself is determined particularly by the availability of light. Nutrients are rarely limiting in estuaries as they are carried in from adjacent coastal waters and with the freshwater inflow as well as being produced by decomposition and recycling processes within the estuary itself. The principal restriction on primary production in most of the estuary is the high turbidity – this limits phytoplankton growth in the water column and restricts microphytobenthos, macroalgae and sea grasses to a narrow littoral zone. Phytoplankton production may be further limited due to the flushing of the population out of the estuary.

3.4b DETRITUS

The principal source of organic matter in estuaries is detritus, which forms the basis of the estuarine food web. Most of the permanent fauna of the estuary are supported by detritus, either directly, as the detritivores, or indirectly, as predators of the detritivores. Estuaries are, therefore, similar to rivers in the importance of detritus inputs (see **Section 2.4b**). Indeed, much of their primary production is not utilised directly by grazing organisms, but incorporated into estuarine food webs as detritus. The sources of detrital material vary between estuaries but include autochthonous material, such as the remains of saltmarsh plants and mangroves, and allochthonous inputs, washed in by the river and also brought in from the open sea. Allochthonous material includes the carcasses of freshwater or marine organisms washed into the estuary and killed by osmotic stress, as well as marine macrophyte remains, while detrital inputs from the river, at the lower end of the river continuum (**Section 2.7b**), are dominated by FPOM, and the physical structure of adjacent wetlands, acting as traps for large particulate detritus (**Section 7.3c**), ensures that most export into the estuary is of FPOM or DOC broken down by processing within the wetland (Lefeuvre *et al.*, 1994). Most estuarine detritivores, therefore, are adapted to consume FPOM, and the shredding functional group is relatively rare.

Estuarine detritivores, in common with their freshwater equivalents, are unable to utilise much of the detrital carbon directly, as it is too refractory. They derive little nourishment from plant material itself, but rely instead upon it being conditioned by microbial action. In a process little different from that in rivers (**Section 2.4b**), estuarine detritus is utilised by a range of specialist decomposers – bacteria and fungi – which contain the necessary enzymes to break down and assimilate the refractile material and, in some cases, are able to synthesise amino acids from inorganic nitrogen. Predatory protists living on the particles consume these primary decomposers, and each other, creating a microscopic food chain on the particles. Most estuarine detritivores digest off the entire microbial community which grows on the detrital surface, including microbial predators; they also digest any labile organic matter present in the sediment including, in the case of intertidal or shallow water populations, microphytobenthos.

The rate at which detritus is conditioned is determined by its surface area. Microorganisms are restricted to the surface of detrital particles by their requirements for oxygen and dissolved nutrients, so the smaller the particle, the greater the microbial activity per unit volume it will support. Small particles, as a consequence, are more nutritious to detritivores than are large ones. The smaller detrital particles are poorer in carbohydrate but richer in protein than larger, fresher material, as a result of degradation of complex structural carbohydrates and the synthesis into microbial biomass (Figure 3.10). Physical damage in the gut of the macrofauna means that the particles egested tend to be smaller than those ingested, but they are often bound up into faecal pellets which are large and heavy and so sink relatively rapidly. Once on the sea floor, the mucus binding them together breaks down and the particles are colonised again by microbes, the increased surface area to volume ratio producing a greater relative area over which aerobic microbial breakdown can occur. This allows a higher relative biomass of microbes to be supported and so gives smaller particles a higher food value for the benthos. Thus, while progressive reingestion leads to the digestion of the more labile portion of the detritus, this may be compensated for by the development of richer microbial assemblages. Successive passages through macrofaunal guts lead to progressively smaller particles until they are too small to be handled by macrofauna and the remaining degradation proceeds by microbial activity.

Filter feeders are uncommon, despite the high density of detritus particles in suspension, probably because the concentration of suspended

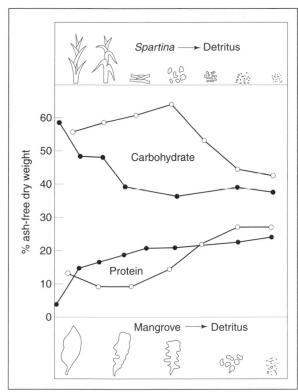

Figure 3.10 The changing composition and physical structure of *Spartina* (○) and red mangrove (●) leaves during conversion from living plant material to fine detrital particles. From McLusky (1989).

inorganic sediments means that they would catch large numbers of useless mineral particles, severely reducing the efficiency of their filtering apparatus. The majority of macroinvertebrate detritivores rely instead upon collector-gathering as a feeding mechanism. Most are infaunal species, feeding on detritus which aggregates on the bed of the estuary, while at the same time remaining in their burrows. They feed using appendages, with which they typically collect the entire surface layer, removing organic matter and egesting mineral particles. The European lugworm (*Arenicola marina*) is a good example of an estuarine detritivore (Figure 3.9). It lives in a U-shaped burrow, spending most time in the bottom chamber, but periodically reversing up the tail shaft to defecate at the sediment surface. The tail shaft is kept clear of sediment and water is drawn down it to provide a respiratory current over the gills, after which it

is pumped up the head shaft. The head shaft is filled with sediment, kept semi-fluid and oxygenated by the respiratory flow, which is ingested by the worm. The depression at the top of the head shaft preferentially traps small organic particles and the oxygenation of the head shaft sediments may stimulate bacterial conditioning of this material and production of bacterial biomass, hence the term 'gardening behaviour' for this activity (Hylleberg, 1975).

Decomposition and deoxygenation

High concentrations of detritus in estuaries mean that microorganisms can become very abundant, their large density leading to a heavy oxygen demand and, beneath the sediment surface, almost inevitable anoxia. Only the surface 2 or 3 mm is oxidised by oxygen from the overlying water. Below the RDL, sediments are usually black due to the buildup of iron sulphide, and decomposition proceeds by anaerobic processes which are much slower than the aerobic ones. There is increasing evidence, however, that some species of nematodes utilise the special conditions around the RDL for chemoautotrophic production by migrating across the RDL, carrying chemoautotrophic symbiotic bacteria into alternately reducing and oxidising concentrations. When beneath the RDL, they load up with reduced organic material, which is then oxidised using oxygen when above the RDL, yielding metabolic energy in the form of carbohydrates (Ott & Novak, 1989; Ott *et al.*, 1991; Polz *et al.*, 1991). This is analogous to the chemoautotrophy occurring in hydrothermal vents in the deep sea (**Section 5.6b**), but is, however, still ultimately based on solar radiation as the source of reduced compounds in the anaerobic breakdown of organic matter.

Anoxia of the water column is less common than that of sediments, but has frequently been observed in estuaries polluted by wastes containing high levels of organic material, such as sewage. As these wastes are degraded, they strip oxygen out of the water column and can cause widespread anoxia and the death of fish and other aquatic organisms. If this occurs, decomposition still proceeds but using the less efficient anaerobic pathways, and noxious gases such as hydrogen sulphide are liberated.

3.4c ENERGY BUDGETS

Energy flow in estuaries is more complex than that in rivers because, in addition to longitudinal and lateral interactions based upon the single direction of flow of the river, there is the complication of tides alternating the direction of flow of sea water. Rivers entering an estuary act as a source of energy and nutrients. Estuarine tides, by pushing back inflows from the river as the tide rises, can create tidal conditions in fully freshwater wetlands upstream, but the effect of this is generally to reduce export of wetland production into the river, rather than supplying inputs from the estuary itself (Simpson *et al.*, 1978). Saline wetlands on the periphery of an estuary may act as a net source or a sink, depending upon the structure of the wetland. On the Atlantic coast of the USA, immature saltmarshes act as a sink for dissolved and particulate materials, whereas mature saltmarsh is a source, exporting materials into the

estuary (Dame, 1994). European saltmarshes, in contrast, are generally net importers of energy, probably because they have little or no vegetation in the mid-intertidal zone, an area occupied by *Spartina alterniflora* in North America (Dame & Lefeuvre, 1994).

This difference is illustrated by the carbon energy budgets for two estuaries shown in Table 3.2. In the Dollard Estuary in the Netherlands, the main sources of carbon are from outside the estuary and phytoplankton production is very low, being limited by turbidity. In contrast, in Barataria Bay, Louisiana, the main source of carbon is the large stands of *Spartina* marsh in the estuary, but phytoplankton and microphytobenthic production are also important. These two estuaries represent extremes on the continuum of estuary type (McLusky, 1989). There are clearly large differences between them, but both act as traps for nutrients and POM, which are consumed and recycled within the estuary, although much is eventually exported into the coastal sea.

Table 3.2 Organic carbon budgets, expressed as g C m^{-2} yr^{-1} (with percentage), for the Dollard estuary (Netherlands) and Barataria Bay (Louisiana)

Source	g C m^{-2} yr^{-1}		Sink	g C m^{-2} yr^{-1}
Dollard Estuary				
Particulate C from North Sea and River Ems	37 100	(46%)	Consumed in estuary	35 560 (44.1%)
From potato flour mill	33 000	(41%)	Utilised in water column	7200 (8.9%)
Phytoplankton primary production	700	(0.9%)	Utilised in sediment	18 200 (22.6%)
Microphytobenthos primary production	9300	(11.5%)	Buried in sediment	9900 (12.3%)
From saltmarshes	500	(0.6%)	Bird feeding	260 (0.3%)
			Dissolved C to North Sea	45 040 (55.9%)
TOTAL	80 600		TOTAL	80 600
Barataria Bay				
From saltmarshes	297	(39.6%)	Consumed in estuary	432 (57.6%)
Phytoplankton primary production	209	(27.9%)	Exported to sea	318 (42.4%)
Microphytobenthos primary production	244	(32.5%)		
TOTAL	750		TOTAL	750

Sources: adapted from van ES (1977) (Netherlands) and Wolff (1977) (Louisiana)

3.5   Community structure

Estuarine food webs are relatively simple, as the range of species capable of tolerating the fluctuating environment is small and the majority have ecologically similar roles. The harsh physical conditions and fluctuating salinity of estuaries may suggest that their community structure should be dominated by disturbance. Secondary production can, however, be very high, those species which can tolerate the conditions reaching very high densities. This, in turn, gives scope for competition or predation to be important structuring processes.

3.5a   COMPETITION AND PREDATION

Given that detritus is such an important food source for estuarine species, one would expect competition for it to occur. There is, however, little evidence for competitive interactions. Some species apparently utilise different parts of the detrital resource spectrum, particularly particles of different sizes: Fenchel (1975) and Fenchel & Kofoed (1976), for example, have shown that the range of particle sizes ingested by two species of the mud snail *Hydrobia*, which correlates with snail size, differs where the species occur together at a site from the sizes ingested by each species when they occupy a site alone. While this represents one of the most widely quoted examples of character displacement, there are a number of serious problems with interpretation of data from such 'natural field experiments' due to, for example, the difficulty of getting truly matched sites (see Cherrill & James, 1987).

Subtle differences in salinity tolerance allow closely related species to replace each other along the estuarine gradient (Figure 3.11). Here one can envisage the equivalent niche being occupied along the estuary by a series of species which differ in their salinity tolerance, so that their competitive ability for resources varies, depending upon the environmental conditions.

Most of the secondary production in estuaries is in the macrofauna of the intertidal flats, whose populations are subject to intense predation pressure. Some predators, such as ragworms (*Nereis*), predatory gastropod molluscs and nemertene worms, occur as permanent residents of the estuarine benthic habitat, but the greatest predation pressure is applied by temporary inhabitants of the estuary, which exploit both the infaunal predators and the detritivores directly. At high tide, fish move on the intertidal flats to feed, while at low tide these areas can support vast densities of wading birds (Figure 3.12). Temporary predators are seasonal in their occurrence, wading birds using estuaries either on migration in the spring and autumn or as winter feeding grounds, while fish predation tends to be greatest in summer when adults are building up reserves for the winter and the following breeding season and when young fish are present. The production consumed by migratory predators is exported from the estuary when they migrate away and, in the case of birds, feeding is at low tide on mud flats while much defecation will occur in terrestrial roosting sites, with energy consequently being lost from the estuarine system (this may be compared with concentration of energy around roosts in freshwater wetlands; see **Section 7.3b**).

The role of predation in structuring estuarine benthic communities is equivocal. Some studies have concluded that it is important, in that epifaunal predators, birds and fish, reduce invertebrate densities, preventing competitive exclusion and helping to promote a diverse guild of deposit feeders. The estimated consumption of prey biomass by wintering birds in Europe, for example, varies from 6% in the Grevelingen Estuary in the Netherlands to 44% in the Tees Estuary in northern England (Baird *et al.*, 1985). However, other studies have shown no effect on deposit feeder communities of excluding epifauna (Frid & James, 1988). This may be because infaunal predators make use of the extra production, a form of competitive release. Alternatively, it may be that the epifauna selectively predate infaunal predators in preference to deposit feeders, as they tend to be larger, and therefore represent more valuable prey. Moreira (1997) estimated that wintering birds were consuming 12% of benthic biomass in the Tagus Estuary in Portugal, mainly in the form of a single bivalve species, *Scrobicularia plana*. He suggested, however, that much of this consumption was of the feeding siphons of the bivalves, rather than the entire

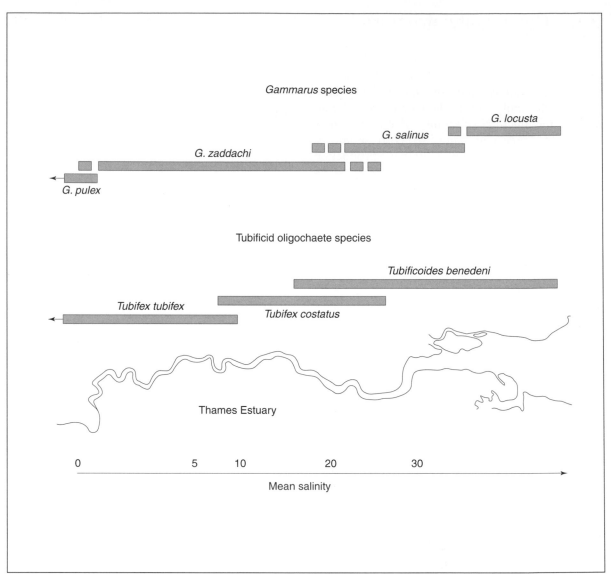

Figure 3.11 Zonation of macroinvertebrates along the Thames Estuary in relation to salinity. Several closely related species may occur within the same estuary, partitioning the habitat according to the salinity tolerance of each.

organism. Bivalves are able to regenerate lost siphons, providing a continuously renewed food supply for birds.

3.5b SPECIES DIVERSITY

Estuaries often contain a high diversity of habitats within a small area, including rocky shores, sand-flats, mudflats, saltmarshes, sand dunes, lagoons and subtidal sediments. However, with the excep-tion of the more terrestrial habitats, diversity within each habitat is usually highest at the sea-ward end and decreases up-estuary (e.g. Barr *et al.*, 1990), largely as a result of the progressive loss of species intolerant of low or fluctuating salinity and the absence of a specialist estuarine fauna to replace them (**Section 3.3a**). The domi-nance of soft sediments is also a determinant of diversity, however, as it limits the fauna to those species able to tolerate or exploit this single habi-

ments in the Thames Estuary is an area of particularly high diversity, because dredging has increased habitat heterogeneity in a location sheltered from physical disturbance by the steep sides of the channel (Attrill *et al.*, 1996).

An exception to the low biodiversity of soft sediments is the avian fauna. In estuaries on migration routes, and in which the climate is ameliorated by oceanic influences, a high diversity of wading birds is recorded. Estuaries on the west coast of the UK, for example, have resident winter populations of species unable to cope with the harsher conditions found in estuaries on the coast of mainland Europe, and support internationally important populations of many species (UK Department of the Environment, 1994).

Estuaries are utilised by many fish species as nursery areas. The young may be released in the estuary or the spawning site may be located so that currents carry the larval fish into the estuaries. Here the young benefit from reduced competition with the adults, reduced predation pressure and rapid growth by exploiting the high densities of infauna and planktonic detritivores (Harden-Jones, 1968).

3.6   Succession

Geologically, estuaries are short-lived. Most of those we see today were formed when sea levels rose at the end of the last glaciation and many will have disappeared given a similar length of time into the future. The reason for this is that estuaries act as zones of accumulation of sediment, by which process they are gradually infilled. Accretion of sediment allows colonisation by plants which stabilise mudflats and enhance further accretion and vegetation development. In the absence of strong currents or storms, coastal wetland vegetation will gradually encroach deeper into the estuary. Alluvial sediments raise the estuary above sea level, enhancing terrestrialisation or development of freshwater wetlands, while longshore drift may form a bar across the mouth of small estuaries, eventually excluding inflow of sea water and creating a lagoon which gradually becomes fresh water.

Intermittent exclusion of sea water leads to widely fluctuating conditions. Lake St Lucia, on

Figure 3.12 Predation in estuaries. (a) At low tide, large flocks of birds feed on the exposed benthos of the mudflats. Here, as the tide rises, oystercatchers (*Haematopus ostralegus*), formerly dispersed throughout the mudflat, aggregate on exposed rocks (Tanskey Rocks, Dee Estuary, northwest England). (*Photo by S. Dobson*) (b) Bite marks in the sediment provide evidence for fish feeding activity at high tide. (*Photo by C. Frid*)

tat; solid substrates, such as sunken ships, will produce zones of dramatically increased diversity. The shipping channel dredged through the sedi-

the Indian Ocean coast of South Africa, is a lagoon connected to the sea by a channel, the Narrows, 10 km in length. Maximum freshwater flow into the lagoon is during the summer, when excess water readily discharges to the sea through the Narrows and salinity in the lagoon ranges from negligible levels at river mouths to 35 towards the estuary mouth. During drought periods, however, water ceases to flow out through the Narrows, whereas occasional tidal incursions flow in, followed by evaporation which produces salinities typically approaching 50 towards river mouths. Hypersalinity is compounded by strong littoral drift, which can temporarily close the mouth of the estuary, stopping further marine incursions which would dilute the lagoon water; under these circumstances, salinities of up to 100 have been recorded. The biota of Lake St Lucia is a fluctuating mixture of marine and freshwater forms, the salinity fluxes creating instability and, occasionally, extensive mortality (Orme, 1975). In due course, sedimentation will dam the Narrows and the lake will become fresh water, but until such time the conditions, and therefore community structure, will remain unstable.

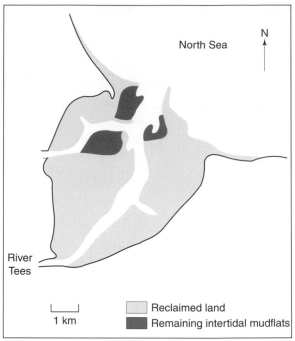

Figure 3.13 The extent of former tidal mudflats and saltmarshes reclaimed from the Tees Estuary, northeast England since the early 19th century. Most is now used for industrial development.

3.7 Human impacts on estuaries

3.7a DEVELOPMENT ON ESTUARIES

Estuaries have been utilised by humans for many thousands of years. Initially they were good sites for the collection of shellfish and for hunting fish and birds. Later they provided important transport functions, with trading vessels using the relative shelter of estuaries to unload or as a route inland. As a result, trading centres developed on estuaries and these later became large towns and cities. Seven of the world's 10 largest capital cities are built on estuaries and it is estimated that, in the UK alone, around one-third of the population lives in towns and cities associated with estuaries.

The extensive tidal flats of estuaries have long been seen as easy sites of land claim, to form grazing meadows or other agricultural land. Large areas of land around the Wash in eastern England were claimed from the sea as early as Roman times. In other estuaries the land is utilised for industrial development (Figure 3.13), with the advantage that the estuarine waterway provides a good route for transport of raw material and products. The development of urban and industrial centres on estuaries has frequently been facilitated by the availability of good building land on the wide level floodplain and by land claim of intertidal flats. Land claim removes the most productive part of the estuarine system – the tidal flats – fundamentally affecting its overall productivity. It also tends to increase sedimentation in the main channel, which then raises the costs of maintenance dredging for port operators and may affect the ability of the estuary to assimilate waste products. Most large estuaries have lost at least some of their natural intertidal areas to land claim and many are now constrained to a channel flowing between artificial banks.

3.7b POLLUTANTS IN ESTUARIES

As the population living adjacent to an estuary grows, so does the need to dispose of waste, and the proximity of the estuary makes it a convenient waste disposal route. Initially the dominant waste inputs were organic material, particularly sewage, but as industry developed and chose estuarine locations for ease of transport, so industrial waste disposal in estuaries increased. It is estimated that the combined discharges from the estuaries of the Elbe, Humber, Rhine, Scheldt, Tees, Tyne and Wear are second only to atmospheric deposition as a source of contaminants into the North Sea (North Sea Task Force, 1993). The use of estuaries for human waste disposal has led to many environmental problems, including the buildup of heavy metals from industrial wastes in the sediments and the food chain, including their presence in fish for human consumption, and the production of long stretches of anoxic conditions in estuaries receiving large quantities of organic pollution.

If a pollutant is discharged continuously into an estuary from a point source, it will reach a steady-state distribution in which the quantity of pollutant added is equal to the quantity of pollutant lost at the mouth. Therefore, we can model the flushing of the pollutant in the same way that the overall flushing time of the estuary is calculated (see **Box 3.2**), so that it is possible to make quantitative predictions about the distribution of pollutants and advise on the siting of discharges and rates of input which can be accommodated. Well mixed estuaries have the lowest capacity to deal with pollution, because the residual flow is weak and the total net outflow of pollutant loaded water equals the river inflow. So the Thames Estuary can deal with as much pollution in the lower estuary where it is 30 km wide as the River Thames at Reading where it is 20 m wide! The intuitive approach, that a large area and strong tidal currents equal good flushing, has led to problems in estuaries such as the Thames, Severn and Humber. This problem can be exacerbated by horizontal circulation, in which a discharge near the estuary mouth on the left bank (Northern Hemisphere – the right bank in the Southern Hemisphere) is carried a considerable distance up

estuary before being mixed into the outward flow (Figure 3.4). In fact, the greatest capacity for flushing a pollutant out to sea is the partially mixed estuary where the total outflow, and therefore dilution capacity, is the freshwater inflow plus a large saline inflow. However, care must be exercised not to discharge into the region of up-estuary flow near the bottom.

In many countries, recent decades have seen considerable improvement in the treatment of wastes before discharge to estuaries, relieving many of the problems in urban and industrialised estuaries. However, there is growing concern that changes in land use practice in the catchment are affecting the ecology of many estuaries, including a number of rural, and previously assumed to be pristine, systems. The main area of concern is eutrophication (**Box 6.2**). The application of high doses of, often artificial, fertilisers combined with changes in land use, such as deforestation, has increased nutrient loads entering the estuary via the inflow waters. In many estuaries, the growth of dense mats of filamentous green algae, such as *Enteromorpha*, appears to be linked with these increased nutrient levels (Raffaelli *et al.*, 1989b). The algal mats blanket the mudflats, smothering sea grass beds and infauna, while the reduced contact between the sediments and the water column brings anoxic conditions right up to the sediment surface, leading to the death of most infauna and changes in the rate of organic matter breakdown and nutrient recycling in the system.

3.7c BARRAGES

The fundamental importance of the dynamic physical regime to the functioning of the estuarine ecosystem is clearly revealed when physical barriers are erected across the estuary which interrupt these natural processes – see Gray (1992) for a review. Barrages or dams may be erected for a number of purposes, including providing permanent water bodies for amenity reasons (e.g. Cardiff Bay barrage in South Wales), preventing up-estuary penetration of water carrying high concentrations of pollutants, providing storm surge barriers, or generating electricity from the power of the tides. Storm surge barriers, such as the Thames Barrier in London, are designed to allow

BOX 3.2   ESTUARINE FLUSHING AND THE CONSERVATION OF SALT

Flushing time

It is possible to calculate an estuary's flushing time, the time it takes for the average particle of water to move through the estuary. To do this we use the mixing of salt water as a marker. The flushing time (T_F) is given by

$$T_F = Q / R \qquad (1)$$

where Q is the volume of river water in the estuary and R is the river inflow rate.

In reality this is calculated by measuring the fractional freshwater concentration (f) in a number of sub-divisions of the estuary,

$$f = \frac{S_s - S}{S} \qquad (2)$$

where S_s is the salinity of sea water and S is the salinity (tidal average) at a particular point in the estuary, then

$$Q = \int f dv \qquad (3)$$

(i.e. integrated over the entire volume of the estuary). This is a very laborious method, requiring a large amount of data to be collected.

Estuarine tank model

An alternative is to use an analogue approach, such as the tank model. Here the estuary is visualised as a basin or water tank with a tap allowing in fresh water, another allowing in saline water and an overflow pipe through which the outflow water leaves the estuary. Such models assume that the sea is well mixed so that the salinity of the inflowing sea water is not influenced by the salinity of the outflowing estuary water. If we assume a steady state, then the amount of salt entering the estuary will equal the amount of salt leaving. If the salinity of river water, $S_R = 0$, the river inflow is R per tide, the salinity of sea water is given by S_s and the volume moving in per tide is P, the volume of the tidal prism, then the incoming volume of salt is given by

$$(R \times 0) + (P \times S_s) \qquad (4)$$

The amount leaving the estuary is the total outflowing volume ($R + P$) multiplied by the salinity of the outflow (S), i.e.

$$(R + P) \times S \qquad (5)$$

These two must balance, so that

$$(R \times 0) + (P \times S_s) = (R + P) \times S \qquad (6)$$

Rearranging gives us

$$S / S_s = P / (R + P) \qquad (7)$$

From this we can estimate the fractional freshwater content of the estuary from the following equations:

$$\hat{f} = \frac{S_s - S}{S} \qquad (8)$$

$$\therefore \hat{f} = 1 - \frac{S}{S_s} \qquad (9)$$

$$= 1 - \frac{P}{R + P} \qquad (10)$$

$$= \frac{R}{R + P} \qquad (11)$$

Therefore, based on the assumption that our estuarine tank is a good model,

$$\hat{Q} = \hat{f} v = \frac{R V}{R + P} \qquad (12)$$

where V is the mean (over a tidal cycle) volume of the estuary. Therefore

$$\hat{T}_F = \frac{\hat{Q}}{R} = \frac{V}{R + P} \qquad (13)$$

It is, therefore, possible to estimate the flushing capacity of an estuary from the river input (e.g. data from river gauging stations), the tidal prism (calculated from published tide tables and nautical charts) and the volume of the estuary (estimated from nautical charts). This approach assumes that the entire estuary is mixed within a tidal cycle. This is not true for most estuaries, but is acceptable for smaller basins.

free propagation of normal tides into the estuary, and are closed only to prevent storm surges penetrating the estuary and flooding low lying areas. If current predictions of sea level rise are accurate, considerably more storm surge barriers will be built in the near future but, as they are only closed relatively infrequently, they have low impact on estuarine ecology.

Barrages constructed to impound water for amenity use or to maintain water quality are often closed most of the time. They therefore act as a barrier to the propagation of tides up-estuary, prevent sediment movement and interfere with migration patterns, although the latter are frequently addressed for fish by the construction of fish passes or 'ladders'. If the barrage is rarely opened, the impounded water body will become increasingly fresh in character, initially taking on the characteristics of a saline lagoon and, if isolation is prolonged, a freshwater lake.

The large tidal range in some estuaries, caused in part by the channelling effect of the estuary on the tidal wave, has led to a number of proposals to build tidal barrages to generate electricity. The basic premise is that the tide flows in through open sluices, which are closed at high tide, impounding the water. After the tide has fallen a certain level, sluices are opened to allow the impounded water to run out through turbines, which generate electricity. At La Rance in northern France, a tidal barrage has been operating since 1966, producing 544 million kilowatt-hours of electricity each year from the 13.4 m tidal range. Pilot scale plants operate in the Bay of Fundy, eastern Canada, and in Russia and China. Unfortunately, no ecological studies were carried out at La Rance before construction, whereas the proposed Severn Tidal Barrage in the UK has seen a large amount of work over many years directed towards predicting the ecological consequences of the development (Mitchell & Probert, 1983; Gray, 1992).

Theoretically, the principal problems associated with tidal barrages are that the reduced flow rates will alter patterns of sedimentation, salinity and flushing of pollutants, thereby affecting water quality. Pollutants discharged above the barrage will be impounded, giving them a longer residence time and potentially a greater exposure to the biota. Riverine sediments will build up above the barrage, but if, as is the case in the Severn, marine sediments normally dominate, the area above the barrage would be starved of sediment. The decreased turbidity could lead to algal blooms, especially if nutrients were also being impounded behind the barrage. Following an algal bloom, or as a result of detrital matter accumulating above the barrier, problems of anoxia could be encountered. Subtidal communities would be directly impacted by the changes in sedimentation and indirectly by any changes in algal production. Intertidal communities would also be affected by the changed tidal regime. Below the barrage, the tide ebbs more slowly than normal, and may never fall as low as previously – reducing both the extent and duration of exposure of the intertidal. Above the barrage, the regime imposed is a rapid flood tide, and a slow ebb with the tidal range much reduced – again significantly reducing the extent and exposure of the intertidal. The most profound effect of this is on the bird fauna, the shortened feeding times and smaller areas available having potentially dramatic consequences for both resident and migrating wading birds. However, these predictions remain untested.

3.8   Summary

Estuaries are zones of transition between freshwater and marine environments. They are complex systems containing many environmental gradients, but are characterised particularly by salinity gradients. The physicochemical conditions in an estuary are determined mainly by relative volumes of salt and fresh water. Tidal influences ensure that conditions are continually fluctuating.

Estuaries are zones of deposition of sediment from both rivers and the sea. Soft sediments, therefore, dominate.

The salinity distribution in the estuary is the primary determinant of the distribution of organisms. Few freshwater organisms can tolerate salinities in excess of 5, while few marine organisms can cope with salinities below 18, although most can survive in salinities between this and full sea water. True estuarine species, which are therefore most common in the salinity range 5–18, are few in number. There appears to be a critical salinity range at around 7–10 which causes a break in faunal distributions.

Estuarine species adapt to sedimentation mainly by adopting a burrowing life style. Planktonic species withstand the net seaward flow by taking advantage of differential surface and near-bed flows, and follow daily or seasonal cycles of movement.

Estuaries are among the most productive of habitats, yet much of this production is based upon detritus derived from external sources and is exported to coastal systems. Primary production is concentrated into peripheral wetlands, that within the water being light-limited, due to turbidity. Most estuarine invertebrates are, therefore, generalist deposit feeders.

Most predators are temporary members of the estuarine fauna: wading birds at low tide and marine fish at high tide. Estuaries provide important feeding grounds for large populations of wading birds and waterfowl and are utilised by coastal fish populations as nursery areas.

In contrast to productivity, diversity is low, a combination of fluctuating salinity, lack of habitat heterogeneity and geological transience of estuaries. Of these, habitat heterogeneity is probably the primary determinant.

Urban and industrial development has taken place on many estuaries, often on land claimed from the sea. Waste produced from these developments has frequently been discharged into the estuary and many estuaries show signs of human impacts, including high levels of heavy metals and sewage contamination.

4

The Coastal Zone

4.1 Introduction

Coastal seas may be defined as those lying between the shore and the edge of the continental shelf, generally at around 200 m depth. They differ from the open ocean not just in their depth, but in the greater significance of physical processes such as tidal mixing and wave action. Inputs from land can influence water chemistry and mixing processes, particularly around the mouths of large rivers, and large discharges of fresh water can extend estuarine conditions (see **Chapter 3**) out

into the open sea, as occurs along the southern coast of Alaska and the mouth of the Amazon. Conversely, a heavily indented coastline in an arid subtropical zone, such as the Gulf of California or the Red Sea, will create areas of high salinity, as evaporation exceeds the rate of mixing from the open ocean. The most important determinant of community structure along the coast itself is the action of tides – the vertical displacement of water which effectively moves the margin of open water up and down the shore at regular, frequent intervals.

BOX 4.1 PRINCIPAL TIDE-GENERATING FORCES

Tides are the response of the hydrosphere to the gravitational attraction of the Moon and the Sun. This gravitational force also raises tides in the Earth's crust, but it is so dense and viscous that they are not visible.

The lunar tide

The Earth and Moon form a single system, revolving around a common centre of mass with a period of 27.3 days. As the Earth is much larger and heavier than the Moon, the common centre of mass lies within the Earth, although offset from its centre. Tidal movements are caused by a combination of centrifugal force, which acts away from the common centre as the Earth and Moon move around it, and the gravitational pull, which acts towards the centre of the Moon.

Ignoring the spin of the Earth on its own axis for now, the Earth–Moon system rotates, eccentrically, about the common centre of mass. The total centrifugal force within the Earth–Moon system exactly balances the gravitational attraction between the Earth and the Moon. It is this balance which keeps the Moon in orbit, so that we neither lose the Moon nor collide with it. The centrifugal forces operate parallel to a line joining the centre of the Earth to the centre of the Moon.

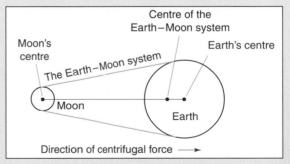

BOX 4.1 – CONTINUED

Every point on Earth experiences the same centrifugal force. The gravitational attraction of the Moon, in contrast, varies with distance from the Moon, as the inverse square of the distance, and is not the same everywhere. Its direction is always towards the centre of the Moon and therefore, except on the centre line, is never parallel to the direction of the centrifugal forces. The result of the centrifugal and gravitational forces at any point on the Earth is the tide-producing force.

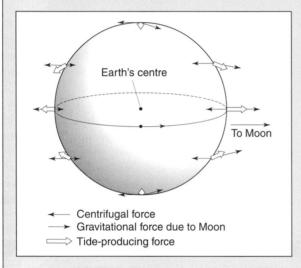

Centrifugal force
Gravitational force due to Moon
Tide-producing force

The tide-producing force has two components, one vertical and the other horizontal. The vertical force acts against the pull of the Earth's gravity, whereas the horizontal component, the tractive force, is essentially unopposed, except by seabed friction, and is the primary mover of water.

The tractive force acts to move water over the surface of the Earth to produce two bulges of water directly towards and away from the Moon. As the Earth rotates upon its axis, a point on its surface will pass under these two bulges of water and experience a semidiurnal pattern of two high tides with periods of low water in between.

Variations in the lunar tide

The lunar tide varies with the Moon's declination. The Moon's position is not fixed above the Equator, but moves 28° either side of the equatorial plane every 27.2 days. When the Moon is at a large angle of declination the plane of the two tidal bulges will be offset, and their effect at a given latitude will be unequal, particularly at mid latitudes. This produces a diurnal inequality in the semidiurnal tides, a large high tide being followed by a small high tide.

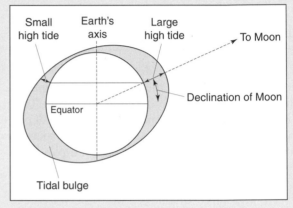

Another source of variation is the Moon's elliptical orbit. At its closest approach to the Earth, perigee, the tide-producing force is 20% above average, while at apogee, its greatest distance away, the force is 20% below average. The interval between successive perigees is 27.5 days.

The solar tide

The Earth–Sun system behaves in exactly the same way as the Earth–Moon system, producing two bulges of water on a line joining the centre of the Earth and the centre of the Sun. However, although the Sun is more massive than the Moon, it is considerably further away, and as a result of the inverse square law, its influence is smaller. The solar tide-producing forces are about 0.46 of the lunar ones.

BOX 4.1 – CONTINUED

The solar tide is affected by the Sun's declination, which varies by 23° each side of the equatorial plane over a yearly cycle. The Earth's orbit is elliptical, thus at perihelion, closest approach, the solar tidal forces are increased, while at aphelion (most distant) they are decreased, but this effect causes a variation of only about 4%.

Interaction of lunar and solar tides

At New Moon, when the Moon and Sun are in line (i.e. the Moon is in syzygy), such that a single line will pass through all three centres of mass, the two tidal bulges are additive and the difference between high and low water is greatest, creating a spring tide. At Full Moon, the Moon is once again in syzygy, and spring tides again occur. These events are (27.3)/2 days apart, i.e. approximately every two weeks.

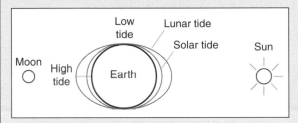

Between the New and Full Moons the Moon is in quadrature, at either first quarter or third quarter. Now the solar tide does not act to increase the height of the high waters, but does increase the height of the low tide, creating a neap tide.

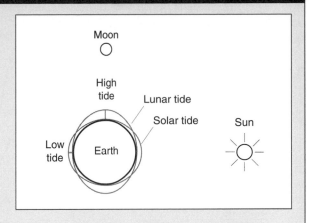

The Highest Astronomical Tide

The Highest Astronomical Tide is produced by the maximum tide-rising force, that is with the Earth at perihelion, the Moon at perigee, the Sun and Moon in conjunction (New Moon), with the Sun and Moon both at zero declination and with the planets in optimum alignment. This combination would produce a tide of greatest height (Highest Astronomical Tide or HAT) and lowest low (Lowest Astronomical Tide or LAT).

At Newlyn in Cornwall, used as the standard for sea level on British Ordnance Survey maps, the normal tidal range is about 3.5 m, the spring tide range is about 5 m, and the HAT to LAT range is 6 m. The next HAT is due in about AD 6580!

4.2 The abiotic environment

4.2a TIDES

Tides are the periodic movement of the sea, generated by the gravitational attraction of the Sun and Moon on the hydrosphere (see **Box 4.1**). The effect of tidal activity is the periodic immersion and emersion of a strip of the coastal zone, as the sea level rises (flood tide) and falls (ebb tide) in sequence, normally twice per day. Additionally, over a period of about 14 days the tidal range follows a spring–neap cycle (Figure 4.1). Spring tides, with the largest tidal range, occur at approximately fortnightly intervals, following which the tidal range decreases to the neap tides (approximately 7 days after the spring tides) and then increases again to the next set of spring tides. Local effects can modify these patterns, especially in bays which may have their own harmonic frequencies. In enclosed seas, such as the Mediterranean, the topography of the basin and the local tide-generating forces produce a tidal range so small that the sea appears tideless, whereas the funnelling of estuaries such as the Baie du Mont St Michel produces a tidal range

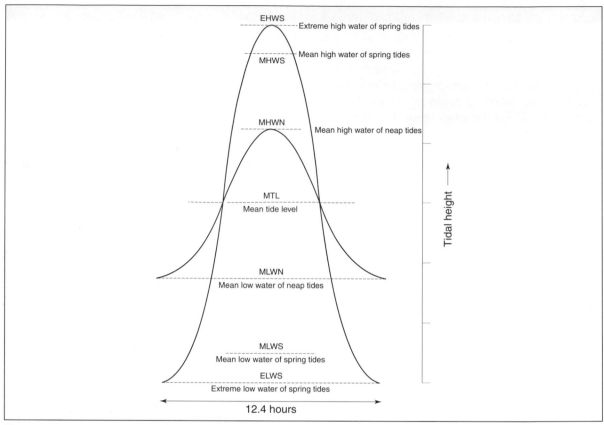

Figure 4.1 A typical open coast tidal curve, showing the symmetrical nature of the flood and ebb and the slow rise from low water followed by a rapid period of flood and a slowing just before high water. The various abbreviations used in describing tidal heights are defined. Note the difference in tidal range between spring and neap tides.

much higher than that experienced along the adjacent open coast (**Section 3.2a**).

Tides create a series of zones at the land–water interface, defined by the degree to which they are affected by the variation in water level. The area periodically covered and uncovered by the sea is referred to as the intertidal or littoral zone, the area permanently covered by the sea being the subtidal or sublittoral zone. Immediately above the littoral is the splash zone, or supralittoral, which, while never covered by the sea, is influenced by the splash and spray of saline waters. To these three zones may be added the supralittoral fringe, which is only covered by splash from storm waves, and the sublittoral fringe, the lower part of the shore only uncovered by particularly low spring tides. The supralittoral fringe marks the lowest extent of terrestrial vegetation, while the sublittoral fringe is a zone of much higher diversity than the littoral zone as a result of the presence of a number of species unable to withstand prolonged desiccation. Note that the term 'littoral' is used in a different context when applied to lakes (**Section 6.3a**).

Tidal variations within the littoral zone create a range of conditions. Only the zone within the range of neap tides is covered and exposed with every tidal cycle, while the highest and lowest parts of the littoral are covered and exposed, respectively, only by spring tides. During neap tides, the very top of the shore is never submerged, while the lowest part is never exposed to the air. A result of this variation in the pattern of inundation is a vertical zonation of physical conditions, which is most clear on rocky shores. Sandy shores retain water within their sediments, which can

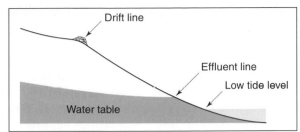

Figure 4.2 Zonation of physical conditions on sandy shores. The water table within the sediment may be higher than the surface water, extending the sublittoral up the shore, although this varies with beach type. The drift line marks the position of high tide, while the effluent line marks the elevation to which the water table extends.

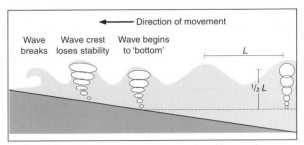

Figure 4.3 Water movement and wave breaking on the shore. $L = 1$ wavelength. See text for more details.

effectively raise the sublittoral to a higher elevation than the low water mark (Figure 4.2), particularly in dissipative beaches, which are low gradient and experience reduced wave action relative to higher gradient reflective beaches.

The intertidal is a harsh environment which varies between extremes of submergence and aerial exposure over very short time periods. A temperate rocky shore in summer, with low water at midday, will be exposed to high light levels, temperatures, desiccation rates and salinity (due to evaporation); when the sea returns, coastal seawater conditions are restored within seconds. In winter, low water just before dawn will expose the shore biota to extremely low temperatures, while rain at any time of year may reduce salinity in pools almost to fresh water in a few hours.

4.2b WAVES AND CURRENTS

Waves are the result of energy being transferred between two fluids moving at different rates. They are a familiar feature at the sea surface, caused by the differential motion of the air and sea, but internal waves are also produced within the ocean along surfaces of different density, such as the thermocline (**Box 1.3**) in the open sea and haloclines (**Section 3.2b**) in estuaries. Waves are transient phenomena which transfer energy but not mass. Water below a wave in the open ocean undertakes a circular path as the wave passes. At the surface, the diameter of this path equals the wave height but, as one goes deeper in the water column, the diameter of the path decreases until,

below a depth of approximately half the wavelength, no motion is felt (Figure 4.3). As a wave enters shallow water, these orbits interact with the sea floor, which exerts a drag, initially deforming the orbits into ellipses as the top of the wave travels more rapidly than the base. As the water further shallows, the drag slowing the base of the wave causes it to become unstable and the wave breaks (Figure 4.3), releasing its energy content. Table 4.1 shows the magnitude of the flows associated with breaking waves; velocities up to 10 m s^{-1} have been recorded on rocky shores, but the flow of a breaking wave is turbulent and velocities above and below these averages will be experienced. Furthermore, the level of wave action varies continuously, the large waves and strong drag forces which occur under storm conditions being interspersed with more moderate conditions and occasional periods of calm.

Table 4.1 The velocity of water at the substrate at 3 m depth and under the breaking wave for waves of various heights. The maximum water velocity associated with a wave occurs at breaking and varies with height of the wave

Wave height (m)	Water velocity at substrata (m s^{-1}) 3 m deep	Breaking
1	0.9	4.4
2	1.8	6.3
3	2.7	7.7

Source: adapted from Denny (1987)

Table 4.2 The effect of particle size on the physicochemical properties of soft littoral sediments

	Fine grained	Coarse grained
Slope	Shallow	Steep
Wave action	Low	High
Stability	More stable	Unstable
Water table	At surface	Sinks at low water
Capillarity	High	Low
Permeability	Low	High
Oxygen penetration	Low	High
Organic matter content	High	Low
Bacteria	Abundant	Few
Redox discontinuity	Present – boundary near surface	Absent, or if present, boundary is deep

While the passage of waves introduces oscillatory motions with periods of seconds, tidal forces produce further oscillatory motions with periods of hours. These forces are strongest where sudden shallows or narrow straits constrain the flow. In the entrance to Lough Ine, a sea lough in southwest Ireland, the ebbing tidal flows reach 3 m s^{-1}, but when the tide turns, velocities up to 5 m s^{-1} in the opposite direction can be recorded only 5 minutes later (Kitching & Ebling, 1967). Tidal currents are comparable in magnitude to flows in stream and river systems, while the flows associated with large ocean waves may exceed anything experienced even in spate conditions in a river.

4.2c THE NATURE OF THE SUBSTRATE

The nature of the sea floor has a profound effect on the communities that develop there. Hard substrates are restricted to areas where water flows are sufficiently strong to keep them clear of sediments or where vertical surfaces have been produced by geological processes. In progressively less dynamic environments, the size of particles comprising the substrate decreases. There is a

clear distinction between 'hard' – essentially non-mobile substrate – and 'soft' – mobile particles of any size. Soft sediment is the most extensive type of environment in coastal seas, covering much of the shore, including the extensive tidal flats of many estuaries, and most of the sea floor.

Particle size is an important determinant of conditions within soft sediments, because a number of environmental properties scale with the size of the particles (Table 4.2). This is partly the result of the processes which cause particles of a particular size to accumulate at a location, but also as a result of the environment produced by the particles themselves. A sediment in which the particles are of a similar size is referred to as well sorted, in contrast to a sediment of many different particle sizes, which is described as poorly sorted.

4.3 Ecological responses to abiotic conditions

4.3a THE TIDAL CYCLE

Only a limited number of species are able to withstand the stressful conditions in the intertidal zone. They are almost all marine in origin, and the shore therefore represents a gradient of conditions in which the lower shore, being immersed for longer periods, is more benign than progressively higher levels. On a rocky shore, the upper distribution limits of most species correspond to some physiological barrier, normally the ability to tolerate desiccation, and therefore many species do not manage to extend above the midshore region. Typically the upper shore contains relatively few highly adapted species.

Sandy shores, too, show some zonation in relation to physical conditions, although it is not so clear as on rocky shores. Normally, up to three zones can be distinguished (Figure 4.4) and the boundaries of these biological zones coincide with physical boundaries (McLachlan & Jaramillo, 1995). As the fauna are mobile, the location of the zones varies each day as the tidal range changes. Reflective beaches support fewer species and fewer zones than dissipative beaches (Figure 4.4).

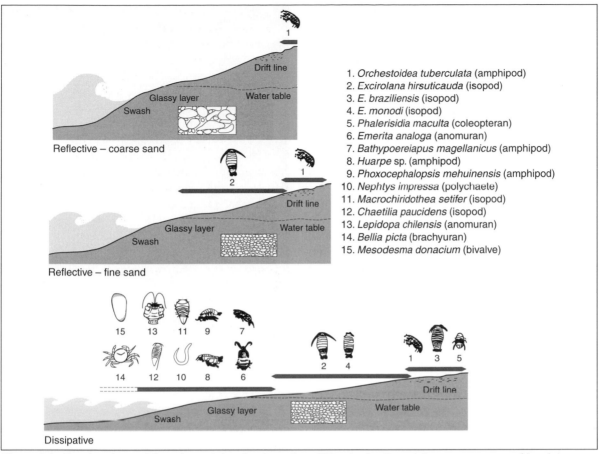

Figure 4.4 Zonation of macroinfauna in sandy beaches in southern Chile, showing the variation across a range of beach types. The insets illustrate the relative particle size on each of these three beaches. Note the absence of the lower zones on the most reflective beaches (from McLachlan & Jaramillo, 1995).

The labelled species in the figure:

1. *Orchestoidea tuberculata* (amphipod)
2. *Excirolana hirsuticauda* (isopod)
3. *E. braziliensis* (isopod)
4. *E. monodi* (isopod)
5. *Phalerisidia maculta* (coleopteran)
6. *Emerita analoga* (anomuran)
7. *Bathypoereiapus magellanicus* (amphipod)
8. *Huarpe* sp. (amphipod)
9. *Phoxocephalopsis mehuinensis* (amphipod)
10. *Nephtys impressa* (polychaete)
11. *Macrochiridothea setifer* (isopod)
12. *Chaetilia paucidens* (isopod)
13. *Lepidopa chilensis* (anomuran)
14. *Bellia picta* (brachyuran)
15. *Mesodesma donacium* (bivalve)

4.3b WAVE ACTION

Community structure in coastal seas is strongly influenced by wave action. Denny (1987) provides a very readable account of the biomechanical aspects of surviving in the surf zone. Organisms in the water column experience the passage of a wave but, if neutrally buoyant, merely follow a circular trajectory, whereas breaking waves exert a drag on benthic biota. In general, a large body form experiences a greater force, creating a selective pressure for small body size in wave-swept environments.

The variability and unpredictability of wave-induced flows has reduced the scope for adaptation by intertidal organisms. Storm waves, in particular, can profoundly affect shore communities. The size of storms tends to follow a log-normal distribution, such that rarely, at intervals of years or even decades, a very large storm occurs. Organisms may, therefore, recruit and grow under calm conditions only to be removed by an unpredictable storm event. Every organism has a certain ability to resist wave action, honed by evolutionary processes to meet its needs. Whether evolution has responded to a rare storm event that occurs at intervals of many generations depends on the other selection pressures operating but, as there is variation in the population, some individuals may survive and some will be lost following the disturbance. Others will survive through being 'sheltered' by topographic features, such as crevices, or other species, including clumps of mussels, which act as refugia (*cf.* **Section 2.3e**).

At the shore scale, there are clear differences between shores varying in their exposure to wave action. Very wave-exposed temperate rocky shores in much of the world support a near mono-culture of barnacles, with occasional mussels (*Mytilus*) (Figure 4.5a). As conditions become calmer, the cover of *Mytilus* initially increases, but then decreases as fucoid algae appear. In the North Atlantic, the fucoid cover varies with exposure: the mid shore of wave-exposed shores is covered by *Fucus vesiculosis* var. *linearis*, which lacks gas bladders, but as the level of wave action decreases, this is replaced by the bladdered form of *F. vesiculosis* and, on sheltered shores, by *Ascophyllum nodosum* (Figure 4.5b). At high lat-itudes, where ice rafting tends to denude the shore each winter, each spring sees a succession from early colonisers through to the summer flush of rapidly growing macroalgae before autumn storms and the return of the ice closes the shore down for winter. This tends to reduce the degree of difference between sheltered and wave-exposed shores.

4.3c THE NATURE OF THE SUBSTRATE

Non-mobile substrates

Hard substrates clear of sediment provide secure anchorage points, allowing sessile filter feeders and macroalgae access to the water column. They are, however, a limited resource in the sea and competition for attachment space is intense, newly exposed hard surfaces – for example as a result of a rock fall, or the legs of an oil rig – being quickly colonised (see **Section 4.5**). Boulders are occupied in the same way, although any movement will lead to partial or total mortality of the attached fauna by abrasion or crushing. Overturning of a particu-lar boulder is a probabilistic event – the larger a storm the more likely it is to be moved. Below a certain mass, boulders are moved so frequently that we can regard them as mobile substrates (see below). As boulder size increases, the probability of being moved within an organism's lifetime

Figure 4.5 (a) Exposed rocky shores are relatively species poor; in this case, there is a zone of black lichen (*Verrucaria* sp.) above a zone of barnacles (*Chthalamus*), with the mid and lower shore covered in mussels (*Mytilus edulis*) (St Ives, southern England). (*Photo by C. Frid*) (b) On sheltered shores, the shore is dominated by algae, while the extreme shelter allows terrestrial vegetation to extend to the very top of the shore, where a lichen zone containing a high number of species merges into the intertidal, with *Verrucaria* extending into the upper shore. The upper shore has a zone of *Chthalamus* and channel wrack (*Pelvetia canaliculata*), the mid shore has a zone of spiral wrack (*Fucus spiralis*) and the lower-mid and lower shore are covered in a dense canopy of egg wrack (*Ascophyllum nodosum*) (Lough Ine, southwest Ireland). (*Photo by C. Frid*)

Figure 4.6 The majority of the bed of coastal seas is covered in sediment, most of whose inhabitants live hidden within the sediment matrix. The seven-armed sea star (*Luidia ciliaris*) is a roving predator within this system. (*Photo by C. Frid*)

decreases, so that large boulders tend to have established communities while smaller boulders have communities typical of early succession stages – they are overturned so frequently that any succession is continually being reset to the beginning (Sousa, 1979).

Mobile particles

Benthic organisms live in intimate contact with the substrate, usually within it (Figure 4.6). Macrofauna will move particles aside as they burrow through the matrix or construct chambers, while meiofauna live in interstitial spaces or on the surface of particles. They are therefore responsive to changes in the physical and chemical nature of the sediment: species occupying a coarse sand beach (well drained, low organic matter, high oxygen) differ from those in a subtidal mud (poorly drained, high organic matter, low oxygen).

Well sorted gravels are highly mobile, so construction of tubes or burrows is difficult. Offshore shingle deposits may be relics of former dynamic environments which are now stable enough to incorporate fine particles deposited more recently; these support opportunistic sessile species attached to the larger stones, epibenthic forms and

an infauna in the fine material in the interstices between the gravels. Sands accumulate in subtidal areas of moderate tidal flows, and in areas with moderate wave action. On the upper shore, the coarse particle size leads to rapid draining at low tide. This, and the mobility of the sediment, serve to restrict macrofauna to crustaceans (Figure 4.4), which are well adapted to withstand desiccation and able to swim in the water column when they are washed out. The higher water content of lower shore sands allows a rich fauna to develop and, in areas of relative stability, extensive beds of biogenic structures may be produced, modifying the environment further. Dense beds of polychaete tubes, for example, act as baffles to reduce near-bed flows (Eckman, 1985).

Muds are deposited only in areas of low flow, such as estuaries and the lee of fringing islands. Their physical nature is described in **Section 3.2c**.

4.4   Energy inputs

Photosynthesis in coastal waters is restricted to the intertidal, shallow areas of the sea floor and the surface layer of the sea. Phytoplankton are responsible for autochthonous production in the water column while, on shores and in shallow water, macrophytes or microscopic algae may be important. On coral reefs, some of the primary production is by symbiotic flagellates – zooxanthellae – living within coral tissues.

In many coastal systems, as in other aquatic systems, primary production is generally exploited only after it becomes detritus. Dead plant material, fronds ripped off by storms, mangrove leaves shed by the trees and dead phytoplankton cells all contribute to the pool of POM, as do faecal material, crustacean moults, shed gametes and carcasses of animals. Production and utilisation of detritus in the oceans is considered further in **Sections 5.4b** and **5.6d**, while its exploitation by benthos is described in **Section 3.4b**.

4.4a   PHYTOPLANKTON PRODUCTION

The physical conditions of light and mixing ultimately control the rate at which phytoplankton growth can occur, but other factors, particularly the availability of inorganic nutrients, may prevent production being expressed at this rate.

Nutrient control of phytoplankton

The rate at which phytoplankton can uptake nutrients can be estimated as a half-saturation parameter, usually referred to as the K_s value. These values differ for each nutrient and between species and, in some cases, different clones of the same species have different K_s values (Carpenter & Guillard, 1971).

Nitrogen is the principal limiting nutrient in marine waters (Elser & Hassett, 1994). Given a thermally stratified water column, no horizontal input of nutrient-rich water and no significant nitrogen fixation by Cyanobacteria, primary production will consist of two components. The first is 'new' production, which utilises nitrate crossing the thermocline by turbulent diffusion. Zooplankton consume some of the production and, in due course, excrete nitrogenous compounds, which are utilised for the second form of production – regenerated production. This model of production, referred to as the Dugdale and Goering (1967) model, provides for a basic rate of primary production, set by the rate of turbulent diffusion across the thermocline, which may be enhanced up to 10 times by nitrogen recycling within the photic zone. This model has been shown to work well in coastal seas and explains the frequently observed phenomenon of a sub-surface chlorophyll maximum. Below the thermocline, light is limiting, but nutrients are available in relatively high concentrations as the result of regeneration by heterotrophs and the lack of primary production. Above the thermocline, a zone exists in which nutrients are present as a result of turbulent diffusion from below and in which light levels allow net primary production, giving a high standing stock of phytoplankton. Some of the production is grazed, liberating nitrogenous compounds which support further, regenerated, production. In the surface layer, nutrient concentrations are insufficient to support net primary production, due to their pre-emption by the populations in the region just above the thermocline.

Eutrophication

Background levels of nitrates in the North Atlantic in winter are typically 12 μmol dm^{-3} while concentrations in rivers flowing into the North Sea are in the range 350–600 μmol dm^{-3}, most of which is anthropogenic input. These waters are diluted by mixing with the saline waters, but concentrations in the coastal waters of the North Sea in winter, before spring bloom utilisation (**Section 4.4c**), are now many times the expected background levels. The spatial distribution of these excess nutrients follows the major sources of inputs, and the interannual variability in river flows and concentrations influences the distribution further. There is, therefore, clear evidence for anthropogenic eutrophication (**Box 6.2**) in the North Sea, but little corresponding evidence for a biological response. Phytoplankton abundance in the North Sea away from the nearshore region declined in the period 1960–80, and while it increased again during the following decade, it still lies below the long-term mean. While the total abundance of phytoplankton has not increased, however, there is evidence for a shift in species composition. Some authors claim that recent 'unusual' algal blooms – producing discoloration (red tides) (e.g. *Noctiluca*), slicks of foam (e.g. *Phaeocystis*), mortality of marine life (e.g. *Chrysochromulina*, *Gyrodinium*) or toxicity in humans (e.g. *Alexandrium*) – are manifestations of such altered species compositions (Reid *et al.*, 1991). Such blooms can occur naturally, so it is unclear whether anthropogenic inputs are increasing the frequency, intensity or duration of such blooms. In the western part of the Wadden Sea (southeast North Sea) there is evidence of an increase in dominance of *Phaeocystis* (cell numbers and duration of blooms) between the mid 1970s and the late 1980s. Total standing stock of phytoplankton and primary production both increased during this period, and eutrophication has been cited as the reason for increased biomass of infauna on the intertidal areas of the Wadden Sea (Beukema, 1992).

4.4b GRAZING CONTROL OF PHYTOPLANKTON

The uptake of light and nutrients by single-celled algae is enhanced by small size, yet relatively large phytoplankton, which should, therefore, be competitively inferior, are numerically dominant.

The probable explanation is grazing pressure (Kiørboe, 1993): larger phytoplankters are only accessible to large grazers, whose long reproductive times ensure that their numerical response to increased phytoplankton abundance only occurs after a significant lag. Large phytoplankton show marked temporal and spatial variability in abundance and their grazers cannot rapidly respond to the increased food which the bloom represents. Only after the bloom develops will grazers become an important check, although, once present, zooplankton can significantly reduce phytoplankton concentrations. Nanophytoplankton are also kept in check by their predators, but these tend to be of the same size order as the algae, with similar generation times, so are able to match any tendency to bloom by rapidly increasing the predation pressure and therefore holding population levels constant.

4.4c PHYTOPLANKTON SEASONALITY

Seasonal variation in the determinants of phytoplankton production results in seasonal patterns of abundance, of which a common feature is a rapid increase in biomass – the phytoplankton bloom. The idealised sequence for the initiation of a phytoplankton bloom consists of four phases, illustrated in Figure 4.7.

1   Photo-inhibition phase, in which high light levels at the surface initially restrict the photosynthetic maximum to an intermediate depth (Figure 4.7a). This production results in an increase in biomass.
2   Self-shading phase, caused by the increase in biomass, which reduces light beneath the upper layers by self shading, so maximum photosynthesis occurs towards the surface (Figure 4.7b).
3   Rapid population growth, exploiting the available nutrients (Figure 4.7c).
4   Nutrient depletion, causing the population to sink until it is concentrated above the thermocline, due both to the physical barrier associated with the change in density and slightly elevated nutrient availability (Figure 4.7d). Photosynthetic production is, however, limited by the low light levels at depth.

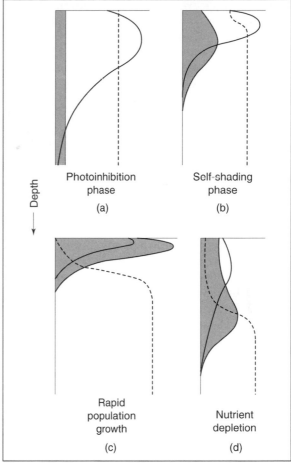

Figure 4.7 The process of bloom development in phytoplankton, illustrating phytoplankton biomass (shaded), daily net photosynthetic rate (solid line) and nutrient concentration (dashed line). See text for more details.

There are four broad patterns of phytoplankton seasonality (Figure 4.8), based upon the pattern of bloom which occurs.

Temperate North Atlantic pattern

In the coastal seas bordering the North Atlantic and in the open ocean, phytoplankton abundance shows a distinct, bimodal, annual cycle (Figure 4.8a). It is at a minimum over winter – low light and a deep mixing depth prevent net production despite the availability of nutrients. In spring, increasing light levels and stability of the water column allow a rapid increase in phytoplankton standing stock – the spring bloom. During summer, phytoplankton biomass falls as grazing zooplankton crop the phytoplankton and production rates become limited by the increasing depletion of nutrients above the thermocline. In autumn, storm waves erode the thermocline and mix nutrient-rich waters up into the surface layer, allowing a second bloom of phytoplankton before light levels and mixing restrict primary production in the winter.

Increasing primary production in the spring provides an increasing food source for zooplankton, whose numbers increase in response, but at a slower rate due to their longer doubling times. This increase is short-lived, as the summer decline in phytoplankton numbers leads to a decrease in zooplankton numbers later in the summer. Zooplankton numbers increase once more following the autumn bloom, but do not become high enough to check phytoplankton growth before winter mixing and low temperatures reduce growth (Figure 4.8a).

This pattern is altered in coastal seas where nutrients from terrestrial sources and mixing by tides alter the balance. In the northwestern North Sea, the autumn phytoplankton bloom tends to be larger and longer than the spring outbreak and zooplankton show a very broad single peak of summer abundance (Figure 4.8b) (Roff *et al.*, 1988).

Temperate North Pacific pattern

In the temperate North Pacific, phytoplankton standing stock remains low for most of the year, with a period of higher abundance in autumn (Figure 4.8c). Zooplankton biomass shows a distinct annual cycle with high levels from spring through the early summer. Therefore, in contrast to the North Atlantic, neither zooplankton breeding nor standing stock is dependent on phytoplankton growth in spring. This is the result of the different life history strategies of the dominant grazers in the two regions. In the Pacific, the nauplii larvae of the copepods *Calanus plumchrus* and *C. cristatus* are hatched from eggs produced by adults at depth during the winter. They migrate up through the water column, as non-feeding larvae, and arrive at the surface in spring (**Section**

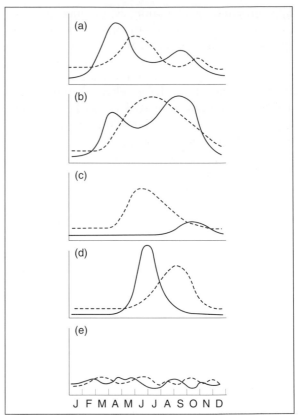

Figure 4.8 Annual cycle of phytoplankton (solid line) and zooplankton (dashed line) abundance: (a) in the temperate North Atlantic, (b) in the North Sea off the northeast coast of England, (c) in the temperate North Pacific, (d) at high latitudes, and (e) in the tropics.

5.7c). These young stages are able to make immediate use of the spring increase in phytoplankton productivity and their grazing pressure limits the standing stock of phytoplankton. It is only in the autumn, when zooplankton numbers decrease, that any appreciable increase in phytoplankton can be observed.

High latitude pattern

At high latitudes, light is limiting for most of the year. As it becomes available in late spring, productivity is extremely high as a result of the abundant nutrients, allowing a rapid and intense phytoplankton bloom to develop (Figure 4.8d). Zooplankton respond to the availability of phytoplankton with their own bloom, which may or may not limit the phytoplankton bloom before the onset of winter brings decreasing light levels and hence decreasing productivity.

Tropical pattern

There is little scope for broad seasonal patterns in the tropics. Rather a succession of increases and decreases in phytoplankton and zooplankton occurs (Figure 4.8e) in response to local weather conditions and the movement of water masses, which bring in nutrients and populations of plankton.

Seasonal changes in species composition

While the broad patterns described above relate to overall biomass, individual species distributions tend to occur as a series of pulses rather than a smooth transition. The early bloom of phytoplankton in the North Sea, for example, is dominated by diatoms but, as silica becomes limiting, they are replaced by dinoflagellates (Maddock *et al.*, 1981). A similar turnover in response to silicon depletion occurs in many freshwater phytoplankton assemblages (**Section 6.4b**).

4.4d BENTHIC PRIMARY PRODUCTION

Rocky shores and the rocky sublittoral

Rocky shores and sublittoral rocky reefs in sheltered, well illuminated waters generally support dense growths of macroalgae, whose primary production in the well illuminated sublittoral kelp forests of California reaches 1000 g C m^{-2} yr^{-1} (Mann, 1982) and, when sheltered from wave action, may exceed 1250 g C m^{-2} yr^{-1} on rocky shores (Hawkins *et al.*, 1992). Physically, these algal forests are structured in the same way as a terrestrial forest. The large macroalgae form a canopy, below which shade-adapted, usually red, macroalgae grow, while below this shrub layer there may be a turf or encrusting film of photosynthetic algae or microbes. The productivity of the lower layers is set by the degree of penetration of light through the canopy and the extent to which nutrients are input. It is also affected by

direct physical abrasion: in wave-swept areas, the fronds of the macroalgae can keep the surrounding area clear of microalgae or macroalgal spores by sweeping over the substrate.

Algal production in coral reefs

Primary production in coral reefs occurs by two mechanisms, macroalgae growing on the reef and symbiotic zooxanthellae, living within the coral tissues. It was originally thought that the low levels of nutrients in the water column controlled algal growth and thus provided a distinct advantage to the zooxanthellae, which recycle nutrients from the waste products of their hosts. However, removal of the fish fauna from a reef, for example by dynamite or cyanide 'fishing', is often followed by an explosion of algae, which can smother coral polyps and bring about a profound change in the reef system (Hughes, 1994). This implies that it is grazing which controls the macroalgal community.

At the base of the reef, corals usually give way to a sandy sediment plain. If sufficient light reaches this plain, algal growth can occur, although it is limited by the availability of suitable attachment sites (coral fragments or shells) and frequency of storm wave dislodgement.

4.5 Community structure in hard substrate systems

4.5a DISTURBANCE

The overriding determinant of community structure on rocky shores is disturbance, particularly through wave action. Benthos are unable to burrow into the substrate but must remain exposed to the full force of waves. Physical disturbance inevitably leads, therefore, to some losses, particularly when storms of unusual strength strike (**Section 4.3b**). Those individuals that are lost release resources, such as attachment space, allowing colonists into the community. In the absence of further disturbance, the most competitive species will eventually dominate, but another disturbance event may reset the succession, allowing less competitive species to coexist. The

Figure 4.9 Patchiness in a mussel-dominated system. Disturbance events, such as the impact of waveborne debris or the failure of mussels to remain attached, create a mosaic of patches. Regenerated resources – attachment space in this case – are colonised and begin to follow a succession towards the 'climax' state. In the meantime, further patches are created by additional disturbance events, so a high diversity system is produced as a result of the mosaic of patches at different stages of the successional continuum. (*Photo by C. Frid*)

extraction has a long history, while today the harvest is mainly concerned with the extraction of alginates and other polysaccharides, that of the kelp *Macrocystis pyrifera* in southern California alone being around 144 000 t yr^{-1}. Harvesting is, in many ways, analogous to natural disturbances that remove the biomass, and as such the effect of harvesting varies with the type of harvest (vegetative fronds, fronds including reproductive structures or whole plants), time of year, areal extent of harvested area and frequency of harvesting (Vasquez, 1995). For example, winter harvesting of *Ascophyllum*, when it is reproductively active, results in very slow recolonisation due to a lack of viable spores. Large-scale and repeated harvesting acts like an increase in natural disturbance frequency, causing a shift in the whole community towards one typical of wave-swept areas.

Archaeological evidence suggests that the coastal habitats of Chile have been exploited by people since at least 700 BC. The principal harvest is gastropods, particularly limpets, for human consumption, but some species of red algae are also collected and sold as a cash crop. Exclusion of humans from experimental areas in the late 1970s showed that the entire coast appears to be in its present state, dominated by barnacles and small mussels, as a result of this long history of, and continuing, exploitation. When the human collectors were excluded, the abundance of the red alga *Iridaea boryana* declined dramatically while the abundance and mean size of the limpet *Fissurella picta* increased (Moreno *et al.*, 1984). The traditional gatherers were effectively managing the shore, unwittingly, to provide a cash crop not otherwise available to them.

4.5b COMPETITION

Interspecific competition contributes to patterns of zonation found among sedentary species on rocky shores. Whereas the upper limit of a species' distribution is determined by its ability to withstand desiccation, its lower limit is generally set by competitive interactions. Coping with extreme physiological conditions requires metabolic energy, so species able to cope with the harsh upper shore environment tend to be poorer com-

patchiness of disturbance events will, in this way, determine the patchiness of the community (Figure 4.9), with frequent disturbance at a small spatial scale maintaining a series of patches at different successional stages (compare with river systems: **Section 2.5b**).

The biomass of fucales and laminarians on the shores and in the shallow sublittoral of temperate regions has attracted commercial harvesting operations in some areas of the world. Small-scale harvesting of seaweeds for iodine and potash

petitors than similar species with less physiological tolerance. The result is that, as one moves downshore into more benign conditions, the upper shore species find themselves in competition with species which lack their physiological resistance but are better competitors.

One of the classic examples of interspecific competition is the study by Connell (1961) of two species of barnacle, *Chthalamus stellatus* and *Semibalanus balanoides*, on rocky shores at Millport in western Scotland. *Chthalamus* generally occurs higher on the shore than *Semibalanus*, yet small *Chthalamus* are able to settle on the lower shore (Figure 4.10). Connell followed the fate of *Chthalamus* young that settled in the *Semibalanus* zone, removing *Semibalanus* from some plots so that they did not encroach on the *Chthalamus*. He found that young *Chthalamus* barnacles kept free of *Semibalanus* did not suffer mortality resulting from the increased submergence time, while in unmanipulated plots, *Semibalanus* undercut, smothered and crushed *Chthalamus* individuals as they grew. Those *Chthalamus* that survived one year in the *Semibalanus* zone were smaller than higher shore barnacles of the same age. Menge (1976) demonstrated that barnacles, in turn, are competitively inferior to mussels (*Mytilus edulis*). Exclusion experiments carried out on rocky shores in New England showed that, in the absence of competition, barnacles thrive in the lower middle shore zone normally dominated by mussels.

A similar process occurs among rocky shore algae, which dominate moderately wave-exposed rocky shores. The mid shore in New England is covered by *Fucus* spp. which are replaced on the lower shore by *Chondrus crispus*. Removing *Chondrus* from plots in the lower shore allows colonisation by *Fucus*, which grows more rapidly than mid shore populations. The lower extent of *Chondrus*, in turn, is defined by grazing pressure from sea urchins (primarily *Stronglocentrotus droebachiensis*), which are confined to the sublittoral (Lubchenco, 1980).

Thus the rocky shore can be seen as a series of physiologically (upper limit) and biotically (lower limit) defined zones. The resultant algal zonation is repeated worldwide but is most dramatic when seen on temperate shores with reasonable tidal ranges. Here the dominant algae differ in colour and form so that the shore, when seen from a distance, appears banded (Figure 4.5).

4.5c PREDATION

The effect of predation on rocky shores is well

Figure 4.10   The distribution of adults and newly settled larvae of the intertidal barnacles *Semibalanus balanoides* and *Chthalamus stellatus*, with an indication of the relative importance of physical (desiccation) and biological (competition) controls (after Connell, 1961).

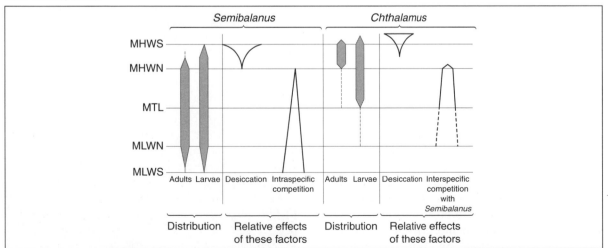

established and, indeed, it was work carried out on rocky intertidal systems that allowed Paine (1966) to develop the concept of a 'keystone' species. The starfish *Pisaster ochraceous*, a common species on coasts of western North America, eats a variety of different sessile species: barnacles, mussels, limpets and chitons. Removal of *Pisaster*, however, results in the loss of many of its prey species as a single, competitively superior mussel, *Mytilus californianus*, monopolises space and excludes other species, including algae (Paine, 1966). *Pisaster*, therefore, is beneficial to several of the species that it predates, by keeping inter-specific competition in check. Similarly, Menge and Sutherland (1976) demonstrated that mussels and barnacles could coexist, albeit in low numbers, in the presence of the dogwhelk *Thais lapillus*, which preyed upon both, but preferentially upon the more competitive mussels.

On most shores, the dominant grazers are gastropod molluscs, while in the sublittoral they are replaced by sea urchins. Grazers tend to be small relative to the macroalgae and only able to exploit the microflora, including newly settled macroalgal spores, which coat the rock surface and may be present as epiphytes on the macroalgae. Consumption of this film may be selective: the periwinkle, *Littorina littorea*, for example, which feeds on seaweed germlings in the biofilm, consumes some species but will avoid others (Watson & Norton, 1985).

4.5d SUPPLY-SIDE ECOLOGY

On many shores, the crucial factor determining which species are present and their abundance is the availability of settling larvae. The importance of a ready supply of new recruits has long been recognised in marine ecology (Thorson, 1950) but the experimental studies of the late 1960s and 1970s emphasised the role of competition for space and the modifying influence of predators – i.e. post-settlement processes. It is now clear that, by chance, the shores used in these experiments were ones which received a good supply of larvae every year. Roughgarden *et al.* (1987) showed that other shores suffer variability in the supply of larvae, due to variation in currents or predation (e.g. larval predation by fish – Gaines &

Roughgarden, 1985), and it is this which controls the type of community that develops. This emphasis on the availability of recruits as a determinant of community dynamics has been termed supply-side ecology. The factors controlling the supply of larvae include hydrography, meteorology and food availability, as well as biotic interactions with other planktonic organisms (larval and the permanent plankton). This represents a new set of challenges to understanding the dynamics of rocky shore communities.

4.5e CORAL REEFS

The physical structure of a coral reef is a function of the interaction between the growing corals, which secrete an exoskeleton of calcium carbonate ($CaCO_3$), and the physical environment, in particular wave action and water movement. As much as 50% of the reef may be covered by living coral colonies (Longhurst & Pauly, 1987). For the reef-building corals, access to light to support the symbiotic zooxanthellae is important, so illuminated space is usually the primary limiting resource (Figure 4.11). Space is also limiting for

Figure 4.11 Space is limiting on hard substrate communities. Among corals, the competition for space – and hence access to light and nutrients for the symbiotic zooxanthellae and the water column for the polyps – manifests itself as overgrowth, often mediated by the use of biologically active chemicals (Namalatu, Ambon Islands, Indonesia). (*Photo by C. Frid*)

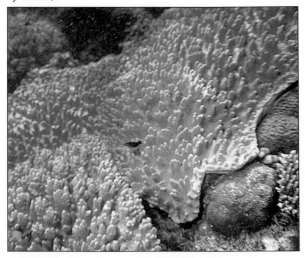

the filter-feeding sponges and soft corals that require access to the water column to feed. Competition occurs through overgrowth, shading and chemical or physical attack, many sessile forms practising antibiosis, or chemical defence of space. Some soft corals, for example, exude chemicals which cause necrosis of nearby hard corals, and the extension of digestive filaments between colonies, often over distances in excess of 1 m, is used in interspecific encounters, with the attacker literally digesting the tissue of the victim (Lang, 1973). Coral reef fish, too, are apparently space limited (Sale, 1984), hence the very rapid colonisation of newly deployed artificial reefs, the fact that specialist microhabitats such as anemone tentacles have a fairly constant density of fish and evidence for interspecific defence of living sites. However, long-term monitoring of reefs shows considerable temporal variation in fish numbers and, while some of this variability may be attributable to seasonal patterns, the majority appears to derive from variations in the arrival of recruits to an area of reef, a further example of supply-side ecology (**Section 4.5d**).

The high diversity of organisms within coral reef systems is maintained by the fact the community is in a non-equilibrium state, determined by a combination of the rate of competitive displacement and a range of disturbances including heat shock, wave action (including the extremes associated with tropical storms), sedimentation, predation (including grazing) and disease. Diversity on a reef generally increases from the surface (frequently disturbed by wave action and heat stress) to a maximum at about 20 m and then declines in the more stable, but increasingly light-limited, conditions. In addition to small or medium-scale disturbance which promotes local diversity, coral reefs are subject to several large-scale disturbances, including large tropical storms (hurricanes and cyclones), climatic fluctuations, such as the El Niño Southern Oscillation (**Section 5.7c**) in the atmospheric and ocean currents over the Pacific, and aperiodic outbreaks of predator populations or disease. These all cause widespread destruction of reef communities, allowing colonisation by dispersing propagules which introduce a further source of variability into the system.

4.6 Community structure in soft sediment systems

4.6a TYPES OF COMMUNITIES

The dominant feature of sediment communities is that they are patchy on any scale of observation – see Thrush (1991) for a review. There are, however, major differences in the species assemblages inhabiting different types of sediments, stimulating attempts to map species distributions by sediment types. The earliest and most extensive of these descriptive approaches was that of Petersen who, in 1914–22, carried out a wide ranging survey of the shallower parts of the North Sea using a quantitative grab sampling technique. From his results he classified the benthos into seven distinct 'communities', which he named after the dominant species (Table 4.3). He implied no linkage between the species in these 'communities', merely that they tended to occur together in space.

There is a clear implication that depth and the nature of the substrate are important in determining which community is present at a particular location. Thorson (1957) expanded Petersen's work and implied an ecological linkage between the species, concluding that similar environments worldwide should have functionally similar communities. While species occurring together do interact, the primary reason they occur together is, however, a need for similar physicochemical conditions. More recent studies in the North Sea have confirmed that associations of species do, indeed, correlate with the distribution of sediment types and other physical factors (Künitzer et al., 1992).

4.6b DISTURBANCE

Several scales of disturbance can be distinguished in marine sedimentary environments (Probert, 1984; Hall et al., 1994). At a small scale (<1 cm²), burrowing and cast production by macrofauna probably influence meiofauna to a greater extent than macrofauna. Combined effects of disturbances at this scale can be large. In the Wadden Sea, for example, it is estimated to be equivalent to the top 35 cm of the sediment being turned over

Table 4.3 Features and key organisms in Petersen's communities from the North Sea

Petersen's community	Description	Key organisms
Macoma community	Shallow, 10–60 m, also estuaries	Macoma, Mya, Cerastoderma and Arenicola
Tellina community	Shallow, exposed, hard sand, 0–10 m	Suspension feeders: Tellina, Donax, Astropecten and Dosinia
Venus community	Open sea, 7–40 m, sand	Venus, Spisula, Tellina, Thracia, Natica, Astropecten and Echinocardium
Abra community	Sheltered waters and estuaries, with reduced salinity, mixed to muddy, organically rich sediments. Increasing sand merges into the Venus community. Increasing silt merges into the Amphiura community	Abra, Cautellus, Corbula, Pectinaria, Nephtys and Echinocardium
Amphiura community	15–100 m, high silt content	Amphiura, Turritella, Thyasira, Nucula, Nephtys and Echinocardium. Increasing sand leads to increasing Echinocardium and Turritella. Increasing silt leads to increasing Brisposis, Thyasira and Maldane
Maldane – Ophiura sarsi community	Soft muds, shallow estuaries to 200 m	Deposit feeders: Maldane and Ophiura sarsi
Amphipod community	Muddy sands generally	Communities dominated by different species of amphipods

every year (Cadée, 1990). At intermediate scales (cm² to m²) biological activity by large macro-fauna – crabs, shore-birds, fish and sea mammals – will cause disturbance, much of which is highly seasonal. Estimates include 26% of mussel beds in a Scottish estuary disturbed per month in winter by eider ducks, and side-scan sonar images revealing 6% of the seabed in the Bering Sea being covered by pits from feeding grey whales. At large scales (dm² to km²), physical processes or human impact are responsible for most disturbance, although biological processes may predispose an area to a physical disturbance, for example by altering sediment stability. Large-scale biological disturbance could include disease outbreaks, population explosions or species invasions and introductions. Storms represent perhaps the most obvious large-scale disturbance, but other causes include deoxygenation events, seafloor smothering (by sediment, dredge spoil, fish eggs, etc.), disturbance by fishing gears, and ice scour in the intertidal at higher latitudes.

One widely observed phenomenon is the effect of disturbance on the mobile fauna. At all scales, from small pits to trawl tracks, immediately following disturbance there is an influx of mobile scavengers, which exploit the individuals exposed at the sediment surface or carcasses of infauna killed by the disturbance. This response is short lived so, although widely reported, experimental data are still scarce (Kaiser & Spencer, 1994, 1996).

Despite the high frequency of small-scale disturbance, benthic communities can remain stable for long periods of time. A monitoring programme has been running off the coast of Northumberland (northeast England) since 1972 at a station in 52 m of water. During the first 10 years, numbers of macrofauna remained remarkably constant. Each year a spring recruitment led to higher numbers in the autumn, which winter mortality reduced by the following spring. In addition to this annual cycle, there was a biennial cycle of alternating high and low years: a low number in March was followed by a high number in September, which was followed by a high March population and subsequently a low number in September. These patterns provide evidence for density-dependent recruitment and mortality (Buchanan, 1993) although, after 10 years of monitoring, this biennial cycle broke down and population values fluctuated markedly. Over 50% of the interannual variation in the spring abundance of macrofauna was explained by interannual variation in the productivity of phytoplankton two years previously (e.g. spring 1992 macrofauna numbers were related to phytoplankton production in 1990). During the study period of over 25 years, the relative abundance of the species of macrofauna present at this site has changed little, and the large interannual changes in abundance have been driven by changing inputs of food.

Disturbance is not necessarily detrimental. Small-scale biological processes, including tube building, pit or burrow digging, generate heterogeneity and provide niches for other, usually smaller, species (Dayton, 1984).

4.6c COMPETITION

Direct evidence for competition in soft sediments is scarce. One proposed mechanism for competitive interaction is the trophic group amensalism hypothesis of Rhoads and Young (1970; see also Rhoads & Boyer, 1983). Suspension feeders need a stable substrate in which to build their tubes, and water currents to bring in food. Deposit feeders, however, need sediments containing organic matter, which requires lower current speeds. At sites of intermediate current speed, deposit feeders will alter the environment to make it unsuitable for suspension feeders: their faecal pellets, released at the sediment surface, have a high water content and, upon disintegration, a small particle size, whose resuspension smothers the larvae of suspension feeders and clogs their filters. Hence one trophic group can exclude the other. The reciprocal may also occur, because tubes of filter feeders stabilise the sediment, reduce the area available to deposit feeders and may intercept sufficient incoming POM to reduce sediment organic matter content, making it unsuitable for deposit feeders (Woodin, 1976).

The generality of the trophic group amensalism hypothesis has been questioned. Wildish (1977) considered bottom roughness and current flows to be the critical factors and suggested, in his trophic group mutual exclusion hypothesis, that both groups are essentially food limited. When current velocities at the seabed exceed a few centimetres per second, then development of a deposit feeding community is inhibited because biologically produced particles (being of low density) are resuspended and removed.

Relicts and founders

Pure competition for space can be distinguished from founder control, in which the first species to recolonise following disturbance is able to monopolise the resource (Section 2.5b). If, for example, a large tube-building filter feeder colonises a soft sediment patch, then the combined effect of the tube and the interception of incoming larvae by the feeding tentacles may effectively prevent certain other species from colonising. However, as competition is much less of a structuring force in soft than in hard sediments, so founder control is less widespread. In contrast to hard substrates, where disturbance events may remove all the macrobiota from a patch, both the nature of the disturbance generating forces and the biology of the fauna mean that most disturbances remove only a proportion of the biota originally present in a patch.

The individuals remaining after the disturbance have been referred to as the relict fauna (Woodin, 1981). They are able immediately to respond to the reduced density of organisms in the disturbed patch and may affect subsequent colonisation. The activities of some species may facilitate re-establishment by others (e.g. Whitlatch & Zajac, 1985; Thrush et al., 1992), the behaviour of tube-building polychaetes and crustaceans, for example, modifying sediment structure to the advantage of deposit-feeding bivalves and oligochaetes (Gallagher et al., 1983). In other situations, however, they can inhibit the colonisation process. Tube-dwelling predators may impede colonisation (e.g. Jensen & Andre, 1993), while burrowing and feeding activities of deposit feeders can inhibit the recruitment of less mobile infauna (Brenchley, 1981; Ambrose, 1984b). There are also neutral relationships between the two groups. McCann and Levin (1989) demonstrated that mobile subsurface deposit-feeding oligochaetes in a tidal saltmarsh creek had no effect upon the settlement of a tubiculous subsurface deposit-feeding polychaete, nor upon molluscs.

4.6d PREDATION

Predation is another process whose role is unclear in soft bottom sediments. Despite predator densities and biomass well in excess of those found on rocky shores, including high densities of wading birds, experimental manipulations in these communities have met with mixed results. Reise (1978), in reviewing the role of epibenthic predators, concluded that the majority of studies showed them to have an impact, but recently a number of studies (Raffaelli & Milne, 1987; Raffaelli et al., 1989a) have shown no impact (see also **Section 3.5a**). One potential reason for this is the usually

overlooked role of infaunal predators. Ambrose (1984a; see also Wilson, 1986) postulated a three-tier system, in which deposit feeders are consumed by infaunal predators which, in turn, are eaten by epibenthic predators. Frid and James (1988) failed to find a response to epibenthic predator exclusion among deposit-feeding species, but did see an increase in infaunal predators. This could have been the result of release from selective predation, competition or a combination of the two.

The algal species occupying the sediment plain at the base of coral reefs (**Section 4.4d**) in the Caribbean are distinct from the species occupying the reef itself. Sand plain species are competitively superior to reef-inhabiting species, but are unable to exploit the reef because of the high levels of grazers, whereas the sand plain provides them with a refuge from grazing (Hay, 1981; Hay et al., 1983). This would also appear to be the case for sea grasses growing in the lagoons associated with the reefs (Ogden et al., 1973). Here, distinct halos of grazed sea grass meadows, delimiting the area exploited by grazers from the reef, can be observed. The reef provides the grazing fish with refugia from predators and so the further from the reef they venture, the higher the risk of predation, hence the halo effect.

4.7 Community structure in pelagic communities

The pelagic environment is a dynamic and complex system in which three-dimensional motions are the dominant feature. Most organisms are advected by the medium rather than being fixed in a particular location. There is usually a vertical reference frame, in the form of light intensity, but no horizontal structures except at boundaries such as the surface, the thermocline and the seabed (Denman, 1994).

Determinants of phytoplankton assemblages

Interspecific differences in response to the temperature and light regime and in nutrient K_s values are important in promoting coexistence of many phytoplankton species in a nutrient-limited environment. If we consider two potentially limit-

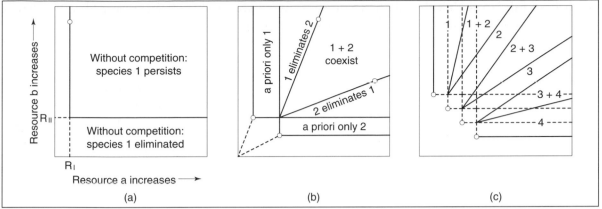

Figure 4.12 Coexistence of phytoplankton species under different concentrations of two limiting resources. (a) A single species (species 1) limited only by the two lower concentrations of each resource. (b) Two species (1 and 2) showing the regions of competitive exclusion and coexistence. Unless both resources are abundant, one species will outcompete the other. (c) Four species showing regions of coexistence based on each resource. Species 1 is the best competitor for resource a, 2 is the second best, 3 the third and 4 the least. The competitive order is reversed for resource b (from Lalli & Parsons, 1993).

ing resources, such as nitrate and phosphate, then each species will require certain minimum levels of both nutrients to survive (Figure 4.12a). If two species attempt to coexist and species 2 is a better competitor than species 1 for both resources, then it will outcompete and eliminate species 1. If, however, species 1 is the better competitor for resource a, but species 2 is the better competitor for resource b, the situation is more complex and coexistence is possible (Figure 4.12b). At low concentrations of resource a, the superior competitive ability of species 1 leads to the exclusion of species 2, whereas at low concentration of resource b species 1 is excluded. When both resources are present in concentrations slightly above these minima, coexistence occurs. If further species are added to the system (Figure 4.12c), more possibilities for coexistence are produced. Adding more types of resource or physical factors such as light, temperature or salinity further increases the scope for many species to coexist.

Determinants of zooplankton assemblages

The tracking, with a short time lag, of phytoplankton production by zooplankton (Figure 4.8) provides evidence for food limitation. There is, however, no evidence for dominance by competitively superior species or for division of the resource, nor, given the generalist and opportunistic feeding in most species, any niche segregation. Therefore, some process must be operating to keep the community in a disequilibrium state. As zooplankton communities are potentially moved and mixed by physical processes, it could merely be the continual movement – horizontal and vertical – of nutrients, phytoplankton, copepods and their planktonic predators that maintains a disequilibrium. However, a number of recent studies have shown that copepod assemblages are able to maintain their integrity in the face of considerable advective flows (Davis *et al.*, 1992; Wiafe & Frid, 1996).

The key role of predation has been emphasised in many littoral systems. The high mobility and low selectivity of marine planktivorous fish reduces the likelihood of their applying a strong regulatory effect, but predatory forms within the plankton are important. Copepod populations in the North Sea are controlled during the winter by their predators – chaetognaths and amphipods (Frid *et al.*, 1994). The number of copepods surviving the winter then influences the rate and size of their summer bloom (Roff *et al.*, 1988), as planktonic predators are unable to apply sufficient predation pressure to control copepods at this productive time. The autumn decline in copepod numbers may be linked to the presence at that time of year of large numbers of fish larvae, but the role of such temporary members of the plankton in the dynamics of the system remains poorly understood.

Interannual variation in zooplankton abundance

There can be considerable interannual variation in the zooplankton community at a single station. The records of the Plymouth Marine Laboratory (Russell *et al.* 1971; Southward, 1974) show a long-term cycle in the English Channel. Until the 1920s, and again in the 1960s, there was a high plankton abundance, the chaetognath *Sagitta elegans* was present and there was a productive herring (*Clupea harengus*) fishery. Between these dates, plankton abundance was low, the herring were replaced by pilchards (*Sardina pilchardus*), and *Sagitta setosa* replaced *S. elegans*. These alter-

ations seem to have been associated with a change in the volume of Atlantic Ocean water penetrating the English Channel.

The annual productivity of zooplankton in the northeast Atlantic correlates with the position of the north wall of the Gulf Stream where it leaves the American coast (Figure 4.13) (Taylor, 1995). To the north and west of the British Isles, productivity is highest in years when the Gulf Stream's track is more northerly, but at the same time these conditions depress production in the northwest North Sea (Frid & Huliselan, 1996) and the lakes of the English Lake District (George & Taylor, 1995). That plankton isolated in lakes respond in the same way demonstrates that it is not a direct interaction between Gulf Stream water and plankton, but rather that the two are responding to a third component. While the

Figure 4.13 The north wall of the Gulf Stream and the relationship between its position and zooplankton abundance around the UK. (a) The position of the north wall off the east coast of the USA during August 1984 (solid line) and its mean position (±95% confidence limits) between 1966 and 1996 (dashed line). (b) The relationship between latitude of the north wall (dashed lines) and total copepod abundance (solid lines) in the northern North Sea, off northeast Scotland and the central North Sea, west of Denmark. Figures have been standardised to have zero mean and unit variance; the correlation coefficient (*r*) between each pair of graphs is given (from Taylor, 1995).

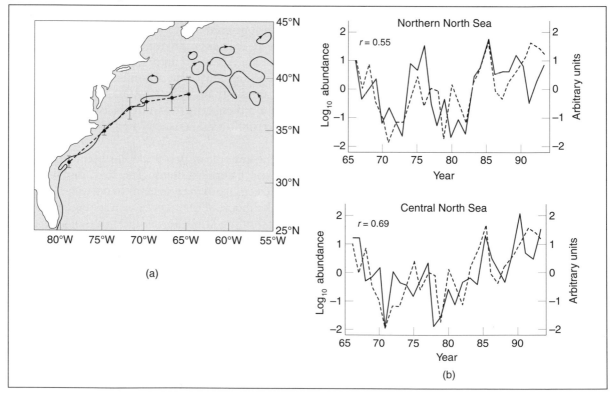

detailed mechanisms behind these relationships are, as yet, not fully resolved, it is clear that meteorological and ocean-scale processes are important in controlling productivity and, in the North Sea at least, the relative abundance of species (Frid & Huliselan, 1996). The Gulf Stream, like most major current systems, varies in strength and position in a complex way, and the meteorological and oceanographic factors which influence its path simultaneously affect plankton production. The most likely mechanism is to do with climatically determined differences in the timing of the onset of stratification relative to the phytoplankton production cycle.

4.8   Succession and change

4.8a   COLONISATION ON NEW SHORE

Hard substrates

Any hard substrate placed into the sea is rapidly colonised by a microbial film, including organic molecules, heterotrophic bacteria, fungi, protists and, in shallow waters, photosynthetic bacteria, microalgae and the early stages of macroalgae. Mobile adults of grazing species may invade this community from adjacent areas at this stage. Mucus from the trails of grazing gastropods adds to the biofilm and may enhance recruitment of seaweed propagules and adhesion of diatoms. This has led to the idea that territorial limpets may use their mucus to 'garden' algae in their territories (Connor & Quinn, 1984). There is also evidence that sessile animals recruit preferentially to surfaces after they have developed a microbial coating (Scheer, 1945; Turner & Todd, 1993). Most pelagic larvae start prospecting for a suitable settlement site when they reach the stage when metamorphosis could occur. There is a 'window of opportunity' during which settlement can occur, at the end of which metamorphosis occurs irrespective of suitability of the site. Thus, early in this period all the settlement cues are required to initiate settlement but, as time goes on, the presence of progressively fewer cues will suffice.

Over time, spores of macroalgae will settle. The microscopic flora is utilised directly by grazers which can also exploit newly settled spores of macroalgae. Once the macroalgae exceed a certain size, however, they become too large for most of the grazers to exploit and will be kept in check by physical abrasion and competition with other macroalgae. Large numbers of grazers can, however, prevent the domination of macroalgae by grazing the sporelings and effectively interrupting the succession.

Soft sediments

In soft sediments, the process of colonisation has been best studied in patches in the 10 cm^2 to 10 m^2 range in shallow waters. For large-scale disturbances, however, studies have tended to follow the fate of a 'natural event', so these studies lack adequate controls and replication is not usually possible. In general, colonisation of small to medium sized patches occurs over a few days by the addition of adults of species from the ambient community, but organic matter accumulating in pits excavated by predators encourages initial colonisation by a different suite of opportunistic species, not previously present in the area.

4.8b   EXCESS SILTATION AND SUBLITTORAL COMMUNITIES

The deposition of new particulate material onto the sea floor is a natural process in many areas, the size and chemical nature of the particles and their rate of deposition being determined by local geological and hydrographic processes. Many coastal seas are, however, subjected to deposition of material at much higher rates than those occurring naturally, through direct dumping of material as a waste disposal operation and excess supply of 'natural' sediments due to changes in coastal defences or land use in adjacent catchments. The latter, in particular, has caused widespread degradation of coral reefs. Deforestation and other changes in land use in the catchments often lead to erosion of soil, which is washed into rivers and transported downstream. In coastal seas, this sediment-rich water discharges from the estuary mouth as a discoloured plume and, as it spreads out, the velocity decreases and the sediment settles onto the sea floor. The extra silt causes direct mortality by smothering the corals, while increased turbidity reduces the light reaching the photosynthetic zooxanthellae. With the death or reduced growth of corals, the reef community shifts: if turbidity is not too great, it may become covered in rapidly growing fleshy algae, but the diversity of the system is generally dramatically reduced and large areas become dominated by a few tolerant species.

Sea disposal of wastes is an economically attractive option for a number of industries which produce significant quantities of solid, low toxicity wastes. The three types of waste which have most frequently been disposed of in this way are mine tailings, china clay wastes and power station coal ash. In each case, the waste undergoes very little chemical change in the marine environment and chemically is often very similar to natural sediments of the area. The principal impacts arising out of the disposal result from the smothering of the natural seabed and its fauna at the disposal site, from changes in the nature of the sediments in the surrounding area, and possibly from effects of the discharge plume on the water column. Dredge spoil is also dumped at sea. This is material removed from the floor of harbours, ports and shipping channels to allow access by large vessels. As such, it is natural sediment of the source area, but, as many ports are sites of polluting discharges, the sediment may be contaminated by pollutants. For economic reasons, disposal of dredge spoil occurs close to shore, and the fine sediments removed from the calm waters of the port may be very different in character from the natural sediments of the dump site. Therefore, dredge spoil causes a direct impact by smothering the fauna and indirect effects through altering sediment particle size and possibly by introducing toxic pollutants. See Eagle *et al.* (1979), Bamber (1984) and Clark (1997) for more detailed accounts of these effects.

4.8c WRECKS AND ARTIFICIAL REEFS

Artificial surfaces in the sea, such as sea walls, piers, jetties, shipwrecks, oil and gas production facilities and similar structures all represent hard surfaces available for colonisation. In general, the communities present on such structures are similar to those on natural hard substrata in the same area. Sea walls and coastal defences tend not to be heavily colonised as their location means they are continually exposed to high wave action and associated sand and sediment scour. Harbour walls often provide an interesting contrast, supporting wave-tolerant communities on the outer face and turbidity-tolerant ones on the inner face.

Much of the ecological interest of artificial structures lies in the opportunity they provide to observe succession. When a wreck sinks or a new sea wall is built we can be certain of the date when the substratum first became available for colonisation. One of the most striking features of the communities which develop on shipwrecks below the photic zone is the importance of orientation in determining the dominant members of the community. While most species can be found on both vertical faces and horizontal structures, their relative abundance is very different, probably as a result of a combination of relative susceptibility to siltation and current. Large anemones such as the plumose anemone, *Metridium senile*, dominate on the vertical faces, while hydroids and bryozoans dominate on the more horizontal areas.

Artificial reefs act as foci for fish. For some species, it is the requirement for hard substrata that attracts them, but many species common on the surrounding sediment plains are also abundant around the reefs. It is unclear whether the increased abundance of fish is a direct response to the increased productivity associated with the extensive epibiotic communities, a response to the changes in the physical environment produced by the reef, or a result of the potential reduction in predation from having a shelter to hide in. Whatever the cause, this phenomenon has been responsible for a large number of projects worldwide in which artificial reefs, made from materials ranging from old tyres to concrete blocks, have been deployed to restore degraded systems or to enhance local fish catches (Wendt *et al.*, 1989; Edwards & Clark, 1992; Clark & Edwards, 1994).

4.9 Exploitation of coastal fisheries

The current global harvest of marine organisms amounts to approximately 86 million tonnes per year and seafood is the source of around 20% of world protein consumption. Over two-thirds of this catch comes from temperate coastal seas, the North Sea alone accounting for around 3.5% of the world fish catch (**Box 4.2**). Worldwide, the fishing industry supports over 15 million people, and Japan, the former USSR, China, USA and Chile are responsible for nearly 50% of the catch.

It is estimated that the Maximum Sustainable Yield (MSY) from the sea is between 100 and 170 million tonnes. Currently, harvest levels are close to the lower part of this range, although many stocks appear to be in an imminent state of collapse. There can, therefore, be no doubt that fishing is a major ecological force in the coastal seas. We might expect three effects of high levels of fishing: an effect on the target population(s), an effect on the ecosystem via a trophic cascade (**Section 6.5c**) and an ecosystem effect of the fishing activity *per se*, including mortality of non-target species, changes in the inputs of POM and direct physical disruption by fishing gear.

Effect upon the target population

Fishing selectively removes the larger individuals in a population. At moderate levels, this removes older, less fecund, fish and so promotes a healthy population dominated by reproductively active individuals, which are the most efficient at converting food to flesh. At high fishing intensities, the population becomes dominated by young fish. In the North Sea the catch of cod (*Gadus morhua*) in the 1990s was dominated by 3–4 year old fish. When fisheries scientists first began studying the fish stocks towards the end of the 19th century, cod bred for the first time at four years old, whereas now they are breeding at three years old, and it has been argued that this is an evolutionary response to the high levels of fishing pressure (Law & Grey, 1989; Stokes *et al.*, 1993).

The trophic cascade

Changes in a target population affect species with which it interacts competitively or trophically. Until the 1940s, the productive, upwelling waters off California supported a fishery for Pacific sardines (*Sardinops caerulea*) which landed over 100 000 t yr^{-1}. When this fishery collapsed, the sardine was replaced by the anchovy (*Engraulis mordax*) (Figure 4.14), and even a relaxation of the fishery did not allow the return of the sardine. While variations in ocean currents and water temperature contributed to this change, these species are competitors and the heavy exploitation pressure on the sardine, along with a decrease in competitive ability due to temperature changes, may have allowed the pilchard to dominate, leading to a new stable community which is resistant to reinvasion by the sardine. A similar explanation has been proposed for the changes brought about by whaling in the Antarctic (see **Section 5.7d**).

Non-target species

The material caught by the fishing process but not required is referred to as the by-catch (Figure 4.15). In some fisheries, this amounts to 75% or more, by weight, of the catch (Weber, 1995) and is usually discarded. While some may be alive, much of it is dead or so moribund as to be easy prey to scavenging predators, thus potentially impacting populations of non-target species. It is estimated that the North Pacific drift net fishery, with an annual harvest of around 300 000 t, sets up to 60 000 km of drift nets each night. In addition to the target catch, these take marine

Figure 4.14 Increase in the population of anchovy (dashed line) following the decline of the Pacific sardine (solid line) off the coast of California (from Levinton, 1995).

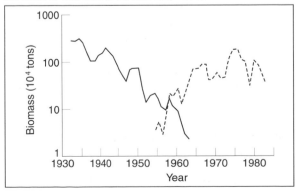

BOX 4.2 THE NORTH SEA FISHING INDUSTRY

The North Sea accounted for 3.5% of the world fish catch in 1983, a total composed of 2.42×10^6 t of fish and 0.16×10^6 t of shellfish. ICES (International Council for the Exploration of the Seas) data show that, in 1913, the North Sea catch was 1.25×10^6 t of fish, increasing to 1.5×10^6 t by 1960. Between 1960 and 1968 it more than doubled, peaking with a catch of 3.44×10^6 t in 1974, since when it has fallen.

Looking at total catch is, however, a rather coarse analysis, particularly because the pattern of exploitation has changed, with increasing quantities used for fishmeal rather than directly for human consumption. By the mid 1980s, fish for human consumption accounted for only 46% of the catch, the remainder being industrial fisheries.

The fish used for human consumption have traditionally been divided, on the basis of the gear used for capture, into demersal species, caught by trawls, and pelagic species, caught by drift nets, seines, etc. With the advent of midwater and surface trawls, this distinction has gone, but variations in the life histories of the two groups still make a convenient distinction for fisheries biologists.

Demersal fisheries

A wide range of demersal fish is exploited, with varying effects upon populations. From 1957 to 1984, the North Sea plaice (*Pleuronectes platessa*) catch increased, as a result of increased fishing effort, from 71 000 to 150 000 t. The more valuable sole (*Solea solea*) catch has remained fairly constant at around 20 000 t. These species are robust and show no sign of overfishing affecting recruitment.

The cod (*Gadus morhua*) catch rose during the 1960s and reached 340 000 t in 1972. Since then, it has declined to below the 1960s level and is now under 200 000 t per year. This appears to be, in part, due to a long-term biological trend rather than just the result of overfishing. Haddock (*Melanogrammus aeglefinus*) appear to be subject to wide natural fluctuations, catches varying between 50 000 and 550 000 t. Currently levels are around 100 000 t and the fishery, mainly dominated by UK vessels, is subject to strict quotas.

As a result of concern over the level of whiting (*Merlangius merlangus*) and haddock taken as a by-catch in the industrial fisheries, an exclusion area was established in the northern North Sea, the 'Norway Pout box', from which young individuals of these species cannot be taken.

Pelagic fishing

Pelagic fishing for food fish is centred on the herring (*Clupaea harengus*) and the mackerel (*Scomber scombrus*). Their life history characteristics make these species highly susceptible to overfishing, culminating in the 5-year closure of the North Sea herring fishery between 1978 and 1982. The lesson has, unfortunately, not been learned and, despite repeated calls from ICES for a ban, the mackerel fishery appears to be in a state of imminent collapse.

It is unlikely that overfishing will ever lead to the extinction of a target species, as it would become uneconomic to fish long before this time. Some by-catch species are, however, susceptible. Skate (*Raja batis*), for example, are taken as part of the catch in trawling operations. Because they are not target species, they are deemed not to be of economic value and no quotas are set on them. Being slow breeders and highly susceptible to fishing, extinction is a possibility.

The industrial fishery

Denmark dominates the industrial fishery. Several small species are taken including sand eels (*Ammodytes* spp.), Norway pout (*Trisopterus esmarkii*), blue whiting (*Micromesistius poutassou*) and sprat (*Sprattus sprattus*). The fishery takes about 350 000 t of Norway pout, and the stock seems robust. Sand eels are fished around the Shetlands, in the northeastern North Sea and in the southern North Sea. Currently about 600 000 t are taken. There is some evidence of a decline, but this is hard to separate from the wide fluctuations in population which this species undergoes.

Sprats show clear signs of stock depletion. Stock estimates of 700 000 t in the mid-1970s had shrunk to under 100 000 t by the late 1990s.

mammals, turtles, birds and non-target fish and probably affect at least some macrozooplankton. Mortality figures are difficult to obtain but estimates are of over 10 000 bird deaths per year.

The discards and offal thrown overboard when the catch is processed and gutted mean that fisheries are beneficial to scavenging species (Table 4.4). Much of the increase in seabird numbers in the North Sea has been attributed to increased food as a result of discarded by-catch and fish offal (Garthe *et al.*, 1996). Similarly, benthic scavengers such as fish (Kaiser & Spencer, 1994), whelks, starfish and hermit crabs (Ramsay *et al.*, 1996) appear to respond to the feeding opportunity that the discards represent.

Physical disturbance

Demersal fishing gears directly impact the sea floor, the passage of a dredge, beam trawl or otter trawl being analogous to a plough or rake being dragged over a field. Large, slow growing and

Table 4.4 Estimates of the fate of material discarded by North Sea non-coastal fishing vessels

	Taken by seabirds (t yr^{-1})	Sinking and potentially available to fish and benthic scavengers (t yr^{-1})
Offal	55 000	7 800
Roundfish	206 000	56 200
Flatfish	38 000	261 200
Elasmobranchs	2 000	13 000
Benthic invertebrates	9 000	140 800
TOTAL	310 000	479 000

Source: data from Garthe *et al.* (1996)

fragile species are most susceptible to damage – studies in the southern North Sea show that beam

Figure 4.15 The catch on deck of a trawler in the North Sea. The valuable part of the catch has to be sorted from the unwanted species – the by-catch – which is then thrown back, by which time most of it is dead or so moribund as to fall easy prey to the following flock of birds. The offal from the gutted fish is also thrown into the sea, adding to the flux of organic matter to the scavenging birds and benthos. (*Photo by M. Gill*)

trawling can lead to decreases of 10–65% in the density of echinoderms, polychaetes and molluscs (Bergman & Hup, 1992).

The physical structure and the creviced nature of coral reefs mean that they are not amenable to towed fishing gear, so fishermen have to use relatively inefficient lines and traps. In some areas, poisons and dynamite have been used to kill fish, which subsequently float to the surface for easy collection. These also cause mass mortality of non-target forms and, in the case of explosive fishing, destruction of the physical structure of the reef (Figure 4.16). Removal of grazing fish and invertebrates, along with mortality of the corals, often leads to the system becoming dominated by rapidly growing algae which prevent reinvasion by coral, providing another example of a change in stable state.

4.10 Summary

Coastal seas are the most productive region of the oceans, and contain a high diversity of environments. The relative ease of study means that we know more about the ecological functioning of intertidal and shallow water communities than the rest of the marine environment.

The abiotic environment in coastal regions is dominated by tides, particularly along the shore itself. The ecology of intertidal areas is primarily a function of the degree of water movement and the underlying geology. This determines the nature of the shore – wave-swept rock, sheltered rock, coarse mobile particles or stable muds. Tides produce clear zonation on rocky shores, in which dominant organisms are sessile, but zonation patterns are less clear on soft sediment shores, where most organisms are mobile burrowers.

Energy inputs in the water column are dominated by phytoplankton production, which generally shows distinct seasonal patterns in response to temperature, light, nutrient ability and grazing pressure. Inputs from rivers can enhance nutrient availability in coastal waters, though this affects species composition of phytoplankton more than overall abundance. Primary production in benthic communities is limited to shallow

Figure 4.16 (a) Unexploited coral reefs are natural high-diversity systems which support a diverse fish fauna (Batu Kapal, Ambon Islands, Indonesia). (*Photo by C. Frid*) (b) Exploitation of these systems by poisons or explosives leads to marked changes in the reef, with an explosion of rapidly growing algae covering the reef and, in the case of explosive fishing, physical break-up of the reef structure (Pombo, Ambon Islands, Indonesia). (*Photo by C. Frid*)

waters, particularly the rocky intertidal and sublittoral and, in clear tropical waters, coral reefs. Detritus is the primary energy source for most subtidal systems.

Community structure in hard substratum systems is determined by physical disturbance and predation, which prevent monopolisation of resources by dominant species.

Competition contributes to patterns of zonation seen on rocky shores. In soft sediment systems, the type of sediment is the primary determinant of community structure. Biological disturbance is important, though its effects may be beneficial to certain species. Benthic community structure is often explained, at least partially, by variability in recruitment ('supply side ecology') and, in soft sediments, by individuals which have survived disturbance ('relicts').

In the water column, there is good evidence for both competitive and predation control of plankton communities, often with the relative importance varying seasonally.

Human impacts on coastal seas include dumping of spoil, which smothers biota, and construction of hard surfaces, which can be beneficial to taxa adapted to rocky substrates. Harvesting of wild populations of marine organisms has major effects, both upon the target species and upon the environment in which they are caught.

5

The Open Ocean

5.1 Introduction

Beyond the continental shelf, the coastal zone is replaced by the open ocean. In oceanic areas, the sea floor is always below the depth at which sufficient light penetrates to support photosynthesis and, with the exception of vent fields (**Section 5.6b**), is dependent for its energy upon allochthonous production.

The water column can be divided into a series of zones. The photic zone, in which there is sufficient light to support photosynthesis, extends to around 100 m depth. Beneath this is the mesopelagic zone, down to about 1000 m, where some light penetrates but not enough to support primary production. Beyond this, and in complete darkness, are the bathypelagic zone (1000–4000 m) and the abyssopelagic zone (4000–6000 m). Only deep ocean trenches, the hadal zone, extend beyond this depth, although the deepest, the Challenger Deep in the Marianas Trench in the western Pacific Ocean, exceeds 11 000 m in depth.

5.2 The abiotic environment

5.2a STRATIFICATION

The thermocline

In the open ocean, a permanent thermocline is present at depths of 500–800 m (Figure 5.1a), effectively isolating surface waters from deep waters. In temperate areas, a second thermocline is produced at a depth of around 30–50 m each summer as intense summer warming at the sea surface, along with a decrease in wave-induced mixing, allows the surface layer to warm up (Figure 5.1b). In addition to this seasonal thermocline, daytime heating can produce a daily thermocline, typically at depths of up to 10 m, which is dispersed each night when the input of solar radiation ceases (Figure 5.1c). In autumn, increased wave action and decreased solar radiation lead to the breakdown of the seasonal thermocline and the water column becomes well mixed again (Figure 5.1d).

Water masses

Below the thermocline, a number of layers in the water column, differing particularly in salinity and temperature (and therefore density), can be identified (Figure 5.2). Distinct bodies of water with differing characteristics are known as water masses and are usually named after their region of formation. For example, Mediterranean Deep Water is present in the eastern North Atlantic at depths of around 1000 m. This relatively warm and saline water mass is formed in the northwest Mediterranean in winter by cool dry winds blowing over the sea, causing intense evaporation and mixing the water column down to depths of 2000 m or more. This water flows out of the Mediterranean under the inflowing Atlantic Water and then sinks and spreads out as it finds the layer of correct density at about 1000 m.

Denser bodies of water attempt to sink beneath less dense ones, so a stable water column

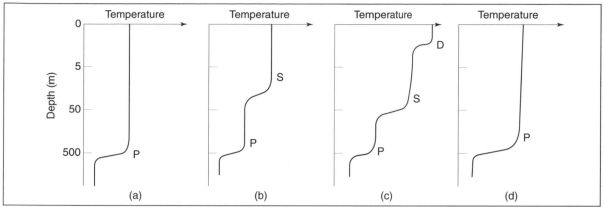

Figure 5.1 Temperature–depth profiles showing seasonal patterns of thermocline development at mid latitudes. (a) Winter. Low inputs of solar radiation and strong wind mixing at the surface produce a deep, well mixed layer. The permanent thermocline (P) is at a depth of 500–800 m. (b) Spring. Decreased wind mixing and increasing solar heating of the surface layer leads to the development of a warm surface layer separated by a seasonal thermocline (S) from deeper waters. As the season progresses the temperature difference across this seasonal thermocline increases and the thermocline depth gets deeper. (c) Summer. The seasonal thermocline is fully developed at 30–80 m and a daily thermocline (D) may be produced by the strong daytime heating of the surface layer. Other near-surface thermoclines may persist for periods of days when very calm conditions coincide with strong heating. (d) Autumn. Decreasing inputs of solar radiation and increasing wind-driven mixing erode the thermocline, making it weaker and shallower before it breaks down completely to give a well mixed surface layer (compare with lakes, Figure 6.3).

is one in which the most dense water is in contact with the sea floor and the least dense is at the surface. The density boundaries between water masses, marked by thermoclines or haloclines, can be significant impediments to the mixing of nutrients, oxygen and pollutants as well as marking breaks in salinity and temperature.

Upwelling

Surface waters and the deep ocean act as separate water masses, each with its own circulation system, connected only in discrete areas where surface waters downwell and deep waters upwell (**Section 1.2b**). The main areas of upwelling occur where surface ocean currents diverge, forcing deep water to rise (**Section 1.2b; Figure 1.3a**). As they are generated by global air circulation processes (**Box 1.1**), these are centres of permanent or predictably seasonal upwelling (but see **Section 5.7c**). In addition to these, however, local conditions, extending over tens to hundreds of kilometres, can cause a breakdown of the thermocline and upwelling of deeper waters. A cold core ring, a cyclonic gyre (**Section 1.2b**) which spins off a major current system, is an example of this (Figure 5.3).

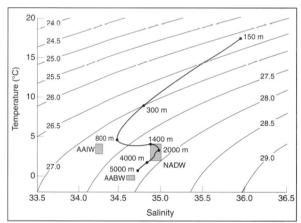

Figure 5.2 A T–S (temperature – salinity) diagram is a widely used tool in oceanography to examine the stability of the water column and identify constituent water masses. The density of saline waters, usually expressed as

$\sigma^t = 1000\times$ (specific gravity − 1) and illustrated here by the contour lines, is a function of salinity and temperature, but is influenced more by temperature, hence the curved σ^t contours. The salinity and temperature of samples at various depths are plotted on the T–S diagram along with the 'core' characteristics of various water masses (boxed regions). In this plot from the tropical South Atlantic, the presence of Antarctic Intermediate Water (AAIW), North Atlantic Deep Water (NADW) and Antarctic Bottom Water (AABW) can all be identified.

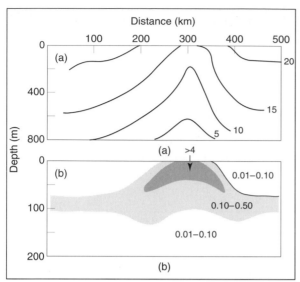

Figure 5.3 Diagrammatic representation of a vertical section through a cyclonic ring in a subtropical ocean. (a) Temperature (°C) and (b) Chlorophyll *a* (μg l^{-1}) (from Parsons *et al.*, 1984).

Movement of surface water into shallows, such as the edge of the continental shelf (the shelf break) and the tops of seamounts, increases water velocity, while frictional interaction with the bottom causes vertical turbulence. This leads to upwelling (**Box 5.1**), which can change otherwise low productivity surface water into a region of high production (Pingree, 1978).

5.2b CONDITIONS IN THE OCEAN DEPTHS

At the sea floor, the physicochemical environment is very constant. Throughout the deep sea, salinity is about 34.8 and water is at high pressure. It is always dark and very cold: AABW temperatures are 0 to -1.8 °C, while NADW is $+1.8$ to -2 °C. In deep trenches, the high pressure causes a heating of the water, which is, therefore, slightly warmer than abyssal waters. Deep basins isolated from the rest of the deep ocean by a shallow sill can be deoxygenated, as the shallow barrier prevents oxygen-rich water flowing into the basin to counter oxygen consumption by decomposers. These deep basins, including the Black Sea, may be anoxic and essentially abiotic due to this physical isolation from the deep ocean circulation (see also deep lakes, **Section 6.2c**). AABW and NADW

are, however, formed in well mixed surface regions and maintain a high oxygen concentration through continual circulation of cold water from the surface. Therefore, most deep ocean waters are well oxygenated and capable of supporting a diverse assemblage of aerobic organisms. Deep circulation also maintains constant conditions across large geographical areas, allowing organisms adapted to the conditions to become widely distributed. There is, for example, no climatic differentiation between areas of the deep ocean.

5.2c THE OCEAN BED

Sediments

The abyssal plain is dominated by soft sediments, many of which derive from phytoplankton. Carbonate sediment is the skeletal remains of coccolithophores and foraminiferans, which have calcium carbonate ($CaCO_3$) skeletons, while siliceous sediment is the remains of diatoms and radiolarians, whose skeletons are formed from silica (SiO_2). Red clays, in contrast, have a relatively small biological component; they are composed mainly of tiny particles originating from continental weathering and carried to the open ocean by wind and currents. Their red colour is caused by small quantities of ferric iron oxide (Fe_2O_3). The thickness of deep ocean sediments can reach several kilometres on the abyssal plain, but their rate of deposition is so slow that, at spreading centres of ocean ridges, they are only a few metres deep and often confined to depressions in the underlying topography.

The distribution of the different sediment types is principally controlled by three interrelated processes: climate and current patterns, distribution of nutrients (which determine surface water productivity) and relative solubility of SiO_2 and $CaCO_3$ as they sink. Carbonate sediments dominate in shallow water overlying mid-ocean ridges; in areas of high nutrient concentration, these derive from foraminiferans, whereas in low productivity regions, coccoliths are the source. Carbonate dissolves most rapidly in cold, deep water, so siliceous sediments dominate in cold waters, where diatoms are most abundant, and in

BOX 5.1   THE PHYSICS OF SHELF BREAK AND COASTAL FRONTS

Consider the potential energy of the water column and the tidal energy. Let R be the ratio of the production of potential energy in maintaining well-mixed conditions (PE) to the rate of tidal energy dissipation (TED):

$$R = PE / TED \qquad (1)$$

We can estimate these two terms in a number of ways and, for a restricted area, many of the terms used in those estimates are constants. However, two terms which vary are the water depth, h, and the average water velocity, $|U|$. We can calculate the stratification parameter, S, from this by:

$$S = \log_{10} [h / (C_D \times |U|)] \qquad (2)$$

where C_D is the drag coefficient.

Low values of S indicate turbulent mixing, while high values indicate stratification. For coastal waters, S usually has a value in the range -2 to $+2$. At intermediate values of S, around 1.5, the degree of stratification and turbulence are just sufficient to stabilise the water column and hold phytoplankton above the critical depth, while also providing sufficient turbulence to maintain a supply of nutrients to the surface layer (Pingree, 1978).

For example, in the Celtic Sea, off southwest England, in summer a front develops, to the southwest of which the water is stratified, while to the northeast strong tidal flows and the shallowness of the water lead to a well mixed water column. The thermocline rises to the surface at the front, producing a surface chlorophyll maximum, in contrast to a deep chlorophyll maximum in the stratified region. The close correlation between the $S = 1.5$ isoline and the surface chlorophyll concentrations is clearly seen in the following diagram. This shows (a) the distribution of the stratification parameter (S); (b) the surface chlorophyll (9–12 April 1975) in the Celtic Sea area of the continental shelf; (c) shows the vertical profile of chlorophyll a (upper) and temperature (lower) along a transect through a frontal region (from Parsons et al., 1984; after Pingree, 1978).

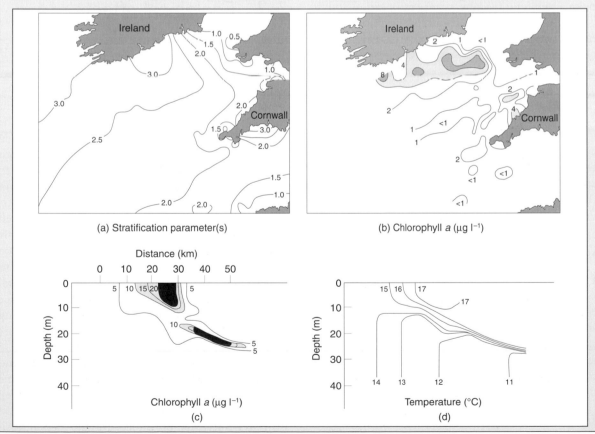

(a) Stratification parameter(s)

(b) Chlorophyll a (µg l^{-1})

(c)

(d)

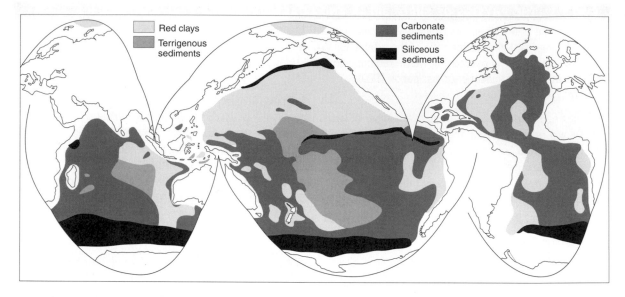

Figure 5.4 The distribution of dominant sediment types in the deep ocean.

deep equatorial regions, where radiolarian activity is highest. In the least productive parts of the deep ocean, where planktonic activity is very low, red clays are the dominant sediment (Figure 5.4).

Trenches

Trenches are long, narrow features, typically with a flat bottom and convex sides, along whose axes currents can be up to 10 cm s^{-1}. They often contain poorly sorted sediments from a variety of sources, including terrigenous sediments, while the trench sides may include exposed rock, providing a wide diversity of niches.

Hydrothermal vents

Hydrothermal vents are localised phenomena in seismically active parts of the ocean bed, in which reduced compounds and, often, heat are emitted into the water (**Box 5.2**). Although accounting for only a tiny proportion of the ocean bed, and very transient in their nature, they are locally extremely important in that they provide optimum conditions for chemosynthesis (**Section 1.4b**).

5.3 Ecological effects of the abiotic environment

The great depth of the ocean limits photosynthesis to a small proportion of its volume, in the illuminated upper layers. The decrease in light intensity from the surface to depth represents the only major environmental gradient in the open ocean (see **Box 1.2**), with light intensities high enough to drive photosynthesis being restricted to the top few hundred metres, even in clear ocean waters.

Water pressure increases with depth, although organisms respond to the external pressure by maintaining the same internal pressure and, so long as they remain within the pressure zone to which they are adapted, suffer no detrimental effects. In the deepest trenches, however, extreme pressures can become an ecological limiting factor, affecting ionic reactions, solubility of gases and viscosity of the water.

Permanent stratification limits circulation and therefore primary production. The thermocline prevents algal cells from being mixed into deep water where there is insufficient light, but also prevents nutrients produced by the decomposi-

BOX 5.2 HYDROTHERMAL CIRCULATION IN THE OCEAN CRUST

Hydrothermal vents are areas of the sea floor where hot water is emitted from the Earth's crust. They were first observed in the mid-1970s by submersibles involved in Project FAMOUS (French–American Mid-Ocean Undersea Study), although their existence had been predicted and hinted at by temperature anomalies discovered in the mid-1960s. Vents occur at ocean spreading centres, the most studied ones being the Galapagos Rift system, the East Pacific Rise and the mid-Atlantic ridge at 21°N.

Once the oceanic crust has been formed (**Section 5.7e**), hydrothermal processes start to occur. Sea water, driven by convection, circulates within the newly formed rock. Chemical reactions between the sea water and the, usually, hot basalt cause major chemical changes to occur. These reactions are the main source of some elements, notably lithium, rubidium and manganese, in ocean waters, while they are an important source of barium, calcium and silicon. It is estimated that about one-third of the sea floor contains active water circulation cells, so it is a widespread phenomenon. About 1.7×10^{14} kg of sea water flows through the oceanic crust every year, and the entire ocean probably passes through the crust every few million years.

There are four types of vents. The most spectacular are the Black Smokers, where hot water, at >350 °C, gushes out of the crust in a dense plume carrying particles of metal sulphide – the 'black smoke'. At temperatures in the range 30–330 °C, the vents appear as White Smokers, carrying particles of barium sulphate. Warm Water Vents have outflows at 10–20 °C, while in Cold Water Seeps the water has undergone chemical change but no heating.

The nature of hydrothermal circulation

Water enters the crust over a wide area, via cracks and fissures, and percolates down through the crust. Hydrothermal circulation can only occur where the rock is permeable, the high degree of fracturing associated with new crust and the lack of a sediment infill partly explaining why it is so common at sites of new crust formation. The figure shows a cross-section of an idealised hydrothermal vent. Sea water percolates down over a wide area and is drawn down and laterally into the region above the magma chamber by the continual rising of heated water. This rises upwards in a narrow plume, carrying with it high concentrations of dissolved minerals which may be deposited among the fractured crust (the stock work) and at the surface.

Magma within the crust is at about 900 °C, and as the crust is thin and, at ridge centres, not covered in a thick layer of sediment, a strong thermal gradient exists. This drives the convection cells, with the hot water rising through the rocks above the magma chamber in a narrow, strongly flowing band.

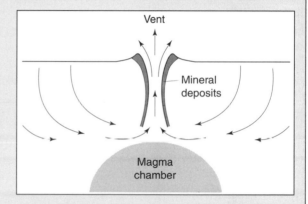

While the flows alter the chemical balance of the sea water, they also affect the rocks, being important in the conversion of basalts into greenschists. Magnesium is completely stripped out of sea water during high-temperature reactions with rock, so its presence in the outflow from warm water vents indicates that their outflow is composed of some hydrothermal water which has mixed with ordinary sea water before emerging. There is no dilution of hydrothermal water from black smokers. As the solution mixes with sea water, precipitates of sulphides, which make up the 'smoke', are often deposited to form a chimney 10 m high from which the vent emerges.

BOX 5.2 – CONTINUED

The transition from one type of vent to another is poorly understood, but can occur at any time. For example, the precipitation of salts within the upper rock layers of a warm water vent may restrict the outflow to a smaller area and so reduce the opportunity for dilution with ordinary sea water, changing the warm water vent into a white or black smoker. Over time, hydrothermal cooling drives the magma chamber deeper, and may be sufficient to solidify it at slow spreading centres. Thus magma chambers and the hydrothermal circulation are relatively short-lived and isolated phenomena, typically lasting for only 15–25 years (Lutz *et al.*, 1985).

tion of material in the deep sea from reaching the phytoplankton. Deep waters are nutrient rich, as detritus raining down from the photic zone (**Section 5.4b**) is decomposed, but little of this is mixed back into the upper layers, where uptake of nutrients by phytoplankton can severely limit their availability. In contrast to coastal seas (**Section 4.4c**) and shallow lakes (**Section 6.3b**), the permanent thermocline caused by the great depth of the oceans means that breakdown of the seasonal thermocline in temperate regions, although resulting in significant nutrient inputs to the photic zone, does not allow nutrients from the deepest part of the water body to recirculate. Only in regions of upwelling are high concentrations of nutrients input to the photic zone, making these the most productive parts of the ocean. Permanent upwelling off the edge of continents can extend over many hundreds of kilometres, while cold core rings produce patches of enhanced primary production typically around 200 km in diameter.

5.4   Energy inputs

5.4a   PRIMARY PRODUCTION

Photosynthesis in the oceans is limited almost exclusively to phytoplankton and cyanobacteria. Floating macrophytes are important only in the Sargasso Sea, in the mid-Atlantic Ocean. Elsewhere, with the exception of the limited primary production at hydrothermal vents (**Section 5.6b**), the ocean ecosystem is dependent on the energy fixed in the photic zone by phytoplankton. Highest ocean production occurs in regions of

intermediate stability where nutrients are mixed across the thermocline but algae are not mixed down into deep waters. Nitrate is generally the limiting nutrient in oceanic waters, although diatoms may be limited by their requirement for silica.

Iron as a limiting nutrient

In the equatorial Pacific and the Southern Ocean, nitrate, phosphate and silicate are present in relatively high concentrations but primary production is low. In these regions, iron may be the limiting nutrient (Chavez *et al.*, 1991; Miller *et al.*, 1991a, 1991b), because, although common in the Earth's crust and in inland and coastal waters, it has low solubility and enters the ocean only in small amounts. The main source is wind-blown dust particles, but the distribution of global winds means that the equatorial Pacific Ocean and the Southern Ocean around Antarctica receive little of this dust.

In 1993 and 1995, the importance of iron in controlling primary productivity in the equatorial Pacific was investigated by releasing approximately 0.5 t of iron, in the form of ferrous sulphate labelled with an inert tracer molecule (so the water with the added iron could be distinguished from the surrounding ocean, even if all the iron was consumed). Within a few days, up to 30-fold increases in chlorophyll concentration and phytoplankton biomass were recorded in the water to which the iron had been added (Martin *et al.*, 1994; Cooper *et al.*, 1996). This has led to speculation about the feasibility of adding iron to the ocean to stimulate primary production and hence removal of CO_2 from the atmosphere to offset anthropogenic increases and global warming.

5.4b SECONDARY PRODUCTION

Transfer of energy to the deep ocean is by detritus sinking from the photic zone. Once it has settled on the ocean bed, some POM is resuspended into the pelagic zone. Resuspension of even small amounts of bottom sediments by internal waves or near-bottom currents can provide a large input of nutrients and POM to the overlying waters. Resuspension is seasonal, as a result of the seasonal pattern of wave action, but is also limited by stratification, which both acts as a barrier to waves interacting with the bottom and effectively isolates the photic zone from any nutrients generated by resuspension.

There is a fairly constant ratio of carbon in the oceans:

DOM	1000
POM	125
Phytoplankton	20
Zooplankton	2
Fish	0.02

Thus POM and DOM represent a large reservoir of organic carbon, whose dominant users are heterotrophic microorganisms.

Composition of POM

Much POM consists of recognisable fragments of phytoplankton, zooplankton, faecal pellets, etc. A large proportion is, however, in the form of amorphous masses, up to 50 mm in diameter, containing bacteria, small algae and protists, along with much inorganic carbonate, or particles less than 5 mm in diameter, with no obvious origin, but possibly either breakdown products or building blocks of these amorphous masses. Surface waters contain semi-transparent flakes, up to 25 mm in diameter, which may be the result of films which form on air bubbles and remain after the bubble collapses.

Most POM is recycled in the top 300 m, so its concentration declines with increasing depth. A large proportion is associated with the surface film, and can be concentrated into slicks by the action of Langmuir Circulation cells (**Box 5.3**).

Typical concentrations are $50-1000\,\text{mg C dm}^{-3}$ at the surface, $5-100\,\text{mg C dm}^{-3}$ at 100 m depth and $<10\,\text{mg C dm}^{-3}$ at 250 m depth. From about 300 m to the seabed, POM concentration is fairly constant.

Biological processing of POM

Biological activity is extremely important in packaging POM. Small particles with a slow sinking rate are concentrated by detritivores into large, rapidly sinking faecal pellets, which, below about 1000 m, are a major component of sinking POM. This transfer is supplemented by vertical migration of organisms which feed at night near the surface, then migrate down at dawn (**Section 5.7a**), often covering a vertical distance in excess of 1000 m (Figure 5.5), and release their faecal pellets at greater depths.

POM particles act as the basal resource in deep ocean systems. The biological repackaging of small particles into faecal pellets and the ease with which phytoplankton cells aggregate into 'flocs', several centimetres across, mean that sinking rates are quite rapid, of the order of 300 m per day, and detritus reaches the ocean floor within weeks of leaving the surface.

Many zooplankton are filter feeders, which do not distinguish between living and dead POM and will gain much of their nutrition from the microbial communities on POM particles, rather than from the detritus itself (see **Section 3.4b**). The same processes occur on POM in the sediments, where deposit feeders strip the heterotrophs off the particles.

In surface waters, the ratio of C : N in POM is 6 : 1, whereas in deep waters this has shifted to 20 : 1, probably because nitrogen is used by bacteria for protein synthesis, while carbon is present in refractory forms. Soluble carbohydrates are rapidly lost from the particles so that, below 200 m, only insoluble carbohydrates are left. Fats generally comprise less than 1% of POC, and they, too, are rapidly re-used by bacteria in the top 200 m. Protein and amino acid concentrations decrease rapidly from the surface to 200 m, then more slowly to 300 m.

BOX 5.3 LANGMUIR CIRCULATION

Langmuir Circulation is the name given to the series of rotating cells set up by moderate winds blowing over the surface of the water (see Stavn, 1971). The cells run downwind and may extend over several hundred metres.

Under conditions of Langmuir Circulation, plankton are passively accumulated into patches which may be several kilometres long but only 1 m or less wide. The figure shows how a steady moderate wind over the sea surface sets up Langmuir Circulation cells. Neutrally buoyant particles remain randomly distributed (A), negatively buoyant particles are aggregated in the upwellings (B), while buoyant particles are concentrated at the downwellings – often forming visible slicks on the surface (C). Actively swimming organisms may position themselves in areas of high relative flows (D), lower velocity flows (E) or the low flow region out of the vortices (F) (after Stavn, 1971).

Accumulation of particles in regions of downwelling and upwelling results in the frequently observed phenomenon of greater variability in samples parallel to the wind than those taken perpendicular to it. A net towed perpendicular to the wind will tend to integrate across the patches, while downwind samples will be either in or out of a patch and hence more variable.

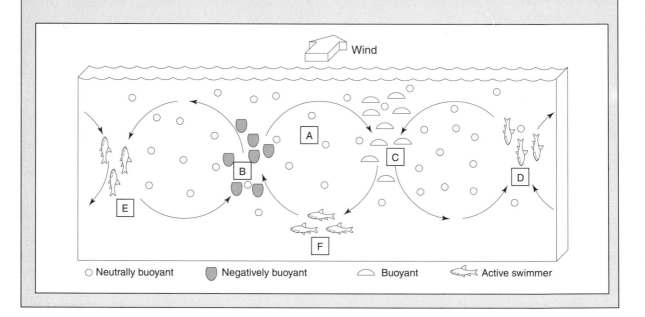

○ Neutrally buoyant   ◗ Negatively buoyant   ◠ Buoyant   🐟 Active swimmer

5.5 Community structure in the photic zone

5.5A OCEAN PLANKTON

Species richness in pelagic communities appears to be similar to that in many terrestrial communities, but the generally wider distributional limits of the pelagic biota mean that the total species pool of pelagic species is much lower than for terrestrial species (Angel, 1994). There is a latitudinal gradi-ent in species richness from the tropics to the poles that mirrors that seen in terrestrial environments. This cline is not, however, constant and there appears to a sharp decline at 40° latitude, which has been attributed (Angel, 1991) to the increased seasonality and greater productivity occurring at the higher latitudes.

The paradox of the plankton

Hutchinson (1961) first referred to the paradox of

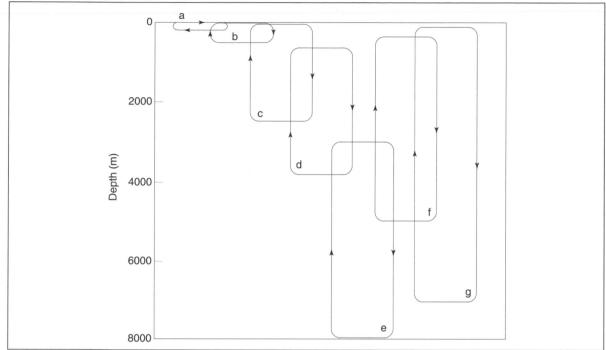

Figure 5.5 Diagrammatic representation of how vertical migrations of different amplitudes and mid-points overlap, allowing material consumed at the surface to be liberated at mid-depths, where it is reconsumed and later liberated at greater depths. **a**: Diurnal vertical migrations in the photic zone. **b**: Diurnal and seasonal migrations in the photic and upper mesopelagic. **c**: Seasonal and ontogenetic migrations including the surface and bathypelagic realms. **d**: Ontogenetic migrations encompassing the bathypelagic and the abyssopelagic. **e**: Migrations wholly within the abyssopelagic. **f**: Migrations including the deep sea and the mesopelagic. **g**: Short-term irregular migrations covering most of the water column (from Raymont, 1983; after Vinogradov et al., 1970).

the plankton: how can so many species co-occur without any distinct subdivision of the resource base and no spatial segregation? The lack of spatial structure and heterogeneity in the pelagic environment sets it apart from all other environments, because there is no scope for niche partitioning based on microhabitat specialisations. Below 1000 m, no light penetrates and only the gradual change in pressure with depth marks the position in the water column, but the majority of species lack specialist pressure-sensing organs, so cannot detect this gradient.

Given the lack of physical structure, the expectation would be for low species richness in pelagic communities. This is not the case. For example, McGown and Walker (1985) showed that 175 species of copepod coexist in the North Pacific in a relatively uniform water mass and that the relative and absolute abundance of each species had

remained constant for over 20 years. Is this the result of competition being reduced by specialisation and niche segregation, or are the communities non-equilibrium ones, continually disturbed by predation, patchy resources or some other factor? In benthic communities, such questions would be tested experimentally. However, the nature of the pelagic environment means that any attempt to enclose a portion, in order to manipulate it, introduces large artefacts which makes interpreting the results of the experiment difficult. An alternative approach which does not suffer from the problem of artefacts is the 'natural experiment', although the uncontrolled and non-replicated nature of such experiments brings their own limitations.

In the central North Pacific, two events have occurred during the last 30 years which can be used as such 'natural experiments' (Dayton, 1984). The first occurred in 1969, when vertical turbulence across the thermocline increased, resulting in increased mixing of nutrient-rich waters up to the photic zone. If competition was an important factor in structuring this community, then increased resources would have allowed those species with high reproductive rates to dominate. Phytoplankton productivity doubled (confirming that they were nutrient limited) as did zooplankton biomass, but the relative abundance of the various zooplankton species did not alter in spite of the change in total abundance. The second experiment occurred as the result of a relatively new tuna fishery, which reduced numbers of top predators in the system by a considerable degree, allowing their prey – planktivorous fish and squid – to increase, and therefore altering predation pressure on the copepods upon which they feed. It did not, however, result in any shifts in the structure of the copepod assemblage. All the consumers of plankton in this system – predatory copepods, chaetognaths, euphausiids, shrimps, squid and fish – are dietary generalists, so, although total predation pressure increased, it did so uniformly across the range of prey species, so no shift in relative abundance occurred. The sum of the predation pressure exerted by this assemblage may be important for maintaining the diversity of the copepod component of the community.

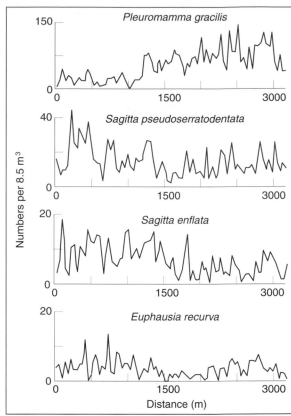

Figure 5.6 Horizontal patchiness of zooplankton occurs at a variety of scales, with large patches superimposed on small patches (from Wiebe, 1970).

Patchiness in plankton distribution

Changes in the physicochemical properties of the water mass, life history variations and short-term migrations account for the heterogeneous distribution of zooplankton in the vertical plane. Spatial distribution of zooplankton in the horizontal plane is also patchy (Steele, 1976). As early as the mid-19th century, it was recognised that plankton were not distributed randomly, but often occurred in dense swarms or blooms. By the 1950s (e.g. Barnes & Marshall, 1951) it was established that zooplankton generally have a more clumped or aggregated than a random distribution. Cassie (1959, 1963) showed that the distribution of the diatom *Coscinodiscus gigas* was non-random, even within 1 m², while Wiebe (1970) described plankton patches on scales ranging from less than 20 m to several kilometres (Figure 5.6). The causes of this patchiness can be

divided into those of physical and biological origin, although observed patches are likely to be a response to a number of physical and biological factors, and even the sampling method used to make the observations!

Physical effects occur over a wide variety of scales ranging from kilometres of advection events, such as upwellings and downwellings, to centimetre scales of random turbulence. Other physical processes influencing spatial distribution of plankton include Langmuir Circulation (**Box 5.3**), frontal systems, and the upwelling and downwelling associated with cyclonic and anticyclonic systems, respectively. Phytoplankton tend to respond primarily to these physical processes and the supply of nutrients. Zooplankton are subjected to the same physical processes, but also undergo a range of biological processes which lead to spatial patchiness. There is some evidence (e.g.

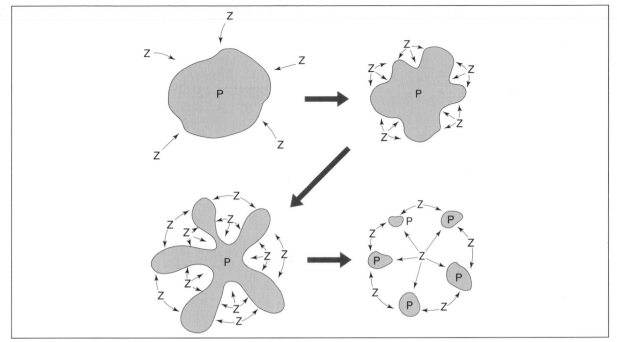

Figure 5.7 Dense patches of phytoplankton (P) attract grazing zooplankton (Z). However, the presence of any inhibitory compounds will be greatest in the patch centre, so grazing tends to occur from the edges. Any irregularities in the patch result in progressive incursions by the grazers, eventually leading to fragmentation of the original patch.

Mackas & Boyd, 1979; Wiafe & Frid, 1996) that zooplankton are able to maintain their patch integrity against small-scale turbulence by active swimming. Zooplankton are attracted to regions of high phytoplankton, and are also able, given that patches may be stable for several months, to increase their numbers more rapidly in regions where phytoplankton are abundant. This is analogous to the ability of phytoplankton to develop dense patches in regions where nutrients are abundant.

Some phytoplankton produce inhibitory compounds, which reach their highest concentrations in the centre of a phytoplankton patch. Grazers, therefore, tend to forage from the edge of the patch inwards, resulting in the fragmentation of the large patch into a number of smaller patches as the zooplankton gain control (Figure 5.7).

Aggregations of copepods in tropical waters and euphausiids in the Antarctic appear to be active social groupings. Whereas many fish shoal to reduce predation pressure, it is difficult to apply this argument of safety in numbers to zooplank-

ton, because many predators require dense patches to ensure that their prey is at a high enough density to sustain them. It has, therefore, been proposed that aggregating and attracting predators gives individuals away from the swarm a respite from predation. This is unlikely to apply to most zooplankton, but may be true for asexually reproducing species and for cladocerans when they are reproducing parthenogenetically.

Predatory plankters such as ctenophores and chaetognaths are capable of very high feeding rates (e.g. Reeve & Walter, 1978; Oresland, 1987) and, in some cases, a clear correlation may be found between increase in abundance of these predators and decline in copepod abundance (Fraser, 1962; Greve, 1981). However, other studies show no such link and the role of zooplankton predators in controlling or structuring grazer assemblages remains to be resolved.

5.5b THE ROLE OF OCEANIC PREDATORS

Low productivity and long food chains in the

oceanic realm limit the biomass of the top predator guild and mean that predators have to forage over large areas to obtain their food. In the tropics and mid latitudes tuna, sharks and toothed whales are the dominant, natural, top predators.

Tuna

Tuna are fast-swimming fish – bursts of up to 20 body lengths per second have been recorded – which never stop swimming. They are negatively buoyant and 'fly' underwater, generating lift from their extended pectoral fins. Their continual motion also allows them to ventilate the gills by forcing water against the gill membranes (ram-ventilation) as they swim with their mouths open, allowing them to meet the oxygen demands of their high metabolic activity. Uniquely among fish, they have a body temperature warmer than the environment, although whether this is simply due to their high metabolic activity generating heat more rapidly than they shed it, or is a case of active thermal regulation – a 'warm-blooded' fish – remains controversial. The oceanic distribution of tuna is probably driven by changes in water temperature (and thermocline position) and the need for well oxygenated water masses. The average density of yellow fin tuna (*Thunnus albacares*) in the Pacific, without any human exploitation, would be one 10 kg fish in every 2.8 km² of ocean (Sharp & Francis, 1976), but tuna form large aggregations which undertake ocean-scale migrations. Three types of aggregation can be distinguished – tuna schools, porpoise-associated shoals and flotsam-associated shoals. Fish in porpoise-associated shoals tend to be larger than those associated with flotsam, which, in turn, are larger than school fish. The size of fish in any given school tends to be similar, probably a reflection of the energetics of maintaining a particular swim speed, while genetic analysis of fish from schools shows a high degree of similarity in the occurrence of rare alleles, indicating that many school members are related (Sharp, 1978). Despite this, the schools appear to form and break up, as smaller groups come together and subsequently separate.

That some tuna shoals are associated with schools of porpoises or dolphins emphasises the similarity in their dietary requirements. It seems strange that, in a low production system, two potentially competing species would operate together. Our knowledge of the ecology of the open ocean is still so limited that it is not known what benefits the species may confer on each other to offset the potential negative impacts of competition. A possible explanation is that, while food density is low on average, both species require large aggregations of prey – social swarms, aggregations at fronts or cyclonic ring upwellings – within which food may not be limiting.

Sharks

The precise role of sharks in oceanic communities is poorly understood (Wetherbee & Gruber, 1990; Cortes & Gruber, 1990). Most sharks are dietary generalists with broader diets than other fish from the same region (Ellis *et al.*, 1996), although differing habits, mouth morphology and dentition lead to relatively low dietary overlap in co-occurring species (Ellis *et al.*, 1996). In larger species, the dietary overlap is potentially greater but competition may be avoided by spatial separation, either vertically in the water column or temporally, as many species show seasonal migrations between oceanic areas and shelf waters (Clarke & Stevens, 1974).

Toothed whales

While some species of dolphin and porpoise feed with tuna on squid and small fish near the surface, the majority of open ocean species of toothed whale also take large amounts of mesopelagic fish, particularly lantern fish (Myctophidae), for which they dive to depths of up to 250 m. There is some evidence that different species of oceanic dolphin feed at different depths and times of day, dividing the food resource (Gaskin, 1982). At close range, all oceanic dolphin and porpoise species utilise vision for hunting but, in addition, many species can locate prey by sound and, in some cases, by active echo-location. The animals emit broadband clicks, their well developed hearing being used to gain information about the environment from the reflections and echoes of these clicks.

Sperm whales (*Physeter macrocephalus*) feed

mainly upon squid, avoiding competition with other species through their large size (males up to 20 m, females up to 12 m in length) and by foraging at greater depths. They have been recorded at 1200 m depth and indirect evidence suggests that occasional dives may exceed 3000 m. Females and juveniles remain in low latitude waters, while males range throughout the oceans (Rice, 1989), providing an interesting example of a species which avoids intersexual competition for resources.

5.5c BALEEN WHALES

In contrast to toothed whales and tuna, which feed predominantly in low and mid latitudes, baleen whales generally undergo migrations between high latitude feeding grounds and low latitude breeding and calving grounds, allowing them to exploit the high, but short-lived, productivity of the high latitudes while calving in warm waters – which may reduce neonatal mortality. Navigation during these migrations often involves movement parallel to a coastline by following bottom contours, supplemented by direct visual observation of the coastline, while oceanic species such as blue whale (*Balaenoptera musculus*), which have good visual acuity, may navigate using the position of the sun and the stars (Herman *et al.*, 1975).

Baleen whales are filter feeders. A gulp of water containing macrozooplankton prey is taken into the mouth and the tongue is pushed up and back, driving the water out through the filter of baleen plates in the roof of the mouth and moving the food mass to the back of the buccal cavity to be swallowed. The various species of baleen whale appear to specialise on different prey groups or in different locations (Figure 5.8). In the Southern Ocean, most species exploit krill (*Euphausia superba*), a large crustacean which aggregates into dense swarms. Humpback whales

Figure 5.8 (a) Differences in food consumed by rorqual whales (Balaenopteridae: minke whale *Balaenoptera acutirostrata*, fin whale *B. physalus*, blue whale *B. musculus,* sei whale *B. borealis*, humpback whale *Megaptera novaeangliae*) and Right Whale (Balaenidae: *Balaena* spp.) in different oceans. Fi = fish, Eu = euphausiids, Co = calanoid copepods, Sq = squid, Am = pelagic amphipods. (b) Krill (*Euphausia superba*) is the dominant euphausiid in the Southern Ocean and, along with the phytoplankton upon which it feeds, provides the basis for many Antarctic food webs. Although rarely exceeding 7 cm in length, it aggregates in vast swarms and provides the main food for all southern populations of baleen whales, from the 10 t minke whale to the 150 t blue whale.

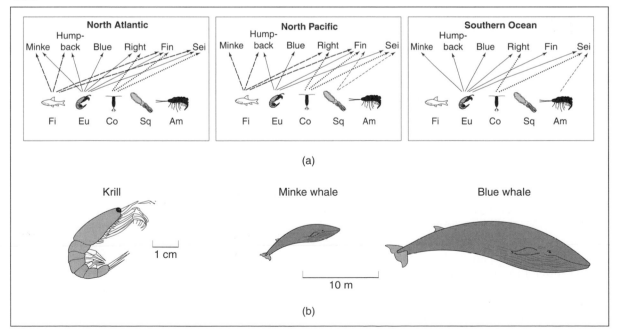

(*Megaptera novaeangliae*) actively enhance concentrations of prey by 'bubble netting' (Jurasz & Jurasz, 1979), which may be carried out by a solitary individual or a group working in cooperation. The whale swims in a circle below the prey, while emitting bubbles of air from its blow hole. As these bubbles rise, they form a barrier, a bubble curtain. Rising up and swimming in smaller circles, the whale concentrates the prey within the bubbles before finally swimming down and then rising vertically – mouth agape – through the prey aggregation.

5.5d PRODUCTIVITY AND FOOD CHAIN LENGTH

Most of the ocean is oligotrophic, exceptions being high latitudes, which show a strongly seasonal pattern of productivity, and upwelling regions where high productivity is sustained by nutrients from beneath the thermocline. In relatively productive high latitudes, euphausiids such as krill directly exploit phytoplankton and, in turn, are exploited by large filter feeders such as baleen whales and seals. In oligotrophic waters, however, phytoplankton are smaller than in more productive regions, because the uptake kinetics for scarce nutrients favour small cells with high surface area to volume ratios. They are too small to be grazed directly by macrozooplankton, and extra microzooplankton and mesozooplankton links are inserted into the food chain. Ironically, therefore, low energy waters have longer food chains, with the associated loss of energy, than high energy waters. The lower inherent production and the greater number of steps in the food chain mean that few large predators can be supported in oligotrophic areas of the ocean.

5.6 Community structure on the ocean floor

Of the 270 million km² of the Earth's surface covered by abyssal plains, the total area quantitatively sampled by all the sampling programmes to date adds up to less than 50 m² (Gage, 1996). They have, however, been relatively well sampled compared to trenches, for which most of our knowledge is derived from a handful of Russian studies in the Pacific (Gage & Tyler, 1991).

The macrofauna of abyssal plains is dominated by nematodes, polychaetes, bivalves and pericarid crustaceans. The Indian, Pacific and Atlantic Oceans are separated at depths of about 2000 m into three distinct basins, with a high degree of species endemism in each basin, although Indian and Pacific faunas are more similar to each other than either is to the Atlantic. There appears to be an observable faunal change at 6000 m, below which amphipods, polychaetes, bivalves, holothurians and echiurids increase in proportion, while echinoids, asteroids, sipunculids, ophioroids, coelenterates, bryozoans and fish decline in importance. Endemism is high in trenches, as much as 75% in some Pacific trenches, which further suggests a specialist fauna distinct from that on the adjacent abyssal plain.

5.6a BENTHIC DIVERSITY

Species diversity of macrofauna in deep sea sediments may be comparable to that of tropical rainforests and coral reefs (Grassle & Maciolek, 1992). Diversity increases from the continental shelf down the slope to a maximum at about 3000 m, with a subsequent decrease down to 6000 m, beyond which it remains relatively constant. This pattern is not, however, universal (Gage, 1996).

Two groups of theories, which are not mutually exclusive, have been proposed to explain the high diversity of the deep seabed fauna.

Environmental stability and habitat complexity

Sanders (1968) originally developed the stability–time hypothesis, his argument being that, as the deep sea is a very stable environment and has been in existence in this form for many millions of years, the organisms have evolved to reduce competition, so individual niches are very narrow and many species can be accommodated. Recent evidence from video and camera studies shows that the deep sea floor is not the unstructured constant environment described by Sanders, but shows considerable heterogeneity. Thus, coexistence can be promoted without the need for extreme levels of niche specialisation. Furthermore, whether the required dietary specialism occurs in the deep sea remains unclear, as gut analyses of the larger fauna indicate that generalists and non-selective sediment feeding dominate.

Non-equilibrium dynamics and biological disturbance

Dayton and Hessler (1972) advanced the view that deep sea diversity could be maintained by the activities of a large number of unselective predators holding populations below their carrying capacity. Thus resources were not limiting, allowing additional species to invade the community. The subsequent realisation of the importance of disturbance in generating small-scale patchiness in marine communities (**Section 1.7b**) has furthered the case for considering deep sea communities to be non-equilibrium ones. The maintenance of a spatio-temporal mosaic, through the action of foraging predators, grazers, bioturbators and detritus falls, is responsible for continually creating patches of underexploited resource available for colonisation. Each patch then follows a succession towards the climax community but, meanwhile, new patches have been created. So the system at any one time contains a mosaic of patches at different stages of the trajectory from newly disturbed to climax state and has a high overall diversity.

5.6b ECOLOGICAL PROCESSES AT HYDROTHERMAL VENTS

Hydrothermal vents (**Box 5.2**) have been compared to oases in a desert for deep sea biology. They differ from the surrounding abyssal plain in the availability of hard substrata but, more importantly, the autochthonous production occurring in response to the emissions being produced (**Section 1.4b**).

Vent plumes contain around 10^6 bacterial cells per litre, representing a productivity in excess of the overlying mid-ocean surface waters. The bacteria generally occur as clumps approximately 100 μm in diameter, at the interface between the two water types, where temperatures are not too high and oxygen is plentiful. They are preyed upon by attached filter feeders, tube worms,

bivalve molluscs and, in Atlantic systems, swarms of shrimps. Predators and scavengers are also present, usually in the form of crabs.

Many of the organisms present at the vents contain endosymbiotic bacteria. The vent mussel *Bathymodiolis thermophilus* possesses enlarged gill tissues which contain chemosynthetic bacteria, but the mussels retain the ability to filter feed and so can exist away from the vent plume. The entire nutritional requirement of the clam *Calyptogena magnifica* can be met by endosymbiotic chemoautotrophic bacteria. One of the most dramatic discoveries at vents in the east Pacific is large colonies of the tube-living worm *Riftia pachyptila*, which lacks a mouth and gut but has a highly vascularised set of gills and whose body is packed, up to 50% of its mass, with endosymbiotic bacteria (Gage & Tyler, 1991). The worms live in the mixed flow conditions close to the vent, where they can extract carbon dioxide, sulphides and oxygen from the water, and contain haemoglobin which enables them to withstand periods of anoxia. Time lapse photography shows that the worms regularly retract into their tubes, to reduce exposure to anoxic conditions as the flow regime fluctuates, and to reduce predation, often in the form of gill nipping, from fish and crabs (Tunnicliffe *et al.*, 1990).

Vent fields are transient phenomena, as changes in flow regime, precipitation of minerals in the channels and collapse of chimneys can all stop the hydrothermal flow and hence the supply of energy to the chemoautotrophic system. The specialist fauna must, therefore, be able to colonise new vents and so avoid extinction when the vent expires. Given the distance between vents, dispersal must be via the water column, and two possible routes exist. First, the hot rising plume of vent fluid could be utilised to lift larvae high into the water column where the lateral shear of the currents distributes them over a wide area. Second, there are currents flowing along the axis of most mid-ocean ridge systems, into which the release of larvae will disperse them to new vent sites on the ridge. While the latter method is more targeted to suitable habitats, vents sites are not distributed evenly along ridges and the former method will distribute larvae over a wide area – although much of it will be unsuitable environment.

5.6c OTHER REDUCING ENVIRONMENTS

Methane gas seeps

Hydrothermal vents are not the only reducing environments in the ocean, and the discovery of chemoautotrophic food webs at vents has stimulated research in environments such as methane gas seeps. At these sites, both free living and endosymbiotic chemoautotrophic bacteria have been observed and it has been suggested that the presence of methane gas seeps supporting chemoautotrophic communities contributes significantly to the productivity of some areas of the ocean (Judd & Hovland, 1989). The fauna at some of these sites contains species similar to those at vents, but their geographical separation from the vents means that they are unlikely to act as 'stepping stones' between vent fields for dispersing fauna.

Whale carcasses

The discovery in 1987 of a partially decomposed whale carcass in the deep ocean off the California coast allowed observations of the impact of large carcasses on the local environment. The input of organic matter from this 21 m blue or fin whale (*Balaenoptera* sp.) carcass had significantly altered the local sedimentary environment, raising the organic content and reducing the sediment oxygen content. In places, the bones and sediment were covered in a mat of the bacterium *Beggiatoa*, a chemoautotrophic species utilising sulphides and oxygen. Anaerobic decomposition of lipids – which are stored in bones for buoyancy and can account for as much as 60% of the skeletal weight of a living whale – released reduced organic compounds and hydrogen sulphide which were utilised by free living and endosymbiotic chemoautotrophs to fix organic carbon (Smith, 1992; Deming *et al.*, 1997).

The bones of the whale had been colonised by clams, mussels, gastropods, polychaete worms and amphipod crustaceans (Allison *et al.*, 1991). While some of these species were members of the background abyssal fauna, others were species recorded previously only from hydrothermal vents, including the limpets *Pyropelta corymba*

and *P. musaica*, which graze sulphur bacteria. It is, therefore, possible that whale carcasses may act as stepping stones for dispersal between seeps (Martill *et al.*, 1991). Approximately 1000 grey whales (*Eschrichtius robustus*) die each year. If 50% of their carcasses arrive at the deep sea floor and they are distributed randomly, then the distance between carcasses, within their limited coastal distribution in the north Pacific Ocean, would be about 9 km (Smith *et al.*, 1989). A similar density of carcasses throughout the oceans would probably ensure effective dispersal for vent-dependent species.

5.6d THE ROLE OF PATCHINESS IN COMMUNITY DYNAMICS

The fauna of the deep sea floor exhibits patchy distributions at a wide range of spatial scales although, given the problems of sampling – both the logistical problems of remoteness and the sparse nature of the fauna requiring large numbers of large volume/area samples – there remains some debate over the degree of patchiness and the causal mechanisms. Analysis of photographs and sediment samples shows that the deep sea floor has variations in the physical environment on scales from millimetres to metres, including mounds, tracks, pits/burrows and faecal deposits, all of which arise from biological activity. Such biogenically produced features interact with the weak bottom currents in the deep ocean to produce further heterogeneity as a result of deposition in the lee of mounds. Superimposed on this physical heterogeneity is the variability associated with the arrival of food material, ranging from aggregations of a few phytoplankton cells to whole whale carcasses (Rice & Lambshead, 1994), and that derived from the variability in the settlement of propagules (Grassle & Morse-Porteous, 1987). Figure 5.9 illustrates the observed patterns of spatial and temporal heterogeneity. They range from short-term aggregations for reproduction to assemblages persisting for many years on hydrothermal vents and, in size, from a few square centimetres to several hundred square metres.

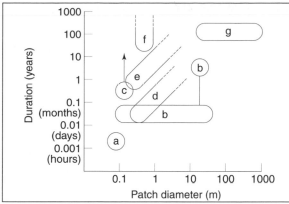

Figure 5.9 Spatial and temporal scales of deep sea faunal patches. **a**: Small-scale social/reproductive aggregations, lasting no more than a few hours. **b**: Slow-moving detritivores, ranging from those feeding on very patchy resources to larger 'herds' feeding on more generally distributed resources. In any one locality, these aggregations will last for only a few days, but the large mobile herds may stay together as a group for very much longer periods. **c**: Meiofaunal patches based on small organic resources. These are very small in size, reflecting the size of the organisms and the resource, but will persist for as long as the resource remains. **d**: Scavenging necrophages attracted to animal carcasses. The size and duration of these patches is directly proportional to the size of the carcass and mobility of the organisms; in the case of whale carcasses (**Section 5.7c**), they may persist for months or years. **e**: Aggregations on plant material. These are similar to those in **d**: but longer lasting, as plant remains are generally more refractory and so attract less active scavengers. **f**: Patches of sessile filter feeders, such as sponges, which are limited to areas where currents bring food to them but, once established, persist for many years. **g**: Patches associated with seeps and hydrothermal vents. (Modified from Rice & Lambshead, 1994)

Organic matter on the sea floor

A key component of the patches identified in Figure 5.9 is the importance of detrital inputs; only vents and seeps are independent of allochthonous inputs from above. It is difficult accurately to estimate the frequency of arrival of organic matter at the sea floor, but there is probably a steady drizzle of material derived from faecal material and moults from animals living in the water column, in addition to pulses of higher levels of deposition due to the arrival of material following blooms in surface waters. This material may arrive only days or weeks after the surface bloom and may be predictable from year to year, giving a seasonality to the deep sea environment.

In some areas, close to the ocean margin, as much as 20% of the carbon in the deep sea sediments is of terrestrial origin. Large pieces of plant material, including tree trunks, saltmarsh plants and macroalgae, are relatively frequently observed, but this is probably largely a function of their refractory nature. This material tends to be utilised by a variety of small infaunal species which colonise the sediment under and adjacent to the plant remains. Offshore (with the exception of the centre of the North Atlantic gyre, below the Sargasso Sea) large falls of plant material are rare and animal carcasses are the main input of carbon in large parcels. Baited camera observations show that animal material rapidly attracts mobile scavengers, particularly amphipods, decapods and fish which consume and disperse the material within a few days. Inputs of large detrital masses, such as whale carcasses, are irregular and infrequent but, once present, may support a localised community for several months, or even years (Figure 5.9).

5.7 Temporal change in oceanic systems

Oceanic communities are in a continual state of flux, the position of organisms changing in response to processes acting at the scale of minutes to those which function over several decades. Much of the short-term variation in plankton distribution can be attributed to physical processes such as wind-driven mixing and 'eddies', while that in the nekton is usually caused by behavioural responses, including predator avoidance, food gathering and shoaling.

5.7a VERTICAL MIGRATION

As the only reference frame is the vertical one provided by the gradient of light intensity, it is perhaps not surprising that the dominant behaviour shown by many zooplankton is movement in the vertical plane (Figure 5.5). Dramatic changes in distribution can occur, many of which can be explained by active behavioural mechanisms – vertical migration in response to seasons, life cycle or even on a daily basis (Harris, 1987).

Ontogenetic vertical migration

Ontogenetic vertical migration refers to a change in depth at different stages of development. It occurs in two basic forms (Raymont, 1983): breeding at the surface, the female rising to lay the eggs; and breeding at depth, following which young animals swim up, not necessarily all the way to the surface. The latter is more common, the copepods *Calanus plumchrus* and *C. cristatus* in the temperate North Pacific providing good examples (**Section 4.4c**). Females lay their eggs in winter and early spring at 500–3000 m depth. Eggs and nauplii float or swim up, reaching the surface in spring as copepodite larvae, which exploit the spring and summer phytoplankton populations to achieve rapid growth. In July, the copepodites, now in their final larval stage (cV), begin to move down, ceasing to feed once at depth. The mature females are non-feed and die after laying. All samples from depth contain both adults and cVs, so it appears that either some mature after one season while others delay for another year, or a proportion never mature.

Diel vertical migration (DVM)

The detailed analysis of ocean plankton distributions from many regions has shown a general pattern of plankton moving downwards at dawn and upwards at dusk, or occasionally the reverse. Diel vertical migration has been observed in polar, temperate and tropical seas and many lakes (**Section 6.5b**). By the 1920s it was fairly well established that the main cue for many species was a particular isolume, or level of light intensity. This explains the phenomenon of 'midnight sinking': the population moves up as a distinct group at dusk as light levels fall and the isolume rises. After dark, without the light cue, the plankton are dispersed over a wide depth range by random movements. At dawn, the isolume reappears, so the plankton regroup near the surface and then move deeper as light intensity increases. While this optimal light level may explain the cue used by many species, others start to migrate up hours before sunset, nor does it explain the evolutionary advantage of reverse migration or of moving the equivalent of up to 100 000 body lengths per day (see **Box 5.4** and **Section 6.5b**).

5.7b SEASONALITY

At latitudes greater than 40°, ocean productivity is highly seasonal (**Section 4.4c**). Seasonal changes in the tropics and subtropics may be driven by ocean-scale phenomena – the monsoons over the Indian Ocean and Indo-Pacific region, for example. Seasonal migrations of species such as whales and tuna may bring a seasonality to otherwise non-seasonal areas. At high latitudes, seasonality is driven by the production cycle (**Section 4.4c**). The flocculation of phytoplankton cells and production of faecal material by zooplankton exploiting the phytoplankton bloom all aid in the rapid transfer of this material to the deep sea, whose faunas also experience seasonal production at high latitudes. Our knowledge of the response of meso- and abyssopelagic faunas to this seasonality is very limited. In the deep sea, time lapse photography, used to follow the fate of settled material derived from the phytoplankton bloom, shows that while pelagic detritus arrives as a relatively uniform covering, it is moved by bottom currents to accumulate in depressions and the lee of mounds (Rice & Lambshead, 1994). These patches then persist for many months and possibly between years, and may be an important source of spatial heterogeneity in the deep sea benthic environment (**Section 5.6d**).

5.7c INTERANNUAL CHANGES: ENSO

In addition to cyclic seasonal changes, there is a series of aperiodic changes which cause interannual variation in the ocean ecosystem. One of the best known is the El Niño – Southern Oscillation (or ENSO) event. ENSOs are climatic fluctuations centred in the Pacific. They occur every 2–10 years and are indicated by the occurrence of unusually warm water off the coasts of Peru and Ecuador. The term El Niño is the local name for this phenomenon and literally means 'the Christ child', making reference to the timing of the warming of the coastal waters just after Christmas.

ENSOs are a disruption of the coupled atmosphere–ocean system in the Pacific, and it remains unclear as to whether it is the ocean which drives a change in the atmosphere or vice versa. During

BOX 5.4 EVOLUTIONARY MECHANISMS DRIVING DVM

The two main contenders for the evolutionary cause of diel vertical migration are the 'more efficient energy use' or growth rate hypothesis (McLaren, 1969, 1974; Enright, 1977a, 1977b) and the 'predator avoidance' or death rate hypothesis (Zaret & Suffren, 1976; Stich & Lampert, 1981; Lampert, 1989).

The growth rate hypothesis

Migration confers a bioenergetic advantage by reducing maintenance costs. The basal metabolic rate is lower in the cold deep water than at the surface. So, if mechanics of feeding and digestion are such that an organism cannot feed continually, then there is an advantage to spending time in a region of lower costs. It may also lead to an increased life time fecundity, increasing the life span of individuals by slowing growth.

Criticisms of the growth rate hypothesis are as follows:

1 Non-feeding life stages migrate, even though they would gain most from reduced metabolic costs by staying at depth.
2 The intensity of migration often increases with age. Young, rapidly growing individuals often do not migrate, even though they would gain most from the energetic benefits of migration.
3 It cannot account for the generally greater migratory activity of larger individuals, which are most obvious to a visual predator.

4 In polar waters, migration ceases during midsummer, when there is no night. Under the growth rate hypothesis, there would be no advantage to staying in cold deep waters, yet the plankton do (as predicted by the predator avoidance model).

The death rate hypothesis

If the main predators hunt by sight, then predation rates will be lower at depth than at the surface during the day. At night, susceptible organisms can migrate up to exploit the higher productivity of surface waters, avoiding predation under cover of darkness.

Criticisms of the death rate hypothesis are as follows:

1 Many migrators do not go deep enough to avoid visual predators.
2 In the Antarctic Ocean, the main predators are not visual, but are filter feeders, yet migration still occurs.
3 Animals in very deep waters migrate, even though they would never be in the light, even at the top of the migration.
4 Many fish feed near the surface at night to exploit the plankton which have moved up.
5 Salps, medusae and ctenophores are not palatable yet still migrate.
6 Transparent forms should migrate less, as they are less visible; this is not the case.

---

a normal year, hot air over Indonesia rises, and the resultant low pressure pulls air west from the high pressure region in the subtropical South Pacific, creating southeast trade winds (Figure 5.10a). During an ENSO, however, atmospheric pressure over Indonesia remains high and these trade winds over the central Pacific weaken, or may even reverse (becoming westerly) in the western Pacific. The reduction in the trade winds causes the sea surface slope across the Pacific to disappear and the thermocline also becomes horizontal (Figure 5.10b), allowing a large body of warm mixed layer water to flow eastwards, bringing warm water to the coastal areas of Peru and Ecuador and suppressing the normal upwelling. The warm mixed layer water carries with it the nutrient-limited plankton community typical of the central Pacific, replacing the normal coastal pelagic community, which is dependent upon the nutrient-rich upwelling. This, in turn, causes a failure of the fishery, which is based on planktivorous fish such as the anchoveta (*Cetengraulis mysticetus*).

The ramifications of ENSO are much more widespread than a change in the upwelling dynamics and fishery off Peru. Weather patterns

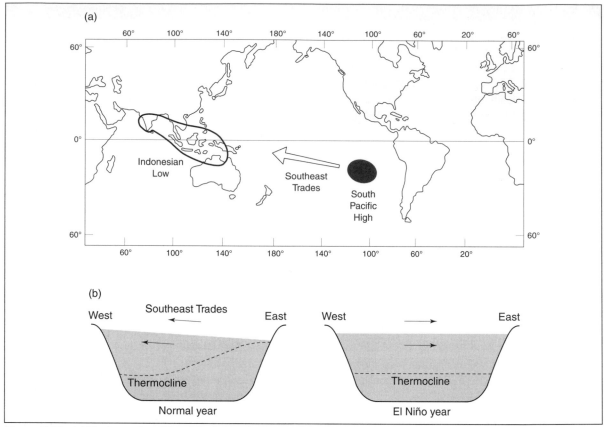

Figure 5.10 (a) The 'normal' position of the Indonesian Low and the South Pacific High and the path of the Southeast Trade Winds produced by the pressure gradient. (b) A section along the Equator in the Pacific in a 'normal' (left) state and during an 'El Niño' (right) event, with prevailing wind and current directions shown by arrows. Note the loss of sea surface slope and the horizontal thermocline during the El Niño event.

over the whole Pacific are altered. Droughts affect normally wet regions, while arid areas suffer torrential and destructive rain storms. Tropical cyclones are also more frequent and track further east in ENSO years, while there is evidence of ENSO events being linked to fluctuations further afield, with, for example, extremely cold winters in Eurasia and North America tending to coincide with ENSO years.

5.7d LONG-TERM CHANGES IN ECOSYSTEM FUNCTION

The Antarctic pelagic food web is centred on krill, which is consumed by baleen whales, seals, penguins, fish and squid. At the beginning of the 20th century, there were large populations of baleen whales in Antarctic waters each summer, consuming around 190 million tonnes of krill each year. Commercial whaling has since decimated these whale populations. Estimates of the consumption of krill for the mid-1980s (Laws, 1985) indicated that baleen whales only accounted for 40 million tonnes and the amount consumed by crabeater seals (*Lobodon carcinophagus*) and penguins had more than doubled. Since the moratorium on hunting, whale populations have increased more slowly than population models had predicted they should, suggesting that the balance of the ecosystem has shifted, the present seal–penguin dominated system being stable and resistant to invasion by whales. If this is the case, which is by no means certain (Fraser *et al.*, 1992), then it is an example of an ecosystem exhibiting multiple stable states. It is also a clear message about the scale and unpredictability of the changes that overexploitation can bring about in the natural world.

Harvesting

The majority of the world's marine harvest is taken from coastal waters (**Section 4.9**), as these are more productive and tend to have shorter, and therefore more efficient, food chains than oceanic regions (Ryther, 1981). In addition, the further the catch has to travel to market from the point of capture, the greater the sale value has to be to cover costs. Therefore, oceanic harvesting concentrates upon exploitation of high value oceanic whales, tuna and squid. Recently, however, 'prospecting' fisheries have developed for species which may potentially yield enough to offset costs, such as krill and deep sea fish. Test-harvesting of Antarctic krill by the Japanese and Russians has led to estimates of a sustainable annual harvest of 100 million tonnes (some estimates actually being double this). One of the barriers to exploitation of krill is how to utilise it: there are no direct routes for human consumption and most proposals for its harvest advocate processing into a protein meal, for use in other products or as a food for livestock. The costs of catching krill in the inhospitable Antarctic, transporting it to consumers in the Northern Hemisphere and processing it, make these proposals far from economic at present. If large scale harvesting goes ahead, however, further major changes in Southern Ocean ecosystems can be expected.

While most harvesting of deep sea fish can be regarded as exploratory, there is a limited number of established fisheries based on deep water species. Off Madeira there is a traditional long-lining fishery for scabbard fish (*Aphanopus carbo*) from depths of 750–1000 m, using baited hooks. The Pacific supports fisheries, on the continental slope to approximately 1500 m depth, for the sable fish or black cod (*Anoplopoma fimbria*), while around Australia and New Zealand there is a trawl fishery on the continental slope and on the tops of seamounts, at depths of 750–1000 m, for orange roughy (*Hoplostethus atlanticus*). In addition to their food value, these fish contain a variety of wax esters in their tissues which are used in cosmetics, specialist lubricants and pharmaceuticals, and they are a good substitute for sperm whale oil. From peak capture rates in the 1980s of 42 000 t yr^{-1}, catches have been declining, leading to concerns that the fishery was based on old, slow-growing fish and will not, therefore, recover. Similar concerns have been voiced over the best known deep sea fishery, the Russian-dominated harvest of roundnose grenadier (*Coryphaenoides rupestris*) and roughhead grenadier (*Macrourus berglax*) in the northwest Atlantic and sub-Arctic. Between 1968 and 1978, catches averaged 83 800 t yr^{-1}, but have since declined, although whether this is a result of exploitation or of long-term cooling of the water masses is unclear.

5.7e OCEAN SCALE CHANGES

The oceanic system has persisted as a continuous entity throughout the period during which life has been present on Earth. Its individual components are not, however, fixed, and all oceans go through a 'life cycle' as a consequence of plate tectonics.

The Earth's surface consists of a series of plates, which move relative to each other. Movement is generated by seafloor spreading, the creation of new sea floor at spreading centres, which form an almost continuous ridge system, that resembles a mountain chain, throughout the major ocean basins. Creation of new sea floor forces the rest to move away and, as the Earth's surface does not change in area, creation must be matched by destruction. Continental crust is less dense and therefore at a higher elevation than oceanic crust so, where ocean and continent are forced together, the continental plate rides over the oceanic plate, which is subducted beneath it, creating an oceanic trench (Figure 1.6). Continental plates, therefore, remain relatively unchanged in size and shape and can be considered to 'float' over continually changing oceanic plates.

Evolution of ocean basins

The average life span of an ocean is about 200 million years. Thus, as the Earth's oldest rocks

Table 5.1 Six stages in the evolution of an ocean

Stage	Examples	Dominant motions	Characteristic features
1 Embryonic	East African rift valleys	Crustal extension and uplift	Rift valleys
2 Young	Red Sea, Gulf of California	Subsidence and spreading	Narrow seas with parallel coasts and a central depression
3 Mature	Atlantic Ocean	Spreading	Ocean basin with active mid-ocean ridge
4 Declining	Pacific Ocean	Spreading and shrinking	Ocean basin with active spreading axes; also numerous island arcs and adjacent trenches around margins
5 Terminal	Mediterranean Sea	Shrinking and uplift	Young mountains
6 Relict scar	Indus suture in the Himalayas	Shrinking and uplift	Young mountains

were formed about 3800 million years ago (Ma), the oceans have turned over 15–20 times. Individual ocean basins grow from an initial rift, reach a maximum and then shrink, ultimately closing completely. The Atlantic and Indian Oceans, which contain active spreading centres and no major subduction zones, are expanding, while the Pacific is contracting because subduction zone activity outpaces spreading. The rates of movement, averaged over time, are of the order of several centimetres per year.

Several stages in the life cycle of an ocean can be identified (Table 5.1). Rift valleys develop along the line of continental separation. Basaltic magma wells up between the continental blocks, creating crust which is thinner and more dense than continental crust and so lies below sea level. The young ocean basin is shallow and, if influxes of sea water are partially or totally evaporated, then salt deposits build up on the sea floor, along with the more normal deposition of sand and mud (Stage 1). Sediment from the adjacent coasts builds out into the rift, eventually creating a continental shelf–slope system. As the spreading axis builds away from the coast, the sediment supply dwindles and the continents become increasingly distant from the spreading ridge (Stage 2). The crust contracts as it cools, and abyssal plains are produced, allowing the continental shelf and rise system to become fully developed. At this stage (Stage 3), the continental margins are approximately parallel to the spreading centre. In due course, one or more destructive plate margins will be formed, as a result of continental collision or new continental rifting (Stage 4), and the ocean begins to disappear (Stage 5).

Figure 5.11 shows the relative position of land masses at three times during the past 170 million years. During the Jurassic Period (Figure 5.11a), about 170 Ma, the continental plates were joined together as a single land mass, called Pangaea, and there was a single ocean, Panthalassa, with an arm called the Tethys Ocean. By the Cretaceous Period (Figure 5.11b), about 100 Ma, the continental

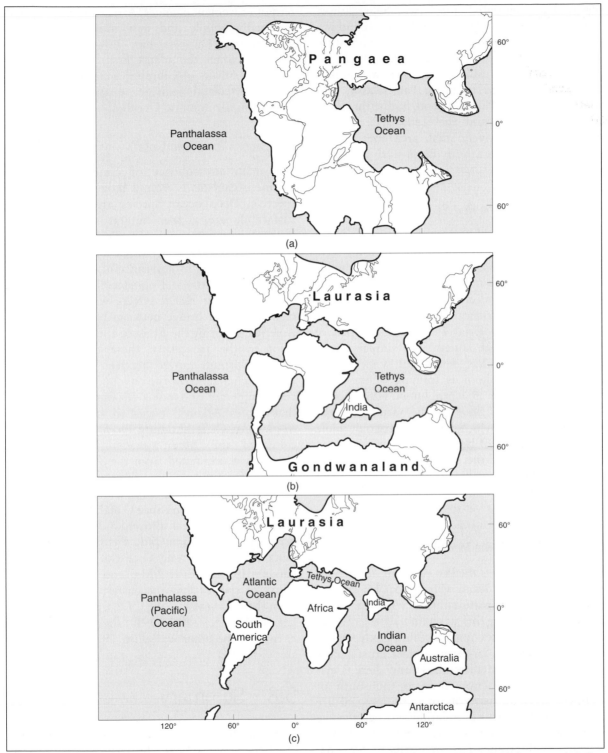

Figure 5.11 Reconstruction of the distribution of the continents: (a) 170 Ma, (b) 100 Ma and (c) 50 Ma. Note that coastal shelf seas are not differentiated from continental land masses.

plates had separated into two aggregations, Laurasia and Gondwanaland. Gondwanaland was beginning to fragment, causing contraction of the Tethys Ocean. By the Eocene Period (Figure 5.11c), around 50 Ma, the Atlantic and Indian Oceans had started to form, Panthalassa, now identifiable as the Pacific Ocean, had shrunk considerably in size, and the Tethys Ocean was confined to a relatively small area covering the present-day Mediterranean Basin and southwest Asia.

Birth of an ocean: the Red Sea

The clearest example of a young ocean today is the Red Sea. Extensive evaporite deposits were produced when the embryo Red Sea was connected intermittently to the Mediterranean. Since this closed and the connection to the south opened, there has been considerable infilling with terrigenous and pelagic material. In the southern part of the Red Sea, a ridge system very similar to the mid-Atlantic ridge has developed, while to the north, new ocean floor is forming in the areas greater than 1000 m in depth, but no rift system is apparent. The sea floor in the vicinity of the southern rift system is 5 million years old, while that in the vicinity of the deeps is 2 million years old or less. It would therefore appear that the Red Sea axial zone is a northward-propagating zone of separation that opened up properly in the south about 5 Ma, but has yet to do so in the north.

Death of an ocean: the Mediterranean

The Mediterranean is the last remnant of the once extensive Tethys Ocean (Figure 5.11), created when the African plate collided with the Euro-Asian plate, cutting off a section of the Tethys Ocean. Its floor is a complex realm, composed of many minor plates. In general, older crust occurs in the east of the Mediterranean and there is evidence for a subduction zone to the south of Cyprus. Thus the patterns of crust removal are complex and no clear correlation between the age of the sea and tectonic activity appears to exist.

The Mediterranean is an ocean in the final stages of its life, as the African plate is consumed under the Euro-Asian plate. Thus, unless the pattern of movement changes, Africa and Eurasia will eventually collide and new mountains will be thrown up. The sea has, however, had one reprieve: when the plates first collided around 7 Ma, the Straits of Gibraltar were closed and the isolated Mediterranean Sea evaporated, only to refill from the Atlantic Ocean about 5.5 Ma.

Implications for ocean biota

The main consequence of plate tectonics for marine organisms is from a biogeographical perspective. Deep ocean species are unaffected by surface climate, as their habitat is relatively constant throughout the world. They are, however, fragmented by oceanic ridges and shallow seas and, particularly, by severance of oceanic connections when continental plates collide. One of the most important recent effects was the development of a land bridge between North and South America, isolating the Atlantic and Pacific Oceans. Prior to the merger of these two continents, oceanic currents moved between them, allowing biotic exchange. Now the only oceanic links are in cool temperate and polar regions, which means that tropical Atlantic species are isolated from the tropics elsewhere. Atlantic biota have, however, colonised the Mediterranean basin because, although it originated from the Tethys Ocean to the east, its only modern connection to the main oceanic system is to the west. Construction during the 19th century of the Suez Canal, a marine channel without locks, has allowed a direct interaction between warm water Indo-Pacific and Atlantic biota for the first time since the creation of the Panama Isthmus over 2 Ma, and has allowed an influx of species into the eastern Mediterranean from the Red Sea, so-called 'Lessepsian migration' (e.g. Golani & Galil, 1991), though few species have gone the other way (Por, 1978).

5.8   Summary

The majority of the oceanic realm is a low productivity environment. Surface productivity is nutrient limited at low latitudes and seasonally limited by low light at higher latitudes. Important exceptions to this occur at regions of upwelling. The sea floor and the water column below the photic zone are dependent upon allochthonous production and the cycling of organic matter. Transfer of detritus to the ocean depths is enhanced by detritivores, both by packaging it into faecal pellets, which sink relatively rapidly, and by vertical migration, often over great distances.

The oceanic water column can be regarded as a series of layers varying in their salinity and temperature. The boundaries between these water masses may act as a barrier to the movement of plankton and so provide some structure to this otherwise homogeneous environment. The abyssal plains are covered by soft sediments, mainly of biological origin.

In the water column, most heterotrophs appear to be generalist and opportunistic in their behaviour – food webs are structured by size. No single species or group of species, including the larger mobile predators, appear to be functional 'keystone' species. Low productivity and patchiness of resources means that large nekton are generally very mobile, foraging over great distances.

Species diversity at the sea floor appears to be promoted by small-scale – often biologically produced – disturbances, such that these systems are non-equilibrium ones. The patchy, unpredictable arrival of detritus inputs accentuates this patchiness. These communities are species-rich compared to most terrestrial ones, but the total species pool in the oceans is much smaller than on land, each species having a much larger geographical range. Deep ocean trenches, in contrast, appear to support a fauna which is both distinctive from that of the abyssal plains and often shows a high degree of endemism within a given trench.

Hydrothermal vents represent areas of primary production in the deep sea and support a specialist fauna, including grazers, filter feeders, scavengers and predators, many of which are restricted to vent environments. The problem of dispersal between vent fields may be reduced by the use of the reducing environment associated with large carcass falls as 'stepping stones'.

Outside the tropics, the oceans are seasonal, with the seasonality in surface production giving a seasonal pattern of organic flux into the deep sea. In addition, the oceans undergo other temporal changes on time scales of months to decades. Some of these patterns, such as ENSO, have major climatic consequences over large geographical areas.

Despite their size, oceans are not permanent, but follow a clear 'life cycle' of formation, spreading and then contraction, powered by plate tectonics.

6

Lakes and Ponds

6.1 Introduction

A lake may be defined as a body of water, encircled by land, whose outflow, if present, is small relative to its volume. Lakes fed by rivers can be distinguished from water bodies fed only by rainfall, groundwater or occasional inundation, such as ponds, oxbow lakes and, in coastal areas, lagoons, but ecologically these water bodies share important similarities and so all are considered in this chapter (Figure 6.1). Pools, backwaters and other permanent dead zones in rivers also share functional similarities with lakes, emphasising that the boundary between a river and a lake can often be very blurred.

Lakes, ponds and other enclosed water bodies are often referred to as standing waters, or lentic systems, as opposed to rivers, which are flowing,

Figure 6.1 Two contrasting lakes. (a) A cirque lake, formed by scouring at the head of a former glacier and fed mainly by runoff from a small, high altitude catchment. The catchment is dominated by slowly weathering rock, with little vegetation, and the lake is deep and oligotrophic (Lochnagar, Scotland). (*Photo by M. Dobson*) (b) An oxbow lake, formed when a river cut off a former meander and now fed by groundwater and occasional floods from the parent river. The catchment is well vegetated alluvium and the lake is shallow and eutrophic (River Bollin, northern England). (*Photo by M. Dobson*)

BOX 6.1   TYPES OF LAKE BASIN

Geomorphologists recognise around 100 different lake types, based upon the origin of their basins, but they can generally be placed into three structural categories.

Depressions in bedrock

Suitable sites include those caused by glacial ice scouring out a depression, forming long, thin lakes in glacially eroded valleys, or more rounded cirque lakes near the tops of mountains, marking the head of a former glacier. Other sites are formed by tectonic activity, raising the ground to create shallow basins, such as that now containing Lake Victoria, or lowering the ground to produce rift (or graben) lakes, collapse of cave systems in limestone areas, volcanic activity and even the impact of meteorites. Bedrock depressions include the largest lake types, and can reach great depths; glacial scour lakes include most of the larger lakes in Canada and northern Europe, notable among these being Great Slave Lake in northwest Canada (maximum depth 614 m, extending to 464 m below sea level; the deepest lake in North America), Mjösen in Norway (720 m; the deepest lake in Europe) and Loch Morar (310 m) in Scotland, as well as the Great Lakes of eastern North America. Volcanic crater lakes can be very deep: Crater Lake in Oregon fills a large volcanic crater and, despite having a surface area of only 55 km², extends to a maximum depth of 608 m. These depths are easily exceeded, however, by the deepest rift lakes: Lake Baikal (1620 m) in Russia and Lake Tanganyika (1480 m) in the East African Rift Valley.

Depressions in sediment

Large areas of sediment left behind following glacial or periglacial activity may contain depressions in which water will collect, creating kettle lakes, which are often short lived; the mosses and meres of Cheshire and Shropshire in England were formed in this way: meres still contain open water, whereas mosses have infilled to become wetlands (see **Section 7.6b** and Figure 7.7). Other lakes occur on fluvial sediments, and may be formed as a river

changes course or shifts sediment around. These include oxbow lakes, formed when a river cuts off one of its own meanders (see Figure 6.1b).

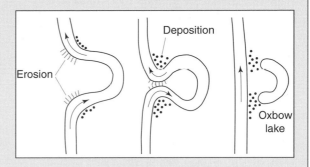

Barrier lakes

A barrier thrown across a valley and acting as a dam will create a lake. Barriers include landslides, lava flows (creating so-called coulee lakes), windblown sand and, in areas of glacial activity, ice barriers. Among the most common, however, are those formed by glacial moraine. Glaciers push out scoured rock fragments, or moraine, and aggregations of this sediment mark the furthest extent of a glacier. After the glacier has melted, these can form effective dams, behind which a lake will develop.

The Finger Lakes of New York are unusual in that they are impounded at both ends by glacial moraine, the southern ends by the debris from an

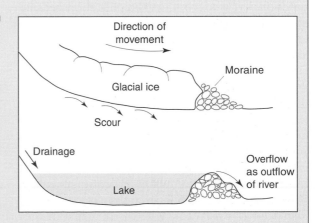

BOX 6.1 – CONTINUED

older ice advance, the northern ends by more recent glacial activity (Cole, 1975).

Barrier lakes form along coasts when longshore drift creates a sand or gravel barrier; complete severance from the sea allows a freshwater lake to develop; otherwise, a brackish lagoon will be created.

Biologically created water bodies

Biological processes create some lentic water bodies, generally small in size. Beaver ponds, formed by active damming of a river, are barrier lakes; *Sphagnum* bog extending across a valley mouth can, similarly, create a barrier behind which a lake will form. *Sphagnum* bog, too, is typically full of small ponds created by depressions in the hummock–hollow sequence of such structures. Ephemeral water bodies which can, nevertheless, be important local habitats for aquatic organisms during dry periods are those created by large animals: alligators in the Florida Everglades, for example, create scrapes which remain water filled during the dry season. Water which collects in hollows in living plants, such as tree holes, supports a specialised community dependent upon the leaf litter which collects within them. The simple but variable communities which occupy these phytotelmata, as they are called, have been used to study the effects of resource availability on food chain length (Pimm & Kitching, 1987).

An exception to the general pattern of biotically created water bodies being small is those produced by human activity. By damming river valleys to create reservoirs, people have created many thousands of lakes, varying in size from those covering a few square metres to reservoirs which extend over several thousand square kilometres. Human activity has also created many flooded depressions in sediment, generally as an accidental by-product of mining or quarrying activities, although in many parts of the world, tiny ponds are dug in large numbers for ornamental or fish-rearing purposes. Gravel pit lakes, for example, simply fill up the depression left after gravel extraction. The Norfolk Broads in eastern England were created when mediaeval peat cuttings were flooded. The soft glacial sediments in Cheshire in northern England contain many ponds formed in depressions created by bombs dropped during the Second World War.

Canals are interesting examples of anthropogenically produced water bodies which, although clearly linear in shape and flowing like a river, generally flow so slowly that they support biota more typical of lakes.

---

or lotic, systems. This is a convenient division but, functionally, is a gross oversimplification because all but the smallest, most sheltered ponds will contain moving water. The differences between lentic and lotic systems relate to the form this movement takes: flow in rivers is unidirectional, proceeding downhill under the influence of gravity, whereas direction of flow in lakes and ponds is less consistent, being affected by, among other things, wind direction and speed, and by convection currents generated by differential heating and cooling in different parts of the water body. Furthermore, the turnover time for water in lentic systems is slower; a water particle in a river is continually displaced downstream, whereas in a lake it may recirculate many times before being lost to the outflow or to evaporation. Absence of a strong unidirectional current allows pelagic communities to flourish so that, ecologically, lakes are more analogous to the open sea than to rivers. Benthic communities, too, share much in common with the open sea.

6.2 The abiotic environment

6.2a WATER LEVEL

Formation of a lake depends upon the presence of a depression, raised on every side, and a supply of water to collect in it (**Box 6.1**). Generally, a lake will fill the entire basin, and feed an outflow river, draining from the lowest point of the basin's edge, but in arid areas, where water input is matched or exceeded by rate of evaporation or loss to groundwater, the depression may be only partially filled, and a saline lake without an outflow will form. The presence of an outflow demonstrates that a basin is overflowing, and therefore the water level will remain relatively constant, changes in inputs being matched by changes in outflow. Fluctuations will, however, occur in response to prolonged or marked changes in rainfall. Equatorial lakes in East Africa, after experiencing low levels during the first half of the 20th century, experienced a sharp rise during the 1960s; the surface of Lake Victoria rose by 2.5 m between 1960 and 1964, doubling its output into the River Nile (Hecky *et al.*, 1994). More impressive, however, are fluctuations in saline lakes, which lack an outlet to limit the degree to which they can rise. Mar Chiquita in Argentina, for example, has a surface area which fluctuates between 2000 and 5000 km², depending upon the rainfall in its catchment. Great Salt Lake in Utah, whose mean depth is variable but generally in the range 4–7 m, has fluctuated in depth by over 5 m between its lowest recorded level in 1963 and its highest in 1873, with a corresponding variation in surface area of 2600–6500 km² (Figure 6.2); this, in turn, is a tiny remnant of Lake Bonneville, a pluvial lake formed by increased precipitation during the Late Pleistocene, whose maximum area was 51 640 km², when its shoreline was 335 m above that of the present-day lake (Goudie, 1992). More spectacular still are arid zone saline lakes which are temporary, drying up completely for extended periods; there are thousands of such lakes in drier parts of the world, most of them small but including Lake Eyre North, fed by intermittent rivers in the desert of South Australia, which can reach a maximum area of 8430 km² (W.D. Williams, 1996).

6.2b THERMAL STRATIFICATION

Lakes share many physical characteristics with oceans, modified by their size and depth. Recognition of these similarities is, unfortunately, confused by the different terminology used by marine and freshwater ecologists. All but the shallowest lakes will undergo stratification similar to that in marine systems, with the development of a thermocline and consequent nutrient depletion (**Section 5.2a**). In such lakes, as in the oceans, dis-

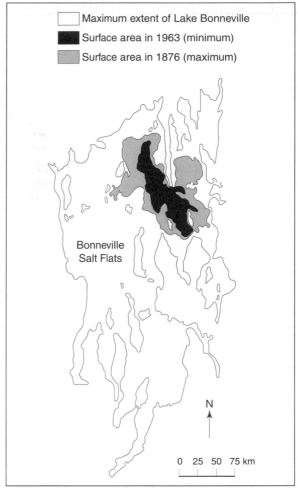

Figure 6.2 Extent of the Great Salt Lake (Utah) and its Pleistocene predecessor, Lake Bonneville. The Great Salt Lake fluctuates markedly in volume and surface area: the maximum (1876) and minimum (1963) water surface areas recorded in historical times are marked (from Burgis & Morris, 1987).

tinct layers can be distinguished, separated by the thermocline, where temperature drops rapidly with depth (**Box 1.3**). The differences between layers are, however, relative: Lake Victoria in tropical Africa, before becoming severely impacted by human activity (**Section 6.7c**), developed a thermocline from January to May, but its hypolimnion, although completely dark, was, at around 23 °C, only 2 °C cooler than the epilimnion (Greenwood, 1994).

An important difference between the physical characteristics of lakes and marine environments is that, whereas the ocean, as a single unit spanning all latitudes, undergoes different stratification patterns in different parts of its water mass, a lake, as a discrete unit, will undergo the same pattern of stratification throughout its area. Only very few lakes large enough to span several climatic zones show different patterns of stratification in different places. This has important implications for nutrient availability, because stratification of the entire water body reduces the opportunity for nutrients to be replenished by processes such as deep circulation and upwelling (**Section 1.2b**).

Patterns of stratification

The pattern of stratification in lakes is determined by latitude, as in marine systems, and altitude. A generalised stratification sequence is illustrated in Figure 6.3, other patterns being variations on this theme. Warm temperate lakes, like temperate oceans, can be described as monomictic, as they

have a single season of mixing, often referred to as the overturn, during the winter and a season of stratification during the summer. Cold temperate lakes are dimictic, stratifying twice per year, once during the summer and again, with warmer water at depth, when they freeze at the surface during the winter, and therefore follow the generalised pattern shown in Figure 6.3. Warm tropical lakes are polymictic, stratifying during the day but with a temperature difference between epilimnion and hypolimnion so slight that mixing occurs overnight. Deep tropical lakes may be continually stratified, like tropical oceans, although severe storms may induce occasional, irregular mixing; these are therefore classified as oligomictic. Certain polar or high altitude lakes are amictic – permanently frozen, their waters never fully mix. The presence of a layer of ice on their surface can result in the development of a reversed thermocline, in which temperature rises with increasing depth beneath the ice, often then to drop again, sometimes appreciably below 0 °C, in very deep lakes (e.g. Priscu, 1995).

Some tropical lakes are monomictic not because of seasonal temperature changes, but because they undergo seasonal variations in depth. Lake Calado is a seasonally flooded lake on the Amazon floodplain, whose maximum depth varies from 1 m in October to 11 m in July, related to the rise and fall of the Solimoes River (MacIntyre & Melack, 1995). When Lake Calado is less than 3 m deep, it mixes fully to the bottom, with no thermocline, but once it has exceeded this depth, stratification occurs. The thermocline depth is variable, but never exceeds 7 m (MacIntyre & Melack, 1988).

Mixing across the thermocline

Mixing in lakes can be induced by wind displacing surface waters. A strong, steady wind will tilt the thermocline by pushing surface waters towards the downwind end of the lake, allowing the hypolimnion to rise at the upwind end (Figure 6.4). Mixing across the thermocline can then occur in one of three ways: (a) the wind displaces the epilimnion so far that deep waters upwell to the surface (Figure 6.4a); (b) continual lateral movement of surface waters causes friction along

Figure 6.3 The stratification cycle of a temperate dimictic lake, showing zones of mixing and the temperature profile with depth during different times of the year. Compare with ocean stratification patterns (Figure 5.1). (a) Spring: complete mixing occurs. (b) Summer: development of a thermocline. (c) Autumn: the thermocline breaks down and mixing occurs throughout; the lake's situation is similar to that during the spring, but the temperature is generally higher. (d) Winter: stratification develops as the surface layer freezes, resulting in a reverse thermocline, with the warmer water at depth.

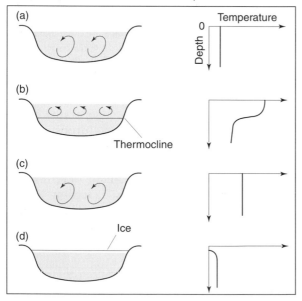

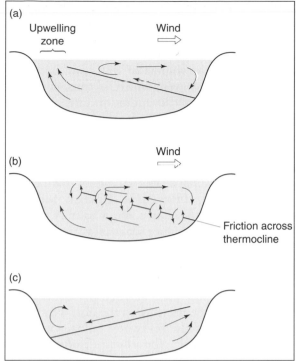

Figure 6.4 Causes of mixing across the thermocline. (a) The epilimnion has been displaced by strong steady wind, allowing the hypolimnion to upwell. (b) Movement within each layer causes friction and turbulence at the thermocline. (c) When the wind in (a) stops, the epilimnion oscillates back and forth across the lake until it reaches equilibrium.

the thermocline, leading to localised mixing across its boundary (Figure 6.4b); (c) when the wind stops, the two layers of water revert to equilibrium but, in the process, the thermocline rocks backwards and forwards in a series of decreasing oscillations (known as seiches), leading to friction and mixing across its boundary (Figure 6.4c).

In temperate zones, decreasing solar radiation during the autumn leads to gradual cooling of the epilimnion and breakdown of stratification, but the process will be hastened by stormy weather, inducing active mixing between the two layers.

Horizontal stratification

It is tempting to see stratification across the thermocline/nutricline as the only structural break in the otherwise homogeneous structure of the water body, but this is a misleading impression of systems whose patchiness, even within such an apparently homogeneous environment is, in many ways, analogous to that of benthic environments. Lakes can generate horizontal flows through differential heating and cooling of various parts of the water body. Shallow shoreline regions, particularly semi-enclosed bays, change temperature more rapidly than deeper offshore areas and, if heated by solar radiation, their water will flow over the cooler offshore water, displacing it laterally.

6.2c OXYGEN STRATIFICATION

A second difference between oceans and lakes relates to oxygenation of deep waters. The deep oceans are kept oxygenated by a global circulation system in which cold, oxygen-rich currents descend near the poles and flow along the ocean bed (**Section 1.2b**). Lakes, lacking the combination of both cold and warm surface zones, have no such currents and replenishment of deep water can be very slow, which, in combination with bacterial respiration at depth, leads to oxygen depletion beneath the upper, mixed layers. Deeper lakes can be completely anoxic in the hypolimnion, a condition typical of oligomictic tropical lakes. Lake Tanganyika in East Africa is interesting in this respect in that it extends across 5° of latitude: its northern end, at 3 °S, is subject to an equatorial climate and oxygen penetrates to a depth of 70 m; its southern end, at 8 °S, is subject to a slightly greater degree of seasonality, increasing mixing and allowing oxygen to penetrate to 200 m depth (Coulter, 1994). In contrast, Lake Baikal in Russia, whose maximum depth exceeds 1600 m, is unique in that it has a complex and, as yet, little understood, water circulation system which ensures oxygenation throughout the water column (Martin, 1994).

Oxygen stratification can be generated or accentuated by photosynthetic organisms. Eutrophication of Lake Victoria since the 1960s has increased the biomass of phytoplankton; as a consequence, the upper layers of the lake have a higher concentration of oxygen than previously, as a result of enhanced photosynthetic rates, while concentrations at depths greater than 40 m are appreciably lower and anoxia, formerly very rare, is common and widespread, probably due to increased inputs of dead and decaying algal cells into the hypolimnion (Hecky *et al*, 1994). At a smaller scale, submerged macrophytes can increase oxygen concentrations in their vicinity and, through diffusion from their roots, can oxygenate bed sediments (**Section 7.3c**), but dense mats of floating leafed macrophytes can decrease oxygen concentrations by impeding exchange with the atmosphere (Carpenter & Lodge, 1986).

6.2d WATER CHEMISTRY

Vertical stratification ensures that marked differences in water chemistry can occur between the hypolimnion and the epilimnion, but horizontal variations are much less profound, the enclosed nature and complete mixing of upper layers ensuring that different parts of a lake's epilimnion will not experience significantly different nutrient status (**Box 6.2**). This is of importance to pollution control because a single point source of pollutant will affect the entire lake but, equally, control at that one point will initiate recovery in the entire water body.

Acidification

Acidification provides a clear illustration of the interconnected chemical status of lakes. A lake is either acid or it is not, with little scope for parts to be acidified while others maintain a high pH. This is not to say that there will not be fluctuations: acid streams, for example, will cause localised elevation of acidity at their mouths, but mixing processes will dilute this input throughout the water body and such patches will only be maintained by constant inputs. Acidification can be countered by using lime as a buffer; this can be added to the lake at a single point and will raise the pH throughout the lake. At Loch Fleet in southern Scotland, lime added to the catchment of several of the small streams flowing into the lake had the same effect: it was washed into the lake at several discrete points but raised the pH to a constant level throughout the entire water body (Howells & Dalziel, 1992).

Saline lakes

Saline lakes are defined as those with a salinity of

at least 3. Inputs of water, however fresh, contain some dissolved salts and a lake lacking an outflow will lose water mainly through evaporation, leaving the salt behind. Salinity, therefore, is determined by the volume of water within which these salts are dissolved, which, in turn, is dependent upon inflow and evaporation rates, and can be very variable. Mar Chiquita (**Section 6.2a**) was, for most of the 20th century, relatively small, with a salinity of 200–300, but increased rainfall since the 1970s raised the volume of the lake such that salinity had dropped to 30 during the 1990s (W.D. Williams, 1996). The Caspian Sea, the world's largest lake, has a mean salinity of just under 13, with only minor seasonal variations, but is significantly diluted by inflow from the River Volga to the north, which accounts for around 80% of inputs to the lake and creates a marked salinity gradient (Figure 6.5). A consequence of this gradient is the presence in the northern fringe of the lake of a fully freshwater fauna, including the zebra mussel (*Dreissena polymorpha*), whereas the central and southern parts of the

Figure 6.5 Salinity gradient in the Caspian Sea during the summer. The figures refer to salinity. Inflow from the River Volga, in combination with increased temperature and aridity towards the south of the lake, creates a marked salinity gradient (from Kosarev & Yablonskaya, 1994).

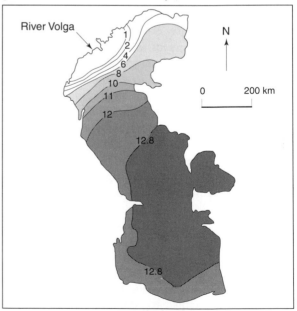

lake have a brackish water fauna (Kosarev & Yablonskaya, 1994).

The salinity of many of the world's saline lakes is being raised by diversion of inflowing water for human use. The most dramatic example of this is the Aral Sea in central Asia, whose two inflowing rivers have, since 1960, been almost completely diverted for irrigation, with the result that, by 1990, its volume had dropped to less than one-third of that in 1960, and its salinity had risen correspondingly from 10 to 29 (Golubev, 1996). The human tragedy associated with the loss of the Aral Sea has been well documented (Pearce, 1995) but effects upon its ecology are much less well understood, although almost certainly equally dramatic.

6.3 Ecological effects of the abiotic environment

Within a given lake, the component of the abiotic environment which fluctuates with the greatest frequency is mixing within the water column. This, in turn, affects light and nutrient availability for primary producers, with consequent effects upon energy budgets for the entire lake. Therefore, this section concentrates upon these determinants of primary production.

6.3a LIGHT INTENSITY

The absorption of light, described in **Box 1.2**, is as relevant to freshwater as to marine systems. High-latitude lakes have strongly seasonal inputs of light, with long summer days and deep penetration into the water column creating an optimum light environment, whereas low penetration and reduced day length in winter ensure that light is severely limiting. Absorption of light is further determined by water clarity: a very clear, clean lake may allow enough radiation for photosynthesis to penetrate several tens of metres into the water column, but coloured humic solutes (such as those originating from peat), suspended sediment and even a high density of algal cells themselves will significantly reduce penetration (Reynolds, 1987). A dense algal bloom, for example, can limit light penetration to the top few centimetres.

In clear shallow lakes, or the edge of deep lakes, light penetrates to the lake bed, allowing the growth of macrophytes and benthic algae. Confusingly, this zone is often referred to as the littoral zone, a term used in marine biology to describe the intertidal (**Section 4.2a**). Here, the term 'lake littoral' is used, to ensure that the two are easily distinguishable.

6.3b NUTRIENTS

The nutrient status of lakes is of fundamental importance in determining their community structure and productivity. There are certain environments, such as marl lakes, in which nutrients, though abundant, are in insoluble forms unavailable to photosynthetic organisms (Mason, 1996) but, in general, the higher the nutrient concentrations, the higher the rate of photosynthetic activity (**Box 6.2**).

Stratification limits the availability of nutrients by minimising their transport across the thermocline (see **Section 5.3c** for a description of the same process in marine environments). Photosynthetically active organisms are confined to the epilimnion by their requirement for light and will normally deplete nutrients to the extent that they become limiting, while at the same time the hypolimnion may contain high concentrations, enhanced by sinking of detritus and even of living algal cells from the epilimnion. Therefore, any process that adds nutrients to the epilimnion in a stratified water body can enhance primary production, and point sources of nutrients from catchment inputs can induce patches of high phytoplankton biomass (Figure 6.6). Wind-induced upwelling from the hypolimnion or mixing across the thermocline will have similar effects but, in contrast to major zones of oceanic upwelling (**Section 1.2b**), is dependent upon strong or steady winds and will be temporary or intermittent.

6.3c VERTICAL MIXING WITHIN THE EPILIMNION

The epilimnion is a layer of mixed water. Some of the larger phytoplankton, such as dinoflagellates,

BOX 6.2   DEFINING NUTRIENT STATUS

The terms oligotrophic and eutrophic are widely used to describe lakes, although precise definitions are difficult, not least because they refer to relative rather than absolute states.

An oligotrophic lake is one with low nutrient levels. Phytoplankton production is low and therefore water clarity is high. Decomposition in the hypolimnion uses up oxygen more slowly than it can be replaced by mixing from the surface, so the water remains well oxygenated.

A eutrophic lake has high nutrient levels and therefore high rates of phytoplankton production. High densities of algal cells reduce water clarity, and decomposition of detritus in the hypolimnion uses up oxygen more rapidly than it can be replaced, leading to reduced concentrations, or even anoxia.

Assessment of trophic status can be made using one or more of the following methods.

1   Nutrient concentration (TP).   The mean annual total phosphorus concentration (i.e. including that within plankton cells within a water sample). Normally expressed as micrograms per litre (μg l^{-1}).
2   Phytoplankton biomass (Chl *a*).   Normally the mean or peak annual biomass is quoted. This is difficult to measure directly, so concentration of chlorophyll *a* (Chl *a*), a component of all phytoplankton whose concentration is directly related to photosynthetic activity, is generally used instead. Normally expressed as micrograms per litre (μg l^{-1}).
3   Rate of primary production (PP).   Measured as mass of carbon assimilated (i.e. converted from inorganic carbon dioxide to organic compounds) per m^2 surface area per day (mg C m^{-2} d^{-1}).
4   Water transparency.   Normally expressed as Secchi depth, the depth measured with a Secchi disc. This is a disc 20 cm in diameter and divided into four equally sized segments, alternately black and white in colour. It is lowered horizontally into the water and the depth at which it just ceases to be visible is the Secchi depth.

Although there are no universally accepted definitions of oligotrophic and eutrophic states, various attempts have been made to quantify them. The table below gives useful approximate values for the parameters listed (from various sources, summarised in Mason, 1996). They allow inclusion of several further categories of trophic status – ultra-oligotrophic, mesotrophic and hypertrophic.

This classification works on the principle that phytoplankton biomass and production change in tandem with phosphate concentration and, in turn, have a direct effect upon water clarity. This is undoubtedly true in a great many cases, but should be applied with caution, as there are many exceptions. **Section 6.3c** describes the example of Loch Ness, oligotrophic in terms of TP and PP, but with a low Secchi depth, not a result of algal cells but of humic substances in the water. Conversely, lakes with high nutrient inputs can be very clear if these nutrients are absorbed by macrophytes (**Section 6.7a**).

| | TP | Chl *a* | | PP | Secchi depth | |
| | | Mean | Maximum | | Mean | Maximum |
	(μg l^{-1})	(μg l^{-1})	(μg l^{-1})	(mg C m^{-2} d^{-1})	(m)	(m)
Ultra-oligotrophic	<4	<1	<2.5	<30	>12	>6
Oligotrophic	4–10	1–2.5	2.5–8	30–100	6–12	3–6
Mesotrophic	10–35	2.5–8	8–25	100–300	3–6	1.5–3
Eutrophic	35–100	8–25	25–75	300–3000	1.5–3	0.7–1.5
Hypertrophic	>100	>25	>75	>3000	<1.5	<0.7

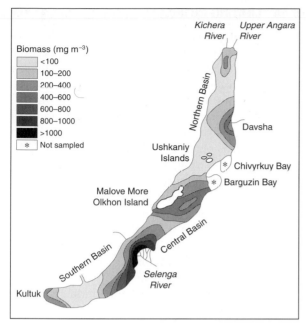

Figure 6.6 Horizontal variations in biomass of phytoplankton in the surface layers of Lake Baikal. The highest concentrations occur around the mouth of the Selenga River, the main inflow, in response to the nutrient load it discharges into the lake (from Bondarenko *et al.*, 1996).

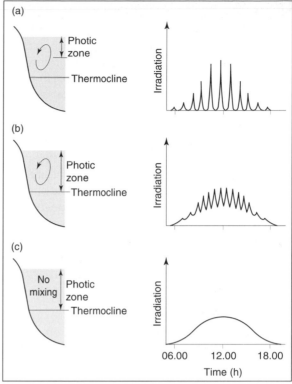

Figure 6.7 The effect of internal mixing within the epilimnion upon photosynthetic activity of a phytoplankter (adapted from Reynolds, 1987). (a) Mixing occurs throughout the epilimnion, but the photic zone extends only half-way to the thermocline: algae are being constantly carried into and out of the photic zone, resulting in photosynthetic activity marked by major peaks and troughs. (b) Mixing occurs throughout the epilimnion, but the photic zone extends to the thermocline: algae are mixed between higher and lower light intensities, but can photosynthesise throughout daylight hours. (c) No mixing occurs. Algae are subjected only to the daily pattern of varying light intensity.

are able to propel themselves through the water and will endeavour to remain in patches of optimal conditions, but their rate of movement upwards is less than the velocity of vertical currents created by surface winds. Rotation of water through the mixed layer is, therefore, too rapid for even motile phytoplankton to counter, so if light penetrates through only a part of the epilimnion but water is being mixed throughout, photosynthetic activity will be limited (Figure 6.7).

Loch Ness, in Scotland, is an extreme example of this phenomenon. It has a summer thermocline at a depth of at least 30 m, but the water is clouded by high concentrations of humic substances, limiting light penetration to a depth of 6–7 m. Therefore, even during daylight hours, phytoplankton may spend only around 20% of the time in the photic zone, reducing their ability to photosynthesise effectively. During the winter, when solar radiation is reduced in terms both of strength and day length, vertical stratification is absent and mixing occurs to the bed (whose mean

depth is 137 m), reducing photosynthetic potential even further. Thus, even though it is oligotrophic, primary production in Loch Ness is constrained, not by nutrient availability, but by light (Jones *et al.*, 1996). It is, in this respect, unusual: oligotrophic lakes are normally clear, allowing deep light penetration, and phosphate is the limiting factor. Nutrient-rich lakes, in contrast, can support such a high biomass of phytoplankton that the algal cells themselves reduce light penetration, confining photosynthesis to a narrow vertical zone close to the surface (**Box 6.2**).

Stratification within the epilimnion

The epilimnion is defined as the upper mixed layer, but calm weather conditions will reduce vertical mixing, leading to the development of internal stratification, with measurable differences in nutrient concentrations, phytoplankton biomass and phytoplankton species assemblages at different depths even above the thermocline (Neill, 1994). Such conditions favour motile phytoplankton, which are able to move vertically within the water column to the zone of optimum light intensity, but are detrimental to heavier or non-motile species, which sink to the bottom of the epilimnion. In sheltered lakes, this stratification can be persistent, but more exposed lakes will be subjected to weather conditions which periodically break it up.

6.4   Energy inputs

Primary production in deep lakes is dominated by phytoplankton, whose productivity is subject to the same constraints of light penetration, nutrient status, mixing and grazing as is that in the sea (**Sections 4.4a, 4.4b, 4.4c**). Attached macrophytes are confined to the lake littoral, generally a region close to the shore although, in shallow lakes, it may extend across much of the bed, whereas in deeper lakes the dominant benthos will be detritivores, relying upon allochthonous inputs from above. In very deep or nutrient-rich lakes, lack of oxygen ensures that the only living organisms are anaerobic bacteria.

A hydrothermal vent (**Box 5.2**), with an associated concentration of bacterial and benthic faunal biomass, has recently been discovered in Lake Baikal (Crane *et al.*, 1991). With so many of the world's lakes in areas of volcanic activity, and even in volcanic crater lakes (**Box 6.1**), it is possible that lake chemoautotrophy is more widespread than has hitherto been considered.

This section emphasises the pelagic system, although most of the constraints upon phytoplankton production affect macrophytes and attached algae as well. Macrophytes are considered in some detail in **Chapter 7**, and potential competition between phytoplankton and macrophytes is returned to in **Section 6.7a**.

6.4A   LIMITING NUTRIENTS

Nitrate and phosphate are normally limiting in aquatic systems, although silicon can become depleted by high diatom biomass. Phytoplankton normally require nitrogen and phosphorus in the relative proportions of 7 : 1 (the Redfield Ratio), so if inputs deviate from this ratio, limitation will ensue. Normally, the major limiting nutrient in fresh waters is phosphate (Elser & Hassett, 1994), and its addition to water bodies, both experimentally and as a pollutant, has been demonstrated on many occasions to increase primary production. Indeed, Schindler and Fee (1974) showed that addition of less than 0.5 g phosphorus per square metre of surface area in small Canadian lakes resulted in algal populations 50–100 times greater than those in control lakes.

Total nutrient input determines biomass of primary producers, but the timing of their addition determines community diversity. Continual input of small doses favours competitive species, resulting in a constant biomass and domination by very few species, whereas addition of the same total concentration of nutrients but in a series of discrete pulses favours opportunistic species: biomass may fluctuate widely, peaking after each addition and then crashing, and different species may become abundant after each input, with no one species being able to maintain domination. Neill (1994) demonstrated that frequent inputs of nutrients to experimental patches of a small oligotrophic lake led to domination by small flagellates, whereas occasional large doses resulted in continually altering species composition in which small flagellates remained rare, though eventually large gelatinous algae dominated.

Nutrient recycling

Nutrient limitation in the epilimnion ensures that any free inorganic nutrients that become available are quickly recycled. Biotic processes such as excretion by zooplankton or fish produce micropatches of nutrient enrichment whose persistence can be measured in seconds before they are destroyed by diffusion, but algal cells that happen to be caught in such a patch may gain their entire daily nutrient requirement even within this short space of time (Neill, 1994).

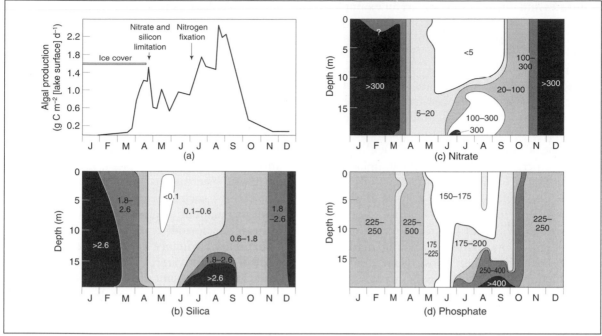

Figure 6.8 Seasonal patterns in primary production and nutrient availability in Lake Esrom, Denmark. (a) Primary production, showing the effects of nutrient limitation. (b)–(d) Nutrient concentrations are displayed as contours on depth–time diagrams, in which depth is shown along the vertical axis and time along the horizontal axis. For a given date, the concentration at different depths is plotted and then points of equal value are joined together. The figures show (b) silicate (mg l^{-1}), (c) nitrate (µg l^{-1}) and phosphate (µg l^{-1}). In Lake Esrom, there is a decline in concentration of all nutrients, but particularly silicon and nitrate, in shallower water during the summer months (modified from Jónasson, 1996).

Autotrophic bacteria are efficient at assimilating dissolved nitrogen and phosphorus at very low concentrations, and in doing so are in direct competition with algae. Their extremely small size, however, ensures that they do not sink into the hypolimnion so nutrient stock that has been incorporated into algal biomass remains in the epilimnion. Bacteria are heavily grazed by protists – rotifers, flagellates and ciliates – and even by very much larger water fleas (*Daphnia* spp.), their consumption and subsequent excretion remineralising and recycling nutrients back into the water column (Stockner & Porter, 1988).

6.4b PRIMARY PRODUCTION AS A SEASONAL PHENOMENON

Primary production generally follows seasonal patterns, although the causes of this seasonality differ between temperate and tropical zones.

Seasonality in temperate zones

In temperate zones, low light intensities and temperatures restrict winter production. A peak is reached during the spring, in response to improving physical conditions, but is curtailed in late spring by nutrient depletion, following stratification, and by zooplankton grazing, leading to a midsummer dip in productivity. During late summer, there is generally a second peak, reflecting a change in algal species composition and occasional weather-controlled breakdown of the thermocline. Algal biomass declines rapidly during the autumn, as light intensities and temperatures again fall, despite the influx of nutrients as seasonal stratification ceases (Talling, 1993). This pattern may be compared with the temperate North Atlantic pattern of seasonality observed among marine plankton (**Section 4.4c**). It is illustrated by Lake Esrom in Denmark, a lake in which primary productivity is limited by nitrogen and silicon, the latter being required by diatoms; concentrations of nitrates and nitrites in the water, for example, drop from over 300 $\mu g\,l^{-1}$ in March to 0 $\mu g\,l^{-1}$ by June, whereas phosphate accumulations remain very high throughout the year (Jónasson, 1996). A small spring bloom is, therefore, followed by a drop in production until late summer, when it is warm enough for nitrogen-fixing Cyanobacteria, which are temperature limited, to proliferate. Mixing of the water column stimulates a second algal peak in the autumn, before lack of light and low temperatures become the limiting factors once more (Figure 6.8).

Seasonal changes in the relative abundance of different phytoplankton taxa may occur. Lake Teganuma in central Japan illustrates this well: it is a shallow, hypertrophic lake, in a warm temperate climatic zone, whose planktonic primary production, although showing a peak in August and September, is high throughout the year. There is, however, a marked change in the species composition of its phytoplankton: the green alga *Micractinium* dominates between February and June, but disappears over the summer, to be replaced by Cyanobacteria – *Spirulina* in July and August and *Microcyctis* in September – while a diatom, *Cyclotella*, dominates over the winter (Takamura *et al.*, 1989).

Seasonality in tropical zones

In the tropics, light intensity and temperature are relatively constant, but phytoplankton production follows seasonal patterns related to hydrology. Low flow rates in rivers and lakes, or periods of water storage in reservoirs, create a period of stability, allowing phytoplankton to flourish, whereas, during high flow or water release periods, their numbers decline. In larger African lakes, where such rainfall-related patterns are diminished by long water retention times, even small variations in temperature translate into patterns of stratification and mixing which can, in turn, affect phytoplankton production (Talling, 1986).

6.4c SECONDARY PRODUCTION

Grazing

Phytoplankton are consumed by a range of graz-

ing zooplankters, predominant among them being cladocerans such as water fleas (*Daphnia* spp.). Zooplankton can consume 10–30% of algal biomass per day in summer (Cyr & Pace, 1992), but different species have different vulnerabilities, grazers preferring small, unicellular or unarmed species to large, colonial forms. *Daphnia* has a very high grazing rate and is able to generate 'clearwater phases', even when algal productivity is high, following which its numbers will collapse through food limitation (Neill, 1994).

Exact mechanisms by which algae persist in the face of such grazing pressures are not fully understood, but include daytime recovery to counter nocturnal grazing and modification of community structure in response to predation pressure. Open water, in the presence of fish, supports larger or less motile species, such as diatoms, whereas among macrophyte beds, small, motile forms, more difficult for grazers to catch, dominate. A possible explanation for this pattern lies in water movement: motile species are able to counter sinking and are therefore favoured in the relatively still waters around macrophytes, whereas diatoms require constant mixing to counter sinking, so will be confined to open waters. In macrophyte-free lakes with high zooplankton grazing pressure, however, small flagellates dominate even the open water, suggesting a role for grazing in determining this pattern (Schriver *et al.*, 1995).

In nutrient-limited lakes, grazing may stimulate algal production by recycling nutrients, the digestive activity of grazers releasing remineralised nutrients back into the water column. The destructive activity of grazers also enhances the loss of DOC from algal cells into the water column, and this DOC is incorporated into a microbial loop (**Section 1.6c**), whereby it is consumed by heterotrophic bacteria which, in turn, are consumed by protists. Thus organic carbon which would otherwise have been lost is recycled within the pelagic zone, the bacterial grazers being consumed by larger zooplankton (Stockner & Porter, 1988).

Detritus

Much phytoplankton biomass eventually settles to the lake bed where, along with inputs of detritus from rivers and the lake littoral zone, it provides food for benthic detritivores. Benthic macroinvertebrate communities are dominated by chironomids, oligochaetes and filter-feeding bivalves, all of which feed upon FPOM.

Benthic chironomids can play an important role in organic matter dynamics in eutrophic lakes, because larval growth in sediments is followed by a period of emergence, when pupae rising to the surface are available as food for free-swimming pelagic predators. In temperate lakes, maximum chironomid growth and emergence often coincides with spring and autumn overturn periods, when primary production is high and oxygen is freely mixed to the lake bed. In Japanese lakes, a single species, *Tokunagayusurika akamusi*, can account for over 70% of total benthic macroinvertebrate biomass (Iwakuma & Masayuki, 1983). This species emerges as an adult in very large numbers over a period of approximately two weeks in late autumn, providing a valuable food source for pelagic predators at this time, and around three times as many individuals are predated as emerge. Adults which successfully emerge, however, are effectively transferring energy out of the lake and into surrounding terrestrial systems.

6.5 Community structure

6.5a PREDATION

Predation is one of the primary determinants of community structure in lakes and ponds, fish in particular having a demonstrably strong effect upon numbers of their prey. A complex example of a predation effect was reported by Cryer *et al.* (1986) from Alderfen Broad, one of the Norfolk Broads in eastern England, a shallow, eutrophic lake in which the main zooplankton predator was roach (*Rutilus rutilus*). In years when fish recruitment was poor, a high biomass of large cladocerans predominated in the zooplankton but, when roach under-yearlings were abundant, copepods and small rotifers dominated, cladoceran density dropping significantly at the time they became important components of the diet of young roach; the smallest (*Bosmina longirostris*)

declined first, followed by the larger species (*Ceriodaphnia quadrangula* and *Daphnia hyalina*) a few weeks later, reflecting the gradual increase in size of the young fish. Experimental exclusion of fish from parts of the lake resulted in an increase in both density and individual body size of *Daphnia*. During the 1970s and early 1980s, roach in Alderfen Broad followed a two-year cycle of abundance, which Cryer *et al.* (1986) speculated was related to their predatory influences. A year of high recruitment produced large numbers of young fish depleting the food supply, so that growth and fecundity were low; this resulted in a low number of eggs and therefore few fish present the following year. In the absence of strong predation pressure from fish, zooplankton reached high densities, providing plenty of food for roach, which grew rapidly, leading to higher fecundity the following year and repeating the cycle. Interestingly, this pattern was maintained by another predator, pike (*Esox lucius*), which severely depleted older, and therefore larger, roach; as a result, reproduction was predominantly by roach under three years old, at which age they were feeding upon the same zooplankton resource as were under-yearling fish.

Other examples of effects of fish predation abound. In Lake Kinneret (Sea of Galilee) in Israel, distribution patterns of fish and cladocerans coincide, both being more abundant on the eastern side of the lake where gradients of temperature and oxygen concentration are highest. At a smaller spatial scale, however, fish aggregation leads to localised reduction in zooplankton biomass, maximal fish densities being matched by minimal cladoceran densities (Kalikhman *et al.*, 1995). The fish in question, Kinneret sardine (*Mirogrex terraesanctae terraesanctae*), congregate in dense aggregations which form and disperse every 4–5 days, possibly as a consequence of local over-exploitation of their prey. In several of the Norfolk Broads, predation by roach and bream (*Abramus brama*) reduces densities of benthic chironomids and oligochaetes (Moss & Timms, 1989). Reduction of fish densities in Tuesday Lake, Michigan, resulted in an increase in density of larvae of phantom midges (*Chaoborus* spp.) which, in turn, reduced densities of smaller zooplankton, midge larvae having reached densities towards the end of summer at which they could potentially consume the entire rotifer population within a single day (Elser *et al.*, 1987).

6.5b STRATEGIES TO AVOID PREDATION

Faced with such intense predation pressures as those described above, zooplankton have developed a range of strategies to reduce their vulnerability to predation. In the lake littoral zone, highest densities of grazing zooplankters are found in the vicinity of macrophyte beds, among which they hide during the day to avoid fish predation, foraging in open water after dark, when fish predation is reduced (Moss, 1990). Fish fry will, however, also benefit from the shelter afforded by macrophytes, and can be very abundant in such environments (Carpenter & Lodge, 1986). In open water, there is no such structural heterogeneity and vulnerable species have adopted a range of strategies to reduce predation pressure, modifying morphology, life cycles and behaviour.

Morphological strategies

Cladocerans are important components of the grazing community in many lakes. If subjected to heavy predation pressure by invertebrate predators, they develop structural features which reduce their susceptibility to predation. Juveniles of *Daphnia pulex*, for example, develop neck teeth and elongated tail spines in response to predation by larvae of the midge *Chaoborus* (Figure 6.9). Defences such as these are developed in response to chemical cues originating from predators. They presumably make cladocerans more difficult to handle when caught, increasing their chance of escape, but development of a crest by the Australian *D. carnata*, heavily predated by notonectids, apparently increases manoeuvrability and therefore reduces the number of times they are caught in the first place (Barry & Bayley, 1985).

Maintenance of structures such as crests is energetically expensive, reducing overall growth rates (Dodson, 1989). Therefore, in the absence of predators, they do not develop. Adult *Daphnia* are too large to be eaten by *Chaoborus* and lose the defensive structures that they developed as larvae.

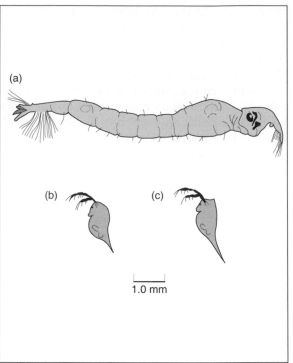

Figure 6.9 Development of structural features in response to predation. (a) Larva of the midge *Chaoborus americanus*, a major predator on grazing zooplankton. (b) Young *Daphnia pulex* grown in the absence of *Chaoborus*. (c) Young *Daphnia pulex* grown in the presence of *Chaoborus*; note the extended tail spine and the tooth on the back of the neck (from Dodson, 1989).

Life cycle strategies

Cladocerans are eaten not only by various size classes of invertebrate predators but also by much larger fish, which selectively take larger individuals. The complexity of interactions between these groups is illustrated in Figure 6.10. In the absence of fish, medium-sized individuals are most at risk from predation (Figure 6.10a), so juveniles grow rapidly until they are too large to be eaten by midge larvae, after which they will reproduce. In the presence of fish, however, they will never grow too large to be eaten, but small individuals, less attractive to fish, are more likely to survive (Figure 6.10b). As Figure 6.10 demonstrates, this is not simply an interaction between fish and cladocerans, but also incorporates smaller predators, which feed on very small cladocerans but, in turn, are eaten by midge larvae. Abundant midge larvae keep numbers of these small predators down, reducing predation pressure on very small cladocerans, so the optimal reproductive strategy adopted by cladocerans in the absence of fish is to produce many small offspring. Where fish are present, however, cladocerans concentrate on producing relatively large offspring to reduce the risk of predation by small predators (Lynch, 1980).

Behavioural adaptations

Fish are predominantly visual predators, whose foraging is effectively confined to the photic zone during the hours of daylight. Therefore, invertebrates which are susceptible to fish predation adopt a strategy of vertical migration, descending at dawn and rising to feed at dusk. This, in turn, may induce their prey species, which are too small to be at risk from fish, to adopt the opposite strategy. Fish, too, will migrate if they are subject to predation by piscivorous fish. Juvenile sockeye salmon (*Oncorhynchus nerka*) in western North America spend the night 20–30 m below the surface but descend during the day to depths of 80–120 m. In Babine Lake, British Columbia, this induces a complex pattern of vertical migration: sockeye eat the cladoceran *Daphnia longispina* but also the larger calanoid copepod *Heterocope septentrionalis*. *Daphnia* does not migrate but *Heterocope* avoids salmon predation by descending at night. This, in turn, induces the small cladoceran *Bosmina* to rise at night, to avoid *Heterocope*, its main predator (Clark & Levy, 1988).

Avoiding predators is not the only adaptive value of vertical migration. For example, descending to the cold hypolimnion for part of the day reduces metabolic activity and therefore expenditure of energy, so less food is required (Lampert, 1989). However, Neill (1990) showed that, when *Chaoborus* was eliminated by trout from Gwendoline Lake in British Columbia, the calanoid copepod *Diaptomus kenai* ceased to migrate vertically, but remained in the upper layers, with the phytoplankton upon which it fed, throughout the day. Three years after the removal of *Chaoborus*, its reintroduction induced reinstatement of vertical migration by *Diaptomus* within four hours. Interestingly, *Chaoborus* itself will not cease to migrate if fish are removed, although the intensity of migration will be significantly reduced.

Diel vertical migration, often over much greater vertical distances, is also well documented in marine environments (**Section 5.7a;** Figure 5.5). The two main hypotheses proposed to explain its occurrence are summarised in **Box 5.4.**

6.5c THE TROPHIC CASCADE

The example of cladoceran response to changing predatory pressures illustrates the way in which a top predator, in this case the fish, can have a direct effect on two trophic levels by consuming both cladocerans and their main invertebrate predators. The fish also have an indirect effect, however: although they do not eat rotifers, they can modify their abundance indirectly by consuming midge

Figure 6.10 Effect of predation on size of dominant cladocerans: (a) fish absent, (b) fish present. The width of each arrow is proportional to the intensity of predation and the size range least impacted by predation is encircled. See text for more details.

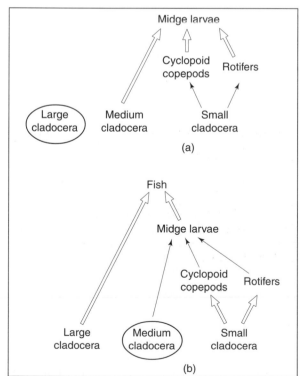

larvae (Figure 6.10). Indirect effects such as these can be translated indirectly throughout the entire food web, in a process known as the trophic cascade (Carpenter *et al.*, 1985). It is best illustrated by using an example in which two trophic levels are increased to four (Figure 6.11). In Figure 6.11a, phytoplankton biomass is kept in check by zooplankton grazing; zooplankton, in turn, are limited by food availability. Addition of a planktivorous fish (Figure 6.11b) reduces the biomass of zooplankton, which are now limited by predation; the fish have had a direct negative effect on biomass of zooplankton which therefore leads to an indirect positive effect on phytoplankton biomass, as grazing pressure is reduced. Addition of piscivorous fish (Figure 6.11c) reduces biomass of planktivorous fish but, indirectly, releases zooplankton from predation pressure and allows them to increase in numbers, thus having a negative effect on phytoplankton biomass. Addition of a new trophic level in each case has a direct negative effect on the one immediately below it but, at the same time, the effect cascades down the food chain, with alternating positive and negative effects.

6.5D SPECIES DIVERSITY

Dispersal abilities

Dispersal abilities of lake species can be contrasted with those inhabiting rivers (**Section 2.6a**). The relatively short life span of most lakes (**Section 6.6**) ensures that their component species are well adapted for dispersal. Small planktonic species, including algae, bacteria, fungi, rotifers and cladocerans, have resting stages such as spores and cysts which are both highly tolerant to desiccation and small and light enough to be wind dispersed. These species are widely distributed, many of them being cosmopolitan and limited in their distribution by water quality at a given site rather than geographical barriers (Neill, 1994).

In contrast to river species, the dominant insects in lentic waters derive mainly from groups with strong flying abilities, such as dragonflies and water beetles, which have little difficulty in dispersing to new sites. Dragonflies and aquatic birds such as ducks carry with them algae and small

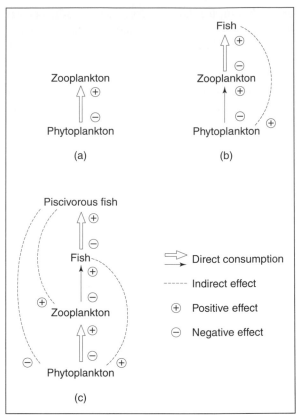

Figure 6.11 The trophic cascade, showing changes as two trophic levels are increased to four. The width of each arrow is proportional to the intensity of predation and positive and negative effects of each interaction are marked. See text for more details.

zooplankton (Maguire, 1963), contributing to the dispersal of these taxa. Other lentic specialists, such as amphibians, have a terrestrial phase in their life cycle during which they can walk to a new site.

Lentic water bodies which require the most advanced adaptations are those which are temporary in nature. Species occupying temporary or intermittent lakes and ponds require three main adaptations: stages in their life cycle that are resistant to desiccation, such as terrestrial adults or the ability to aestivate during the dry season; good powers of dispersal; and the ability to be adaptable in their use of the resources available (Watson *et al.*, 1995; D.D. Williams, 1996). Organisms which possess these adaptations benefit from their ability to exploit an environment in which resources may be plentiful but specialist predators absent. Anuran amphibians (frogs and toads) are typical of temporary ponds; they are generally excluded from permanent water bodies by fish predation upon the tadpole stage of their life cycle but, to counter this, possess a highly mobile and essentially terrestrial adult stage.

Endemism and ancient lakes

The well developed dispersal abilities described above ensure that isolated water bodies are rapidly colonised. Geographically close lakes will share a common pool of species, and endemism is rare, because few lakes are stable enough for the geological time scales that speciation requires, and continual dispersal of individuals reduces the potential for genetic isolation.

It is for this reason that the ancient lakes of the world are special. Their age has allowed speciation to occur among groups with poor dispersal abilities, the most famous examples being the gammarid shrimps in Lake Baikal (around 1000 species) and the cichlid fishes of the East African Great Lakes (600 species in Lake Malawi alone, plus the haplochromines of Lake Victoria discussed in **Section 6.7c**). For endemic species to develop in any numbers, however, stability is also required. Lake Kivu in Rwanda and Zaire (Congo) is one of the world's oldest lakes, but has a low species richness and an immature plankton community because of volcanic activity within the last 10 000 years which literally cooked the lake and destroyed all life within it (Dumont, 1994); presumably before this event it supported a very diverse assemblage of species, including many endemic forms, but recolonisation has been by widespread, opportunisitic species and those able to live in rivers, which were able, therefore, to find refuge in its catchment during the volcanic event.

6.6   Succession

The major difference between lakes and oceans is that lakes have measurable life spans. While oceans are created and destroyed over geological time (**Section 5.7e**), there is a continuity to the marine environment as a whole, whereas lakes are relatively isolated from each other and inevitably will be destroyed eventually, along with the aquatic communities which they support.

Lake formation can be very rapid. As soon as a basin is created in the presence of a supply of water, it starts to fill with water (**Box 6.1**). The creation of reservoirs by artificially damming valleys demonstrates the speed at which this can occur, most filling within a few months of dam closure. One of the most rapid was Lake Kainji on the River Niger in Nigeria, which covers a maximum area of 1280 km^2 and has a volume of up to 15.7 km^3, yet reached its full size just 2½ months after dam closure in 1968, but even the enormous Lake Volta, the largest man-made lake in Africa, reached its full extent of 8845 km^2 and volume of around 160 km^3 within five years (John *et al.*, 1993). The Salton Sea in an arid region of California was created by accidental diversion of water from the Colorado River, via irrigation canals, into a desert depression. The leak was repaired within two years, but not before a lake covering 891 km^2 and with a volume of 6.8 km^3 had been created (Carpelan, 1958). Natural lakes can be assumed to fill with this, or perhaps even greater, rapidity. Reelfoot Lake, on the Kentucky–Tennessee border, is reputed to have come into being almost overnight after a series of earthquakes in 1811 created depressions into which the River Mississippi spilled (Cole, 1975).

The fate of all lakes is the same: as soon as formation is complete, they start to fill in. This is because, being concave depressions and input by rivers carrying sediment, they are natural zones of deposition: a river entering a lake loses its momentum, stops flowing and deposits its load. Even ponds, without river inputs, will accumulate sediment, whether wind blown or transported by biological agents. An inevitable consequence of this is eutrophication (**Box 6.2**), which will stimulate productivity and, in turn, accelerate the further build-up of organic matter.

Lakes are relatively barren at first, with few animals and plants and limited sediment and nutrients. Initially, therefore, productivity is low, most nutrients coming from the catchment. Lack of sediment and nutrients keeps macrophyte growth low and plankton losses may match or even exceed production if there is a large outlet. This is a relative condition: a pool formed by a beaver dam over rich forest soil will be sediment-rich compared to one formed in a glacial hollow, but each lake is barren at birth relative to its later stages. Shallow lakes with a large littoral zone will, however, become highly productive once nutrient balances are established, and will rapidly acquire organic matter. Even large lakes, once production becomes high relative to losses, rapidly infill and will eventually become wetlands, a process explored further in **Section 7.6b**.

The process of succession to a wetland can be surprisingly rapid: the East Anglian Fens, for example, had lost most of their open water a few thousand years after formation. Deeper, cleaner lakes persist much longer, but even the largest have life spans measured in tens or hundreds of thousands of years; the majority of lakes in northern Europe and North America, however large and deep, were formed within the last 20 000 years, with the retreat of glacial ice at the end of the Pleistocene. The size and solidarity of their basins makes bedrock lakes the longest lived and most stable lakes, although volcanic lakes, if formed within the crater of an active volcano, can be destroyed very rapidly in the event of an eruption. The oldest and deepest lakes in the world are those in tectonically active areas, filling the depression made as plate boundaries slip relative to each other. These include Lake Baikal and Lake Tanganyika, both around 20 million years old, which are maintained by the constant subsidence of the basins they fill. Lake Baikal, for example, overlies sediment 8 km deep, enough to have filled it in several times over (Martin, 1994).

6.7   Lakes as functional wholes

The nature of a lake or pond, as an enclosed body of water, ensures that it functions essentially as a single community. Traditionally, community structure in lakes was assumed to be a function of nutrient availability, the primary force acting upon it being 'bottom–up' control, in which competition among primary producers, limited by nutrients in particular, determines structure and productivity of higher trophic levels. More recently, however, development of ideas such as the trophic cascade and predation avoidance strategies has demonstrated an alternative, 'top–down' control, in which predation by tertiary consumers controls the structure of the community. It is unlikely that one such process can control community structure without some effects of the other, but certainly their relative importance can vary, as can be demonstrated by consideration of the perturbation of lake systems in which the modification of a single parameter has wide-ranging effects throughout the entire lake system. Two examples are presented here, involving human-induced modifications: eutrophication by increased nutrient inputs and introduction of predatory fish.

6.7a   EUTROPHICATION

Eutrophication is the name given to enrichment of waters by plant nutrients. This process occurs naturally, but inputs of very high levels of nutrients from human activities, such as fertiliser runoff and discharge of partially treated sewage, can lead to hypertrophy, the presence of nutrients at excessive concentrations. With nutrient availability removed as a limiting factor, photosynthesisers will increase in biomass until they are constrained by space or by shading. At such densities, they can disrupt the entire lake ecosystem, most notably through oxygen depletion. During the day, the water may be supersaturated by photosynthetic oxygen production, but at night the combined effects of respiration and decomposition of detritus may lead to complete deoxygenation, and the consequent death of other organisms living within the lake.

Hypertrophic water bodies are dominated either by macrophytes or by phytoplankton, each flourishing in the presence of high levels of nutrients, but rarely, if ever, do they support high densities of both. It is a common feature of many water bodies that clear water and a high density of macrophytes is replaced by turgid, algal dominated water as nutrient levels rise.

Alternative stable states

Typically, eutrophication will lead to increased densities of macrophytes and algae, but then phytoplankton crops become very large and submerged macrophytes are lost (Mulligan *et al.*, 1976). This is not a straightforward case of algae outcompeting submerged plants, however, because there is a range of possible causes, none of them complete explanations. The most obvious is that floating algae shade submerged plants, but plants such as water lilies (*Nymphaea* spp. and *Nuphar* spp.), which start their growth when algal densities are low and grow to the surface, and floating plants such as *Lemna minor*, which overwinter at or near the surface or among debris at lake edges, also disappear. Other potential reasons relate to increased sediment instability, or even relative shortage of nitrate or carbon dioxide, all of which would potentially favour phytoplankton over macrophytes. Balls *et al.* (1989), using a series of experimental ponds in the Norfolk Broads region of eastern England, demonstrated clearly that it was not simply a case of increased nutrient loading: fertilisation to a level above that experienced by nearby lakes from which macrophytes had been eliminated resulted in no displacement of aquatic plants, and phosphate levels in the water did not increase, despite the inputs. Irvine *et al.* (1989) suggested that a hypertrophic lake will be dominated by one of two alternative states – aquatic plants or phytoplankton. Each is buffered against the other: macrophytes by absorbing extra nutrients and by suppressing the wave action that would otherwise re-suspend bottom sediments and lead to shading, algae by adding to the turbidity that shades potential vegetation growth. Although eutrophic lakes are generally turbid relative to their oligotrophic counterparts, macrophyte coverage exceeding 30% of the total surface area will usually maintain high water transparency, irrespective of nutrient concentration (Canfield *et al.*, 1984). This is because the turbidity is caused by the presence of algal cells, whose densities, in extreme cases, become so great that the water takes on a thick, soupy appearance.

The maintenance of either a macrophyte or a phytoplankton system is affected by secondary consumers, whose activities, once again, will serve to buffer whichever system is in place. In macrophyte-dominated systems, grazing pressure on algae is intense as cladoceran grazers, using macrophytes as predation refugia, are abundant, whereas in algal systems, fish will keep numbers of grazers low, allowing algal numbers to remain high.

Managing eutrophic lakes

From a management point of view, the macrophyte system is usually more desirable than the algal system. Macrophytes disrupt access for boat movements, fishing, etc., but stabilise nutrients by entraining them for long periods within the plants' tissues; in temperate regions, an annual nutrient cycle is set up, incorporating absorption into plant tissues during the spring and then slow release during winter decomposition. Algae, with their short life cycles, cycle nutrients rapidly, leading to a succession of blooms. They can also respond very rapidly to increases in nutrient supply and, in temperate regions, constant death and decomposition of algal cells can exacerbate problems of oxygen availability during the warm summer months, whereas macrophyte decomposition is mainly confined to the winter, when rates of decomposition are slow.

Unfortunately, the macrophyte system is easier to destroy and replace with the algal system than vice versa. Any major perturbation

Figure 6.12 Eutrophication – the vicious circle which maintains high phytoplankton biomass to the detriment of benthic macrophytes.

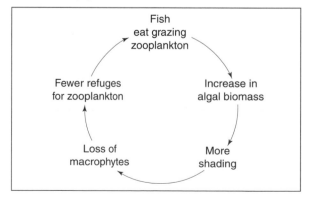

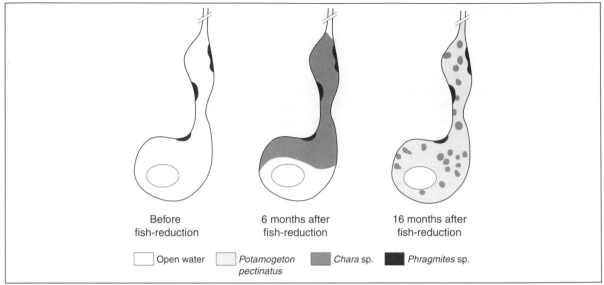

Figure 6.13 The changing distribution of macrophytes in Lake Bleiswijkse Zoom (Netherlands) in response to fish removal (from Meijer *et al.*, 1990).

to macrophytes, such as chemical weedkillers, mechanical damage by boats or excessive grazing, will open up the still nutrient-rich water and allow algae, which can respond very quickly, to move in. Once their numbers increase, turbidity is raised and the opportunities for recolonisation by macrophytes are reduced (Figure 6.12). This is well illustrated by Lake Apopka in Florida. Until the 1940s, this shallow lake, with a surface area of 125 km² but a mean depth of less than 2 m, was exceptionally clear, with a lush growth of macrophytes. In 1947, a hurricane uprooted macrophytes, causing massive mortality and, through their decomposition, releasing nutrients into the water. Within one week of the hurricane, the first algal bloom was reported, and phytoplankton quickly became the dominant primary producers (Carrick *et al.*, 1993). When such a transformation occurs, restoration of the macrophyte system will almost certainly require the removal of planktivorous fish, or severe reduction in their densities, in order to release grazers from predation and allow them to attain high densities. This may be extremely difficult to achieve but, if successful, its effects upon macrophytes can be remarkable (Figure 6.13).

6.7b INTRODUCTION OF FISH

The trophic cascade demonstrates the top–down control by top predators of lake ecosystems. That top predators can have more fundamental effects, completely restructuring food webs, rather than simply altering the relative abundance of other species, has been documented many times through accidental or deliberate introduction of predatory fish to lakes, of which the example of Gatun Lake in Panama is one of the most celebrated. Prior to 1967, Gatun Lake supported a complex food web with 11 common species of fish. Introduction of the piscivorous cichlid *Cichla ocellaris*, a native of the Amazon basin, simplified the food web immensely, predation by this species eliminating seven species and reducing numbers of three others. Only one species, the planktivorous cichlid *Cichlasoma maculicauda*, increased in abundance, probably because *Cichla* eliminated species which had formerly fed upon its fry. Of particular significance was removal of the atherinid *Melaniris chagresi*, formerly an important component of the diet of seasonally present consumers – Atlantic tarpon (*Tarpon atlanticus*) and black tern (*Chlidonias niger*) – both of which disappeared from areas where *Cichla* was present. Black terns were not the only birds affected, kingfishers and herons also being reduced in abundance by the arrival of *Cichla* (Zaret & Paine, 1973).

In contrast to the experience of Gatun Lake, an apparent increase in species diversity was recorded from Lake Nakuru in Kenya following the introduction of the tilapine *Oreochromis alcalicus grahami* to the previously fishless saline lake. This species quickly became abundant, feeding on the cyanobacterium *Spirulina platensis*, but had no observed detrimental effect upon other components of the fauna because *Spirulina* was so abundant and prolific that total consumption by the fish was negligible. What did result, however, was an extension of the food chain in this lake to fish-eating birds, particularly great white pelican (*Pelecanus onocrotalus*), but including more than 50 species in total, whereas, prior to fish introduction in the 1950s, lesser flamingo (*Phoeniconaias minor*), itself a consumer of *Spirulina*, had been the only abundant bird species (Lévêque, 1995).

6.7c LAKE VICTORIA – AN EXAMPLE OF COMPLEX PERTURBATION

Lake Victoria provides an example of a complex interaction between alien species and eutrophication in modifying community structure, and demonstrates that even a water body of this size – the world's second largest freshwater lake in terms of surface area – can be completely modified by human activity. Lake Victoria has suffered from eutrophication, overfishing and the introduction of exotic aliens, all of which have contributed, often synergistically, to its current state (Lowe-McConnell, 1994). During the period 1961–64, heavy rain brought exceptionally high lake levels (see **Section 6.2a**), flooding adjacent papyrus swamps, inputting much organic matter and accelerating eutrophication of the water, which had been occurring gradually for the previous 40 years. At the same time as these high water levels, several exotic fish species were introduced to replace overfished native species. Introductions included Nile perch (*Lates niloticus*), a large predatory species, typically 35–50 kg in weight when full grown. *Lates* was first recorded in Lake Victoria in 1960, although it may have been present since 1954, so deliberate introductions were made in Uganda in 1962. Its increase was initially very gradual, but during the late 1970s and early 1980s its population exploded and it spread throughout the lake. Lake Victoria formerly supported over 300 species of haplochromine fish, all of them endemic, of which around 200 have disappeared or become severely endangered since the irruption of *Lates* (but see **Section 7.7c**). The pelagic zone of the lake formerly supported a large fish biomass (more than 200 g ha^{-1}), of which 40% was accounted for by grazing or detritivorous haplochromines and a further 40% by zooplanktivorous or piscivorous haplochromines; now, 90% of the current fish biomass of around 100 g ha^{-1} is *Lates*. Haplochromine detritivores and grazers have apparently been replaced by a crustacean – the atypid prawn *Caridina nilotica* – and zooplanktivorous haplochromines by the native cyprinid *Rastineobola argentea*. *Lates* now feeds upon *Caridina*, *Rastineobola*, dragonfly nymphs and juveniles of its own species (Figure 6.14).

It is tempting to see the situation in Lake Victoria as a simple case of a dominant predator restructuring the community, but *Lates* persisted at a low density for almost 20 years before suddenly irrupting to dominate the ecosystem. A possible explanation relates to eutrophication and consequent reduction in oxygen levels at depth (**Section 6.2c**). The oxycline is typically around 20–30 m deep in the open lake, and can rise to as little as 5 m depth close to the shore, leading to fish kills and enforced migration of fish inshore where they are more susceptible to netting. Juvenile *Lates* may initially have been kept in check by large piscivorous haplochromines, themselves the prey of adult *Lates*. The reduction of haplochromines through overfishing may have released *Lates* from predation until the adult population was high enough for it, in turn, to become the dominant predator. Once common, *Lates* consumed large numbers of grazers and detritivores which had formerly kept algal biomass in check; their loss led to more algal detritus sinking into the hypolimnion, reducing oxygen levels. Eutrophication had started – and accelerated – before the irruption of *Lates*, as a consequence of land use changes, but its effects, in terms of algal blooms and deoxygenation, may

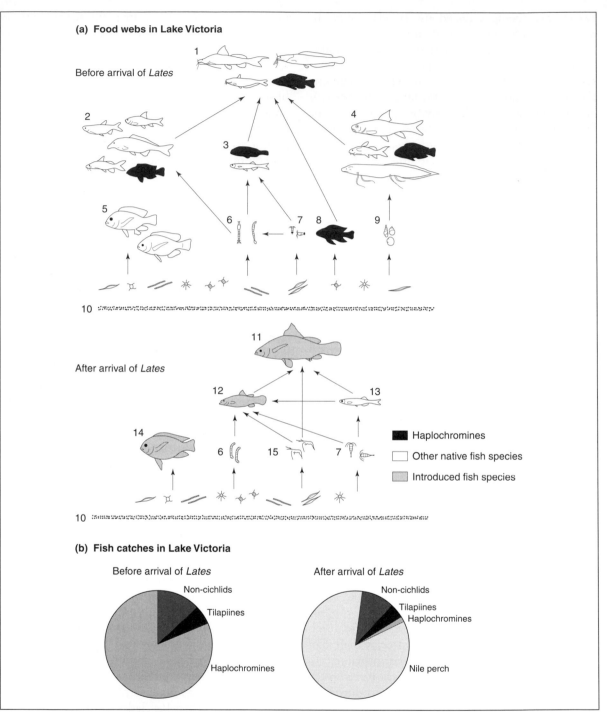

Figure 6.14 The effect of introduction of Nile perch (*Lates niloticus*) on the ecosystem of Lake Victoria. (a) Food web before and after establishment of *Lates*. (1) piscivorous fish; (2) insectivorous fish; (3) zooplanktivorous fish (including *Rastrineobola argentea*); (4) molluscivorous fish; (5) algivorous fish (native species of *Oreochromis*); (6) planktonic insect larvae; (7) planktonic crustaceans; (8) detritivorous and planktivorous fish; (9) molluscs; (10) phytoplankton and detritus; (11) adult *Lates*; (12) juvenile *Lates*; (13) *Rastrineobola argentea*; (14) *Oreochromis niloticus*; (15) *Caradina nilotica* (from Witte *et al.*, 1992). (b) Percentage composition of fish catches in the Nyanza Gulf, Kenya, before and after establishment of *Lates* (from Lowe-McConnell, 1994).

have been kept in check by the large numbers of native haplochromines until *Lates* became well enough established to reduce their numbers. Alternatively, increasing deoxygenation of bottom waters may have forced benthic species inshore, providing more food for *Lates* and enhancing its population growth (Lowe-McConnell, 1994). Confounding the situation is the replacement of zooplanktivorous haplochromines by *Rastineobola*, a species whose population has been enhanced by the arrival of *Lates*. *Rastineobola* predation upon zooplankton is more intense than that of the species it has replaced, so densities of larger zooplankters have declined, with a corresponding reduction of grazing pressure on algae. Primary production is, therefore, much greater than grazing capacity and excess production descends into the hypolimnion. *Caridina*, a species tolerant of very low oxygen concentrations (less than 1 mg l^{-1}), has proliferated as a consequence, as the practically anoxic hypolimnion provides it with a predation refuge from *Lates* (Gophen *et al.*, 1995).

There is a fourth human impact on the Lake Victorian ecosystem: the elimination during the mid-20th century of crocodile (*Crocodylus niloticus*). The effect upon fish assemblages of the loss of this species is unknown, but it is interesting to speculate upon the outcome of *Lates* introduction if this major piscivore had still been present (Lévêque, 1995).

6.8 Summary

Lakes are created in depressions in the Earth's surface within which water collects. An outflow river will dampen large fluctuations in volume, but saline lakes, which generally lack an outflow, can fluctuate widely in surface and volume, in some cases disappearing altogether.

Physically, lakes share much in common with the open sea, undergoing thermal stratification, often seasonally. Lack of mixing between the surface layer (epilimnion) and deep layer (hypolimnion) can result in oxygen depletion at depth; deep lakes, with the exception of Lake Baikal, are permanently anoxic at depth. Horizontal variations in water chemistry are less marked than vertical variations.

Primary production in deep lakes is dominated by phytoplankton, which are subject to the same constraints of light penetration, nutrient status, mixing and grazing as occur in the sea. Primary production in temperate zones is seasonal, limited by temperature and light in the winter and by nutrient depletion and grazing in the summer. In the tropics, seasonal variations in hydrology affect primary production. In shallow lakes, primary production by benthic macrophytes is important, although eutrophication may lead to dominance by phytoplankton.

Predation is the dominant biotic interaction in lakes. Strategies to avoid predation include development of structural defences, life cycle strategies and avoidance behaviour. Predatory fish are often key components of lake ecosystems.

Endemism is rare in lakes, as most species have effective dispersal abilities, in response to the geologically short life spans of lakes, and the temporary nature of some lentic water bodies. Ancient lakes, in contrast, have high levels of endemism.

Lakes act as sinks for sediment and will inevitably infill over time. The successional process involves gradual eutrophication.

Anthropogenic eutrophication and introduction of alien fish species demonstrate that lakes, however large, act as single ecological units.

7

Wetlands

7.1 Introduction

A wetland may be defined as an area of land whose characteristics are determined by the presence of water, either permanent waterlogging or through regular, usually seasonal, flooding. If permanently inundated, this is to a depth shallow enough to allow the growth of emergent vegetation or rooted macrophytes. Within this broad definition are many options for subdivision, reflecting the diverse nature and modes of origin of the world's wetlands, but all share important ecological similarities as a result of the high water table, hence their consideration together here. They do, however, fall into two fundamental

Figure 7.1 Examples of different wetland types. (a) Aquatic marginal wetlands: a fringe wetland marks the edge of a river (foreground); behind it is a flooded levée, marked by terrestrial vegetation, and a flood wetland receiving its seasonal input of water from the river (Danube Delta, Romania). (*Photo by M. Dobson*)

(b) Mires: a fen, sitting in a natural depression in the ground and fed by groundwater (Knockbane, Northern Ireland). (*Photo by M. Dobson*)

types, for which the terms aquatic marginal and mire are here used (Figure 7.1).

Aquatic marginal wetlands

Aquatic marginal wetlands are created by open water bodies – rivers, lakes and the sea – which act as the source of water (Figure 7.1a). They can be conveniently subdivided into fringe wetlands and flood wetlands. Fringe wetlands have a continuous or very frequent (at least once per day) hydrological connection with the parent water body (Figure 7.2a) and are typical of the shallow edges of lakes and slow-flowing rivers, being characterised by emergent vegetation. Flood wetlands are, for most of the time, hydrologically separated from the parent water body, becoming connected only during high water (Figure 7.2b). Typical examples are river floodplain marshes, inundated frequently or for long periods during the wet season. Coastal saltmarshes incorporate both wetland types: areas subjected to daily inundation ('low marsh') are flooded with a frequency and regularity adequate to describe them as fringe wetlands, whereas infre-

quently flooded areas ('high marsh') are flood wetlands. During the interval between flood events, flood wetlands will lose their water through drainage and evapotranspiration, and may, in some cases, dry out completely. The terms 'riverine wetland' (Brinson, 1988) and 'riparian wetland' (Mitsch, 1996) have been applied to flood wetlands, as here defined, but these terms imply application only to freshwater wetlands associated with rivers, overlooking the important functional and ecological similarities these systems share with infrequently flooded coastal systems.

Mires

Mires persist independently of a parent water body, being fed by groundwater, overland runoff or precipitation. They, too, can be divided into two types, minerotrophic (or rheotrophic) mires and ombrotrophic mires, often referred to as fens and bogs, respectively (Moore & Bellamy, 1974). Fens are valley mires, receiving water and nutrients from groundwater and runoff from the surrounding catchment. They are generally nutrient

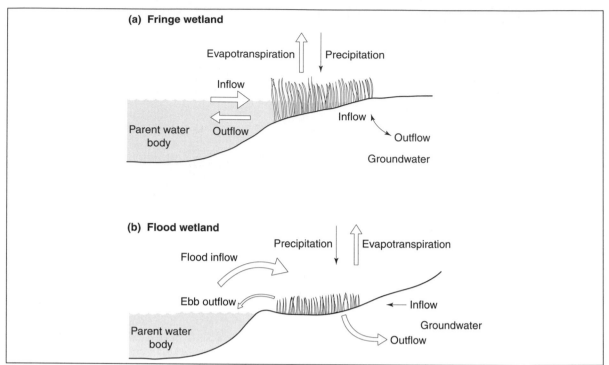

Figure 7.2 Inputs and outputs of water in (a) a fringe wetland and (b) a flood wetland. The width of each arrow is proportional to the volume of water following that route.

rich, unless fed by very pure groundwater (Figures 7.1b and 7.3a). Bogs, in contrast, occur above the water table and are fed solely by rainwater and aerial deposition, so are nutrient-poor (Figure 7.3b). Both bogs and fens are normally permanently waterlogged, ensuring reduced rates of decomposition and allowing partially decayed plant matter to accumulate in the form of peat; they are thus sometimes collectively known as peatlands. Bogs, which have acidic surface water, generally support vegetation characterised by mosses of the genus *Sphagnum*; if the pH rises above 4.5, fen vegetation, characterised by sedges (*Carex*) and woody plants, will take over.

Transitional wetlands

As with all aquatic systems, rigid definitions lead to difficulties with habitats which are clearly transitional. An area of floodplain marsh may be fed by groundwater during the dry season, thereby remaining permanently waterlogged and taking on the characteristics of a fen. Whether it is then classified as a fen or a flood wetland, or simply a hybrid between the two, is a matter of subjectivity, although if its soil is dominated by peat it is probably a fen which occasionally is flooded by a river, whereas if dominated by mineral soils, such as riverine silts, it is a flood wetland with fen-like characteristics. Similarly, as a fen forms over the site of a lake or pond, it passes through a transitional stage, and a distinction must be drawn between a small lake which supports a large fringing wetland, and an open pool formed in a hollow within a mire (see Figure 7.7).

Swamp and marsh

This classification of wetland types is one of many which have been devised in an attempt to categorise this very diverse group of habitats. We deliberately avoid using the terms 'swamp' and 'marsh', both of which have been employed in several, rarely compatible, ways. Fojt (1994), for example, defines swamps as wetlands where the water table is normally above ground level, and

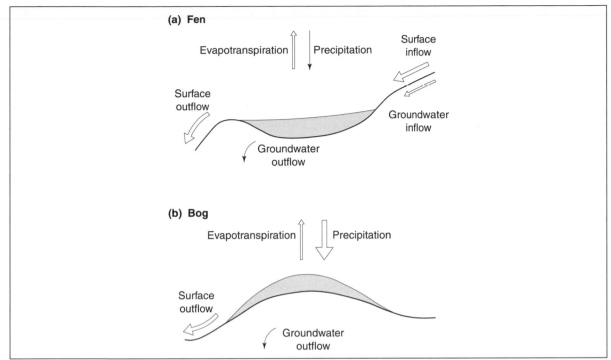

Figure 7.3 Inputs and outputs of water in (a) a fen and (b) a bog. The width of each arrow is proportional to the volume of water following that route. Note that, if the bog is growing, it will retain water and inputs will exceed outputs.

marshes as wetlands where it is normally at or just below ground level, whereas the normal use of 'swamp' in the USA is to refer to a wetland dominated by trees, while 'marsh' is reserved for wetlands dominated by non-woody vegetation (Williams, 1990). These terms are, however, valuable as accepted names for well known wetland types, such as saltmarsh in coastal areas, or reedswamp to describe single-species stands of wetland grasses such as common reed (*Phragmites australis*).

7.2 The abiotic environment

7.2a THE WATER TABLE AND OXYGEN AVAILABILITY

The abiotic environment of wetlands is dominated by the position of the water table relative to the substrate, and whether waterlogging or flooding is a permanent or a seasonal feature. The water table, in turn, determines the concentration of oxygen in the soil. Whereas well drained soil contains many air spaces, these are filled with water in flooded soil. Furthermore, decomposition of organic matter in the soil by microbial action rapidly depletes oxygen. The rate of diffusion of oxygen through water (0.226×10^{-4} cm s^{-1}) is 10 000 times slower than its rate through air (0.209 cm s^{-1}), so the rate at which oxygen is used in respiration easily outstrips the rate at which it can be replaced. Absence of oxygen is, in itself, a problem which wetland organisms need to overcome, but it also has implications for soil chemistry.

7.2b SOIL CHEMISTRY

It is difficult to separate abiotic from biotic processes in wetland soils because, although the anaerobic conditions are, in themselves, important in determining the ecology of wetland communities, they are compounded by indirect effects upon soil chemistry which result from microbial activity. A detailed review of wetland soil chemistry may be found in Ross (1995); a summary of its most important features is included here.

Nutrients

Permanently waterlogged soil is normally very deficient in nitrate, because rates of decomposition of organic matter, and therefore of remineralisation of nutrients, are severely reduced in the absence of oxygen, and because of denitrification by anaerobic bacteria (**Box 7.1**). Seasonally flooded wetlands, on the other hand, go through a drying period when decomposition and nitrification can occur, releasing nutrients back into the system. Fringe wetlands bathed by water with a relatively rapid turnover will have a constantly replenished nutrient supply and can be very nutrient rich.

Toxins

In the absence of oxygen, reducing conditions are created in which toxic chemical species are generated, reduced forms of iron (Fe^{2+}) and manganese (Mn^{2+}), for example, being more soluble, and therefore more chemically reactive, than their oxidised forms (Fe^{3+}, Mn^{4+}). Reduction of these metals, which will not occur until oxygen and nitrates have been completely exhausted, is carried out by anaerobic bacteria. Sulphates (SO_4^{2-}), too, are reduced, in the total absence of oxygen or nitrates, to iron sulphide (FeS) or hydrogen sulphide (H_2S), again by anaerobic bacteria. In the absence of iron, H_2S, which is highly toxic, will be produced as a gas; its release when anaerobic sediments are physically disturbed gives off the distinctive sulphurous smell characteristic of wetland soils. Under extremely anaerobic conditions, methanogenic bacteria reduce carbon dioxide (CO_2) to methane (CH_4), another gas which is toxic at high concentrations.

7.2c INTERACTION WITH OPEN WATER BODIES

Water connections

Aquatic marginal wetlands cannot be considered in isolation from their parent water bodies. A fringe wetland will merge with the open water body which it fringes, and most large wetlands incorporate stretches of open water from which they cannot realistically be functionally separated. Any seasonally flooded wetland, for example, will have channels into which water drains, channels which in managed wetlands are straightened but otherwise equivalent to those which would occur naturally. Saltmarshes and mangals (mangrove swamps) contain networks of drainage channels, permanently flooded or into which sea will penetrate during every high tide. River floodplains may contain relatively large, permanent water bodies such as oxbow lakes, remnants of former river channels (see Figure 6.1a and **Box 6.1**). These have no clear or permanent inflow, but are replenished by groundwater percolation and by occasional inundation during floods. Their equivalents in coastal wetlands are lagoons, generally physically separated from the adjacent sea and virtually tideless, but with some influx of sea water, particularly during spring tides.

Despite being formed or maintained without the requirement for open water bodies, mires will not exist independently of other aquatic systems. If a wetland has a fluctuating topography, some parts will inevitably fall below the water table, allowing open water bodies to form. A major difference between aquatic marginal and mire wetlands, in terms of their relationships to other water bodies, is that, whereas aquatic marginal wetlands owe their existence to rivers, lakes or the sea, mires, as reservoirs of water, actively contribute to the formation of other aquatic systems. Even blanket bogs, maintained solely by rainwater, will almost inevitably act as a source for rivers, and commonly their surfaces are dotted with open pools. This distinction does, however, mask the role of flood wetlands in regulating the flow of rivers. Such wetlands act as reservoirs of excess flood water, much of which will gradually drain back into the channel, dampening major fluctuations in discharge; isolated from its wetlands, a river's discharge may fluctuate rapidly in response to precipitation and, during dry periods, it may cease to flow altogether.

Nutrient and sediment exchange

Fringe wetlands, with their direct aquatic connec-

BOX 7.1   DENITRIFICATION IN WETLANDS

Creation of nitrates by nitrogen-fixing or recycling nitrogen compounds derived from decomposing organic matter is called nitrification, and is effected by a series of microorganisms:

$$\underset{\text{nitrogen}}{\text{Organic}} \overset{(1)}{\rightarrow} NH_4^+ \overset{(2)}{\Leftrightarrow} NO_2^- \overset{(3)}{\Leftrightarrow} NO_3^- \qquad (1)$$

$$\text{ammonium} \qquad \text{nitrite} \qquad \text{nitrate}$$

Stage 1 is the result of decomposition by a range of different microorganisms, and can proceed under aerobic or anaerobic conditions. Stages 2 and 3 are carried out by *Nitrosomonas* and *Nitrobacter*, respectively, both of which are active only under aerobic conditions.

Denitrification is the transformation of nitrate to gaseous nitrogen or nitrous oxide:

$$NO_3^- \rightarrow NO_2^- \rightarrow NO \rightarrow N_2O \rightarrow N_2 \qquad (2)$$

This transformation results from the activity of denitrifying bacteria, which are not limited by anaerobic conditions.

In well drained soil, under aerobic conditions, nitrification recycles organic nitrogen:

$$\underset{\text{nitrogen}}{\text{Organic}} \rightarrow NH_4^+ \rightarrow NO_3^- \rightarrow \underset{\text{nitrogen}}{\text{Organic}}$$

$$\underset{\text{decomposition}}{} \underset{\text{nitrification}}{} \underset{\substack{\text{uptake} \\ \text{by plants}}}{} \qquad (3)$$

In waterlogged soil, under anaerobic conditions, decomposition will proceed only to the ammonia stage, and most nitrates present will be denitrified, although a small proportion will dissimilate into ammonia:

$$\underset{\text{nitrogen}}{\text{Organic}} \rightarrow NH_4^+ \leftarrow NO_3^- \rightarrow N_2$$

$$\underset{\text{decomposition}}{} \underset{\text{dissimilation}}{} \underset{\text{denitrification}}{} \qquad (4)$$

Where waterlogged and aerated soils occur in close proximity, nitrifying bacteria can, ironically, contribute to denitrification (see figure). Nitrification in the aerated soil removes ammonia, creating a diffusion gradient so that ammonium diffuses from waterlogged soil. This, in turn, is converted into nitrate but, because denitrification is removing nitrate from the waterlogged soil, a second diffusion gradient is created, causing nitrate to diffuse into the waterlogged soils, where it is broken down.

tions, exchange nutrients with the open water body, while flood wetlands rely upon the inputs of sediment and, of course, water during flood events, but in turn can be major providers of organic detritus into river food webs. The lateral connections and movements of organisms between rivers and their floodplains are discussed in **Section 2.7c**. Saltmarshes and mangals are often

Figure 7.4 Mangroves of the genus *Avicennia* develop aerial roots, which grow vertically upward, allowing them access to atmospheric oxygen even during high tides (Poka, Ambon, Indonesia). (*Photo by C. Frid*)

obically for short periods, but all will require oxygen eventually. Most species overcome the problems of low oxygen concentrations in the soil by development of aerenchyma (aerated tissues), creating interconnected air spaces within the root system, either within existing roots or, upon flooding, in new roots. The mangrove genus *Avicennia* develops roots which bend upwards, growing out of the soil to allow direct gaseous exchange with the atmosphere (Figure 7.4). Shoots, too, grow in some semi-aquatic species in response to flooding, to restore contact with the open air (Blom & Voesenek, 1996). Oxygen transported to roots reacts with metal ions, transferring them into oxidised, and therefore less toxic, forms, but some wetland plants tolerate high concentrations of toxins by incorporating them into their tissues (Hughes & Johnes, 1995).

Animals, too, have to be adapted to the special conditions of wetlands. Seasonally flooded wetlands will support aquatic species when inundated and terrestrial species when dry, these animals either moving away, becoming dormant or even metamorphosing into a terrestrial life stage when conditions are unfavourable (**Section 7.6e**). Fringe wetlands and other permanently flooded areas support a community reminiscent of lakes except that it tends to be based more on detritus than on phytoplankton. Stagnant water containing large quantities of decomposing organic matter reduces oxygen concentrations but many invertebrates overcome this by breathing air, either rising to the surface to breathe or transporting and storing bubbles of air under water; others pierce aquatic macrophytes and breathe air in the aerenchymae. The greatest effect of wetland conditions is upon organisms living within the substrate, which have to overcome the same problems of oxygen shortage and toxicity faced by plant roots.

closely associated with estuaries, where their formation is intimately connected to the sedimentation process and to which they supply much of the detritus which contributes to the high productivity of so many estuaries (**Section 3.4c**).

Much of the discussion in this chapter, particularly with respect to adaptations of wetland organisms, is equally applicable to the littoral zone of lakes; the distinction between a deeply flooded fringe wetland and a shallow lake is artificial.

7.3 Ecological effects of the abiotic environment

7.3a ANAEROBIC CONDITIONS

Anaerobic conditions in wetland soils require adaptations to overcome the problems associated with respiration and high concentrations of toxins. Relatively few plant species possess these adaptations, although many species typical of seasonally flooded wetlands avoid physiological stress by passing the flood period in a state of dormancy. Some wetland plants can respire anaer-

Zonation

Vertical zonation is commonly seen in wetlands, where a change in elevation of only a few centimetres will create a range of different conditions, each requiring different strategies and therefore supporting different species (Figure 7.5). A series of zones, related to the height of the water table with respect to the sediment surface, can be recog-

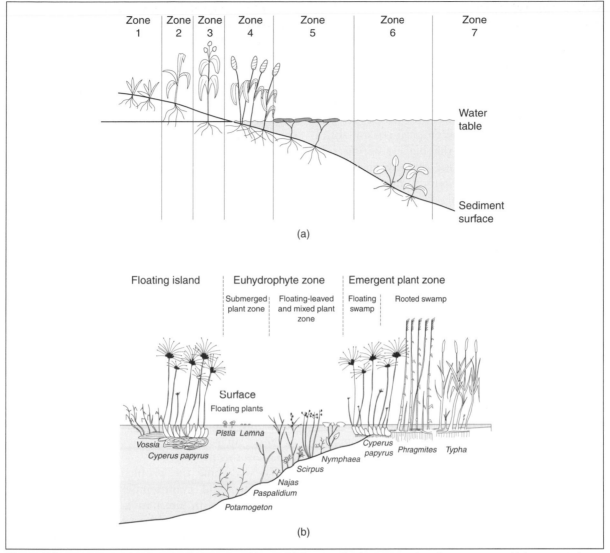

Figure 7.5 Vertical zonation in wetland plant assemblages. (a) A generalised representation of seven zones which occur at the land–water interface, and the life forms of plant species which occupy each, including the position of above-ground structures and roots in relation to the sediment surface and water table. See text for more details. (b) A typical vegetation zonation in tropical African fringe wetlands. Note the floating swamp and floating islands formed by *Cyperus papyrus* (from Denny, 1995).

nised at the land–water interface, representing different sets of conditions to which their inhabitants must be tolerant. These zones are illustrated in Figure 7.5a. Zone 1 represents the fully terrestrial environment, with freely draining, aerated soils. Plants living in zone 2 have roots which are, for the most part, in aerated soil, but may have to overcome problems of anoxia and toxins at depth. Plants living in zones 3 to 6 must be tolerant of permanently waterlogged sediments; in zone 3, their above-ground parts are above the water and, in zone 4, the water is shallow enough to allow emergent species to grow. Zones 5 and 6 are too deep for emergent species, and their flora is fully aquatic (euhydrophytes), while zone 7 represents those parts of the water body beyond the littoral zone which are too deep for light to penetrate to the bed, and so are devoid of attached macrophytes. This type of zonation is particularly clear in fringe wetlands, such as that illustrated in Figure 7.5b, but can be found in most wetland types. Zonation in *Sphagnum* bogs is considered in **Section 7.5**.

Zonation of species analogous to that of marine algae occurs in coastal wetlands, where water level fluctuations are predictable yet frequent. Mangroves occur in tropical coastal zones from mean sea level to the highest spring tide level, within which are clear zones, each with its dominant species. Species-poor Central American mangals are dominated by red mangrove (*Rhizopora mangle*) on the seaward side, where tidal inundation is daily, black mangrove (*Avicennia tomentosa*) where tidal inundation is less frequent, and white mangrove (*Lagunalaria racemosa*) at levels flooded only by spring tides (Golley *et al.*, 1962). Indomalayan mangals are much more speciose, but similar zonations occur (Mann, 1982). Saltmarsh can generally be divided into three vertical zones (Long & Mason, 1983). Low marsh supports very few macrophyte species and can contain large areas of bare mud, although in eastern North America this zone may be dominated by the grass *Spartina alterniflora* (**Section 3.4a**), and in the British Isles increasingly by *S. townsendii*, a hydrid of the alien *S. alterniflora* and the native *S. maritima*. Above the MHW (Figure 4.1) is middle marsh, or turf, extensively vegetated with halophytic grasses, while above MHWS is high marsh, supporting halophytes and some freshwater species, such as common reed (*Phragmites australis*), which will persist so long as freshwater inputs are great enough to flush out occasional saltwater incursions.

Floating vegetation mats

A consequence of anoxia in flooded wetlands is floating mats of vegetation, formed when an interconnected mass of vegetation, generally dominated by a single species, breaks free from the underlying mineral substrate. Such mats float because their aerenchyma tissue makes them less dense than water and also, as they develop, because anaerobic decomposition within the mat generates trapped bubbles of methane, which will keep the mat afloat even if living tissue on the surface is removed (Hogg & Wein, 1988).

Floating mats are especially prevalent in equatorial Africa, where they are known as 'sudd'. They are normally dominated by papyrus (*Cyperus papyrus*), which can form extensive rafts of vegetation held together by interconnected rhizomes, with plants such as *Vossia* growing on the fringes (Figure 7.5b). These mats are created when floating swamp on the edge of a water body breaks free during stormy conditions or when there is a sudden rise in the water table (Denny, 1995).

7.3b NUTRIENTS

A consequence of anaerobic denitrification (**Box 7.1**) is that inorganic nitrogen is generally the limiting nutrient in wetlands. Ironically, the very presence of well-adapted wetland species can contribute to denitrification: some of the oxygen transported into their roots will diffuse out into the surrounding substrate and create an aerobic environment in which nitrifying bacteria can convert ammonium to nitrate; this nitrate can then be broken down into gaseous nitrogen by denitrifying bacteria. It is the presence of aerobic and anaerobic conditions in very close proximity over a large surface area around the roots which enhances this process.

To overcome the problems of nitrate availability, wetland communities typically support plant species with alternative sources of nitrates, including, in Europe, alder (*Alnus glutinosa*) and bog myrtle (*Myrica gale*) which maintain a symbiotic relationship with nitrogen-fixing bacteria in their root nodules. Ombrotrophic mires support carnivorous plants such as sundew (*Drosera* spp.), which obtain nitrogen compounds from insects which they trap and digest. In saltmarsh soils, too, anaerobic conditions promote denitrification and biologically available nitrogen can be a limiting factor to growth. Plants inhabiting coastal wetlands have to withstand the further physiological stress of high salinity, a situation complicated by the high requirement for nitrogen of species such as *Spartina alterniflora*, possibly because nitrogen compounds are required to maintain osmotic balance under saline conditions (Adams, 1990). Plant productivity in estuarine saltmarshes is normally higher in the low marsh than in the high marsh, even when the same species are compared. This can be explained by the frequent influx of nutrient-rich water in low marshes, but also by the lower salinity of interstitial water around the roots, as a consequence of flushing by diluted estuarine water. The interaction between these two factors, and their relative importance in determining productivity, are unclear (Mann, 1982).

Microflora and nutrient availability

Wetland macrophytes, even if submerged, gain their nutrients only from the sediment. They will, however, support a diverse epiphytic microflora of algae which gain their nutrients mainly from the water. There is little transfer of nutrients from algae to macrophyte, although some from macrophyte to algae but, when they die, macrophyte stems, along with the microflora they support, collapse into the sediment. The nutrients absorbed from the water column by epiphytic algae are, in this way, transferred into the sediment and therefore available for macrophytes (Wetzel, 1990). In this way, epiphytic microflora, despite shading macrophytes and reducing their photosynthetic efficiency, can be indirectly beneficial to their hosts.

Vertebrates and nutrient availability

Mobile vertebrates are important in their ability to redistribute nutrients within wetland systems. Wading birds in the Florida Everglades disperse widely to feed but roost and nest aggregated into colonies in trees, creating areas where excretion and mortality are concentrated. Harris (1988) has calculated that, during the late-19th century, there were an estimated 2.5 million wading birds in the Florida Everglades which, assuming 50% of excretion and mortality occurred at roosting sites, would have transferred 400 t yr^{-1} of ash (the inorganic nutrient component of excretory products and corpses) from the wider wetland to relatively small areas around roosting sites. As the number of birds has been reduced by habitat loss and degradation and, until early in the 20th century, hunting for plumes, so the extent of this redistribution of nutrients will have declined significantly.

7.3c WETLANDS AND WATER QUALITY

Aquatic marginal wetlands, being adapted to nutrient-rich environments, can respond to eutrophication by increasing their absorption and use of the extra nutrients. If nutrients are at an artificially high concentration, wetlands can remove the excess and, as such, are valuable in improving water quality. Some nutrients will be incorporated into plant tissue as enhanced growth, but this is normally a small proportion of the total concentrations removed. More important for nitrogen compounds is the nitrification– denitrification process are described in Section 7.3b, in which local oxygenation of soil adjacent to plant roots facilitates conversion of excess nitrates into gaseous components which are then lost to the atmosphere, whereas phosphates are absorbed by microflora or retained in plant litter and sediments (Ross, 1995). Reedbeds are particularly effective because not only can they absorb dissolved nutrients and enhance oxygen-dependent decomposition of organic matter, but the vegetation structure acts both as a net, causing particles in suspension to settle into the sediment, and as an attachment surface for microorganisms (Gersberg et al., 1986). They can, in this way, efficiently strip water of its nutrient load and improve its quality.

Removal of nutrients by soils in aquatic marginal wetlands can have a major influence on water quality. Pinay and Décamps (1988) estimated that a 30 m wide strip of riparian woodland along a tributary of the River Garonne in southwest France would be enough to remove all of the nitrate entering the groundwater from surrounding agricultural land. Trémolieres et al. (1991) demonstrated that the same process can work in reverse. The River Rhine in eastern France inundates its floodplain with heavily polluted water. As this water infiltrates the soil, it is cleansed of excess nitrates and phosphates such that the water which enters the groundwater is significantly less polluted than the river water. This process is biologically controlled, in that the areas with the most developed wetland vegetation are most efficient at purifying the water.

The ability of wetland vegetation to clean water is being exploited commercially, with beds of emergent reeds (*Phragmites*) or cattails (*Typha*)

Table 7.1 Wetland productivity: net primary productivity (NPP) ($g \, m^{-2} \, yr^{-1}$) of different freshwater wetland types

Latitude	Bog	Fen	Aquatic marginal
Polar (65–90°)	100–300	100–333	–
Boreal (55–65°)	300–700	400–700	500–1000
Temperate (30–55°)	400–800	400–1200	700–2000
Tropical (0–30°)	600–1200	–	1500–4000

Notes: Figures quoted show the normal range – examples of extremely high and extremely low productivities are given in the text. No attempt has been made to distinguish between different aquatic marginal wetland types, because of the range of definitions employed. For examples of productivity in coastal wetlands, see Table 3.1. *Source*: from data in Aselmann and Crutzen (1989).

proving most successful. Water treatment wetlands can be created and maintained with relative ease; natural wetlands, too, can be effective, but will suffer reduction in species diversity, as nutrient enrichment favours the most competitive species at the expense of others (**Section 7.5**). Excess nutrient inputs may eventually destroy macrophytes in permanently inundated fringe wetlands, effectively destroying the wetland and creating an open water environment. This process normally proceeds according to the mechanisms described in **Section 6.7a**, in which eutrophication of lakes leads eventually to domination by phytoplankton, but can be caused by more subtle changes. In the Norfolk Broads, in eastern England, there is a clear relationship between nitrate loading of water and the loss of stands of *Phragmites australis*. As nitrate concentration increases, *Phragmites* grows more vigorously, increasing the proportion of above-ground to below-ground growth. Most of the losses in the Norfolk Broads have been from a growth form known as 'hover', which consists of floating mats of *Phragmites*; these depend upon their root and rhizome mat for mechanical strength and become unstable if emergent shoot growth is too high, making them vulnerable to erosion (Boar & Crook, 1985).

7.4   Energy inputs

7.4a   PRIMARY PRODUCTION

Wetlands support some of the highest and some of

the lowest productivity values recorded (Table 7.1; see also Table 3.1). At one extreme is reedswamp, whose productivity can be matched only by tropical rainforests and the most intensively managed agricultural systems, while at the other are ombrotrophic mires, some of whose productivities are on a par with those of tundra or desert ecosystems.

The most productive wetlands are fringe wetlands, bathed in a continually replenished source of nutrients to replace those scavenged by bacteria or incorporated into sediment. Single-species stands, such as reedswamp or papyrus swamp, are dominated by species which, despite being perennials with the capacity for year-round growth, are not woody, so that little energy is expended on growing or maintaining non-photosynthetic structural features. Such wetland dominants are essentially giant leaves. Furthermore, living in an environment where water is plentiful, they have no need to limit transpiration rates. Seasonally inundated flood wetlands can also be highly productive, the flood period bringing in sediments and nutrients while the dry season allows aerobic decomposition of detritus and consequent nutrient release. In *várzea* floodplains along the Amazon, the grass *Echinochloa polystachya*, which grows very rapidly and can achieve productivities approaching $10\,000 \, g \, m^{-2}$, absorbs large quantities of nutrients from the river. Dry-season decomposition of this species, which grows at the lowest points on the floodplain, releases nutrients which are carried by rising floodwaters to higher levels so that, while one generation is absorbing nutrients from the river, the decomposition products of the previous generation ensure that flood waters which penetrate further into the floodplain remain nutrient-enriched (Piedade *et al.*, 1997).

The least productive wetlands – ombrotrophic mires – are also dominated by non-woody species, but are limited by permanently low nutrient availability. Despite this limitation, they can have surprisingly high productivity values: Clymo and Hayward (1982) quote a typical value of 800 g m^{-2}yr^{-1} for *Sphagnum* growing in pools in British bogs, somewhat higher than the productivity of temperate grassland, although productivity on hummocks is typically less than a quarter of this value.

High net productivity can be maintained indefinitely in fringe wetlands if decomposition rates or removal of detritus by the parent water body match production, suppressing accumulation of organic matter. Blanket and raised mires accumulate organic matter, as a result of extremely low rates of decomposition in the cool temperate environments in which they usually form, but by raising the water table as they develop (**Section 7.5**), continued domination by *Sphagnum* is assured. In other wetland environments, such as rheotrophic fens, accumulation of organic matter can lead to relative lowering of the water table and an increased proportion of species adapted to drier environments. Flood wetlands, too, experience reduced water stress during the dry season, allowing more terrestrially adapted species to persist. In such situations, total biomass may be higher than in fringe wetlands, but net productivity is lower.

7.4b SECONDARY PRODUCTION

Exploitation of detritus

Despite the high productivity of wetland plants, relatively little is consumed by herbivores (Berrie, 1976). Most macrophytes, and particularly emergent species, have tough cell walls and high lignin content making ingestion difficult. Instead, consumption is mainly after death, by detritivores; conditioning is important in improving palatability of detritus derived from autochthonous wetland plants, just as it is with respect to allochthonous inputs to other aquatic systems (see **Sections 2.4b** and **3.4b** for discussion of conditioning in rivers and estuaries, respectively). The high productivity of many wetlands generates large volumes of detritus, this standing stock being enhanced, in the case of fringing and flood wetlands, by detritus from external sources washed in from the adjacent water body; wetland plants act as traps for algae, detached pieces of macrophytes and detritus originating from the pelagic zone (Pieczynska, 1993).

Ironically, detritivores often rely upon macrophytes as structural habitat features, benefiting from their high surface area. In Tivoli South Bay, a small wetland on the Hudson River in New York, the detritivorous chironomid *Cricetopus* sp. accounts for 73% of chironomid larvae in early summer. Although a consumer of fine particulate detritus, it uses the dominant macrophyte, water chestnut (*Trapa natans*), as an attachment structure, reaching densities of 5000 m^{-3} on the underside of its leaves (Findlay *et al.*, 1989); numbers of chironomids decline, however, later in the year, possibly as a result of heavy predation but also because the water chestnut plants become more emergent, reducing underwater surface area available for colonisation.

Grazing

Despite the general preference of aquatic invertebrates for detritus, some herbivory does occur, particularly when alternative food sources are scarce (Jacobsen & Sand-Jensen, 1995). Crayfish are omnivorous, adults eating mostly vegetation and detritus; they prefer fully submerged species to emergent forms and can affect macrophyte numbers both through direct consumption and by cutting plant stems near the base (Nyström & Strand, 1996).

True grazers on macrophytes are found among mammals and birds. Barasingha (*Cervus duvaucelii*), the endangered swamp deer of southeast Asia, relies heavily upon submerged macrophytes as a source of sodium and will actively seek otherwise nutritionally poor species from ponds and ditches (Moe, 1994); moose or elk (*Alces alces*), which occurs widely in North

America and northern Eurasia, is another deer species which habitually feeds upon aquatic plants, apparently choosing sodium-rich species (Fraser *et al.*, 1980). Perhaps the most effective mammalian grazers, however, are the sirenians, mainly marine but including the American manatee (*Trichechus manatus*) which moves freely between marine, estuarine and freshwater habitats, and the only exclusively freshwater species, the Amazonian manatee (*Trichechus inunguis*). This latter species, which weighs up to 450 kg, feeds upon aquatic and semi-aquatic macrophytes, consuming about 8% of its body weight per day. The movements of this species are determined by the hydrological cycle of the Amazon. As the rivers rise, between December and June, manatees spread into the *várzea* and *igapó* (flooded forest) areas, to feed on the lush new growth of macrophytes; when river levels drop, manatees migrate into perennial lakes where, if macrophytes are in short supply, they will eat detritus off the lake bed, or simply not feed at all (Rosas, 1994).

7.5 Community structure

The soil conditions, the risk of inundation and, in flood wetlands, the seasonality of the inundation cycle, all make a wetland an extreme environment for rooted plants. The precise physiological tolerances of most wetland plants ensure that community structure is intimately related to the water table. Conditions may be so extreme that no species can be adapted optimally to more than a narrow range of requirements and will be outcompeted elsewhere.

Adaptations to permanently waterlogged conditions can lead to problems living in well drained soils. Some wetland species have little control over transpiration rates from their leaves and will dry out rapidly in the absence of a constant supply of water. Others, growing shallow roots to avoid anoxia, have little capacity for extracting water from dry soils, but wetlands support many species, adapted to waterlogging and low nutrient levels, which are physiologically able to survive or even flourish in well drained soil (Hughes & Johnes, 1995). Most of these species are, however, con-

fined to wetlands by their poor competitive abilities elsewhere, as adaptation to waterlogging leads to strong specialisation and therefore a competitive disadvantage against terrestrial species if the environment dries up. This is illustrated by changes wrought to the nutrient-poor Pinelands wetlands in the coastal region of New Jersey, USA, parts of which have undergone drying and nutrient enrichment as a consequence of nearby urban development (Ehrenfeld & Schneider, 1991). Changes to water quantity and quality have little effect upon the overall physical appearance of the habitat, nor on the relative abundance of the various life forms of plants: trees, shrubs and herbaceous vegetation. What does occur, however, is a change in species composition, as a result of two processes. Lowering the water table allows the soil to dry, removing the constraints of toxicity and low oxygen concentrations which had previously impeded invasion by terrestrial species, while nutrient enrichment allows them, once established, to grow rapidly. Wetland plants, adapted to a normally nutrient-poor environment, are low in stature and slow-growing, and in the presence of nutrients are outcompeted by the more vigorous terrestrial species, which have taller stems, broader leaves and more rapid growth rates. Ehrenfeld and Schneider (1991) found that the trend following urbanisation was towards increased species richness, but that this was actually hiding a loss of wetland species and their replacement with terrestrial plants, rather than a simple mixing of the two sets of species assemblages.

Sphagnum *mires*

Sphagnum species growing in peat-forming mires are unusual in that they can control and enhance the water table to their own competitive advantage (**Section 7.6b**). *Sphagnum* mosses lack roots, whereas most of their potential competitors are rooted vascular plants, so *Sphagnum* strategies for reducing competition involve creating adverse conditions below ground, to suppress root growth. Waterlogging clearly impedes non-wetland species, but *Sphagnum* also increases the acidity of its environment and reduces nutrient availability, its leaves intercepting atmospheric

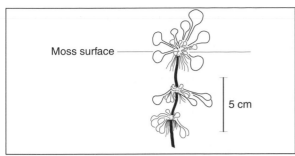

Figure 7.6 Growth form of *Drosera rotundifolia* in *Sphagnum* bog. Each leaf rosette represents a shoot generation, the buried rosettes being previous years' growth, now dead (from Svensson, 1995).

nutrients before they can penetrate the surface layers, and through slow mineralisation as a result of reduced decay rates. Finally, its poor heat-conducting properties ensure that the below-ground parts of the bog remain cool. Suppression of vascular plants increases light availability and reduces water loss through transpiration, both of which maintain optimum conditions for *Sphagnum* itself (van Breeman, 1995).

Sphagnum shoot growth can exceed 10 cm yr^{-1} in pools, but is typically 1–5 cm yr^{-1} in hummocks. Vascular plants growing with *Sphagnum* in peat-forming systems must, therefore, match this growth to avoid being smothered. The growth form of sundew (*Drosera rotundifolia*), for example, comprises a vertical stem and a series of leaf rosettes; stem growth keeps pace with that of *Sphagnum*, but at the expense of successive leaf rosettes, which are abandoned within the *Sphagnum* moss as they become smothered (Figure 7.6). By adopting strategies such as this, vascular plants can maintain their presence in *Sphagnum* bogs. In turn, they have little detrimental effect upon *Sphagnum* itself, although its growth will be suppressed by shading and particularly by accumulation of above-ground litter. The competitive advantage held by *Sphagnum* does, however, require maintenance of the high water table. Drought conditions will benefit vascular plants, which have effective root systems for gaining water. Paradoxically, those with shallow roots, including *Drosera*, rely on the water-conducting capacity of *Sphagnum* for their water supply, so will also suffer under drought conditions (Malmer *et al.*, 1994).

A *Sphagnum* bog consists of raised hummocks, above the water table and often relatively dry, hollows which are permanently waterlogged or even flooded, and flat lawns. Although up to 10 different species of *Sphagnum* may coexist in a single mire, most are confined to a narrow vertical range and can be identified as 'hummock species' (e.g. *S. rubellum* and *S. fuscum*) and hollow species (e.g. *S. balticum* and *S. tenellum*), with a range of species from both groups occupying lawns. Within this division, there is often further, more subtle zonation, in which, for example, *S. fuscum* may occupy the upper part of hummocks and *S. rubellum* the lower part.

Hummock species take advantage of their high capillarity, greater tolerance of low nutrient levels and more stable dead tissue to grow above the open water level and form hummocks, the upper limit for each species being set by its physiological tolerance of an increasingly drier environment and reduced nutrient levels. The determinants of the lower limits to each species are, however, much less clear; transplantation experiments have demonstrated that it is not simply a case of hollow species being more competitive, as hummock species, when transplanted to hollows, have persisted and even thrived. How so many species can coexist when several apparently occupy each niche without any apparent habitat differentiation is also a mystery (Rydin, 1993).

The hummock pool sequence is very effective at reducing runoff and therefore retaining the water table at a level advantageous to *Sphagnum*. The hummocks, however, are more oxygenated and therefore suitable for vascular plant species. So they support the growth of bog shrubs, such as heather (*Calluna vulgaris*) and even trees (van Breeman, 1995). Ironically, the roots of vascular plants form a firm matrix which supports the spongy *Sphagnum*; without this matrix, there is a danger that hummocks would collapse (Malmer *et al.*, 1994). The *Sphagnum*, therefore, relies upon vascular plants to maintain the high water table which gives it the competitive edge over these same plants.

7.6   Succession and change

Wetlands are very dynamic systems, in which patterns of succession and seasonal cyclical change are more marked than in any other aquatic habitat type.

7.6a   ORIGIN OF AQUATIC MARGINAL WETLANDS

The creation of freshwater flood wetlands is enhanced by the sediment-carrying properties of rivers. When a river floods and spreads across its floodplain, the reduced water velocity lowers its sediment-carrying abilities and it deposits material that it is carrying. Coarse materials, requiring the most energy to keep in suspension, tend to be dropped first, close to the edge of the channel, creating a barrier, or levée, which effectively raises the height of the channel rim. The effects of a levée are two-fold: it reduces the number of times a river will spill over onto its floodplain, increasing the seasonal nature of flooding, but at the same time it impedes drainage, so that the wetted area will remain waterlogged for a long period after the flood has subsided.

7.6b   DEVELOPMENT OF MIRES

Fens are created in areas where open water accumulates, including depressions in bedrock or glacial drift. A fen may develop directly as such, but typically is the result of infilling a lake or even a semi-enclosed arm of the sea, evolving, therefore, from an aquatic marginal wetland. The process of vegetation growth will lead to infilling of the aquatic component of the wetland and gradual terrestrialisation through a series of successional stages, each supporting distinctive plant assemblages.

Fen development from a lake

The various stages of the infilling of a lake, known as hydroseres, are illustrated in Figures 7.7 and 7.8. Infilling proceeds from the edge of the lake (Figure 7.7a); submerged macrophytes grow in the littoral zone, producing detritus and facilitating sedimentation by trapping and retaining silt

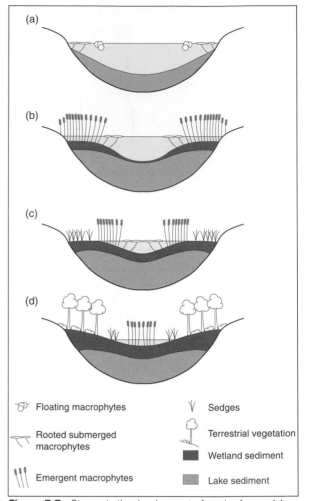

Figure 7.7   Stages in the development of a mire from a lake. See text for more details. (a) Open water with floating macrophytes. (b) Encroachment by emergent vegetation. (c) Infilling with *Carex* fen. (d) Encroachment by terrestrial vegetation.

within their roots and rhizomes. When the water is shallow enough, emergent species, such as *Phragmites*, which can establish in water up to 1 m deep, will invade, often forming large stands (Figures 7.7b, 7.8a). These are very productive, producing large quantities of detritus which accelerate deposition even further until, as sedimentation rises above the water table, species typical of fens, such as sedges, begin to encroach (Figure 7.7c). At this stage, the sediment, although waterlogged, is not generally immersed (Figure 7.8b). Sedge peat will begin to accumulate, mark-

Figure 7.8 Stages in the creation of a fen from a shallow lake. (a) A shallow lake, showing encroachment by emergent macrophytes (Decoy Lake, Orielton, Wales). (*Photo by M. Dobson*) (b) A fen on the site of an infilled lake (Tullanavert, Northern Ireland). (*Photo by M. Dobson*)

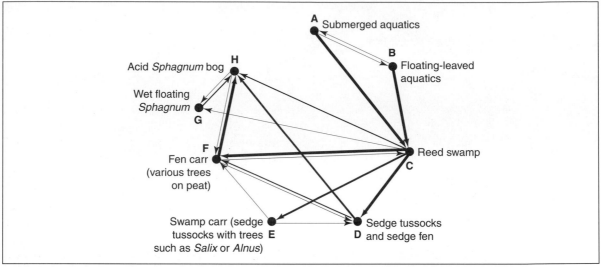

Figure 7.9 Successional stages which have occurred in lake hydroseres in the British Isles, as determined by analysis of peat cores. Arrows indicate direction of change, the width of each arrow being proportional to the number of times this change has been identified. In most cases, the sequence terminates with acid *Sphagnum* bog (modified from Chapman & Reiss, 1992; after Walker, 1970).

ing the transition of the wetland from a fringe wetland to a fen. Once the fen has developed, wetland trees such as willow and alder will establish, increasing detritus inputs and, at the same time, lowering the water table through elevated rates of transpiration. The former wetland, therefore, becomes a fully terrestrial environment (Figure 7.7d).

This sequence of hydroseres, in which each facilitates development of the next by modifying sediment levels, would appear to be the most likely course that wetland succession should take, but, in reality, the successional process is much more complex. Walker (1970) found a range of different sequences from a series of British peat cores, demonstrating that the pattern illustrated in Figure 7.7 is by no means the same in different sites. It may be predicted that the inevitable conclusion of wetland succession is fully terrestrial vegetation, but this scenario, though widely quoted, is not borne out by the evidence. The initial stage, in which reedswamp develops from submerged or aquatic macrophytes, occurs commonly, but reedswamp, in turn, can be replaced by open sedge fen, carr woodland (formed by wetland-tolerant trees growing directly on peat) or *Sphagnum* bog. A series of successional pathways

can be identified, but almost all culminate in *Sphagnum* bog (Figure 7.9), to the extent that Walker (1970) concluded that the true climax of hydroseres in the British Isles is not terrestrial woodland but ombrogenous *Sphagnum* bog.

Bog development

Bogs will form where precipitation exceeds evaporation and drainage is very slow. Establishment of *Sphagnum* further impedes drainage; *Sphagnum* lacks internal water conducting tissues, so draws water by external capillary action through spaces formed as its branches hang against its stem. *Sphagnum* grows in sponge-like aggregations which hold large volumes of water, such that up to 98% of a living *Sphagnum* carpet can be water (van Breeman, 1995). It has no roots and grows from the top, new growth continually shading and killing older parts (Clymo, 1987). The dead tissues collapse and become compacted into a water-saturated, poorly permeable mass, the catotelm, covered by the living layer, the acrotelm, up to 40 cm thick and very permeable. As the moss continues to grow, the bog adds more organic matter to the catotelm, allowing it to rise above the surrounding land and, in turn, raising

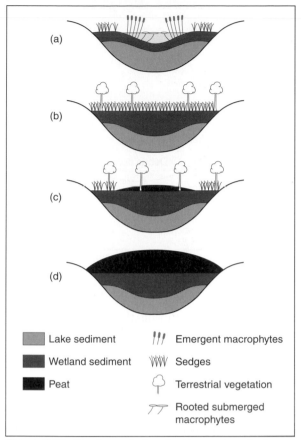

Figure 7.10 Development of a raised bog on top of a fen. See text for more details. (a) Fen encroachment and sedimentation. (b) A mature fen. (c) *Sphagnum* encroachment across the fen.(d) A raised *Sphagnum* peat bog.

Legend:
- Lake sediment
- Wetland sediment
- Peat
- Emergent macrophytes
- Sedges
- Terrestrial vegetation
- Rooted submerged macrophytes

the water table with it. Such raised bogs typically develop over the top of fens, a rheotrophic mire being replaced, through the action of *Sphagnum*, by an ombrotrophic mire. The sequence is illustrated in Figure 7.10, starting with encroachment of fen vegetation in a rapidly infilling basin (Figure 7.10a). Eventually the fen completely dominates the basin (Figure 7.10b). The water table is high, allowing patches of *Sphagnum* to establish. These patches expand and coalesce and *Sphagnum* expands across the fen (Figure 7.10c). As the *Sphagnum* continues to grow, it develops a catotelm, which remains saturated, raising the water table. This allows the *Sphagnum* to expand upwards, creating a raised bog of *Sphagnum* peat on top of fen peat (Figure 7.10d).

Schwingmoors

Succession in kettle hole lakes may proceed directly to *Sphagnum* dominated bog. Floating macrophytes which grow outwards from the bank, such as leatherleaf (*Chamaedaphne calyculata*) in northeast North America, are important in this succession as they provide a substrate upon which *Sphagnum* and various sedges can become established. The peat produced from the partial decomposition of these species is slightly buoyant, creating a mat of peat which floats, albeit mainly below the surface. Organic debris which erodes from the mat, along with planktonic and inorganic debris from the pelagic zone, form a distinct layer of debris peat (Figure 7.11a). Thus kettle hole bogs contain two horizontal layers, the debris peat and the mat peat layer, with remains of leatherleaf in between. The mat peat can be further subdivided into three vertical zones (Figure 7.11a). The outer edge is a zone of thickening of the floating mat, as more organic detritus is deposited, pushing the mat deeper into the water. When it becomes so deep that it comes into contact with the debris peat, further thickening cannot occur, so addition of new peat at the surface results in compaction. Closest to the shore is peat at its maximum density; no further compaction can occur and a zone of equilibrium is produced, in which organic matter addition is matched by decomposition at the surface (Kratz & DeWitt, 1986). Peat encroachment will eventually cover the open water and may overtop the lake centre, leaving a lens of water trapped within the centre of the fen (Figure 7.11b), creating a quaking bog (so-called because the lens of water allows it to move underfoot) or schwingmoor. When the open water is completely covered, the water table is able to rise and *Sphagnum* growth extends upwards, creating a raised bog.

Blanket bogs

Cool, constantly wet climates, in combination with impermeable rocks, allow the development of blanket bogs. Again, *Sphagnum* is the controlling influence, but these are not confined to previously flooded areas, but develop on and spread over flat or gently sloping ground. Blanket

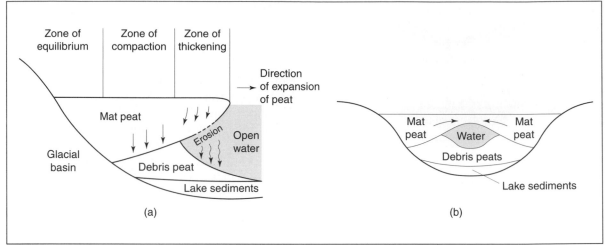

Figure 7.11 (a) Bog encroachment on a kettle hole lake. See text for more details (after Kratz & DeWitt, 1986). (b) A schwingmoor. The mat peat encroachment from either side has merged in the centre, trapping a lens of water.

bogs are features of temperate zones subjected to an oceanic climate, particularly in northwest Europe, and are typical of much of the north and west of the British Isles, where they can extend over large areas. The Flow Country of northern Scotland, for example, is a more or less continuous expanse covering nearly 4000 km² (Ratcliffe & Oswald, 1988).

7.6c ARRESTED SUCCESSIONAL COMMUNITIES

Fringe wetlands along rivers rarely pass beyond an early successional stage, because floods flush out accumulated silt and detritus. Similarly, flood waters moving rapidly over flood wetlands shift sediment around and break down vegetation. Rivers in areas flat enough to develop aquatic marginal wetlands will also tend to change their course frequently, either by gradual erosion or catastrophically in flash floods, unless artificially constrained, and will cut through wetland areas. For these reasons, wetlands along river floodplains can be very heterogeneous, but rarely progress to terrestrial or mire stages. If flood waters rise slowly with little kinetic energy, then physical changes are less likely to occur; encroachment by terrestrial species will be suppressed but other successional processes are unaffected. Succession will remain in an arrested state, however, if the dry season allows the mineralisation of organic layers

that have built up during the flood. If a river's ability to flood is curtailed, by damming or embanking, then terrestrial vegetation will quickly dominate, because the wetland has been cut off from its supply of water.

Fringing marine wetlands may go through cyclical changes in which succession proceeds to a given stage and then is reset by storm activity. Dry land stages will only be reached rapidly if the wetland is actively expanding, for example through rapid siltation.

Cyclical succession in Sphagnum *bogs*

A well established theory associated with ombrotrophic *Sphagnum* mires is the regeneration cycle, a cyclical succession which occurs in the hummock–hollow complex of these environments. The regeneration cycle hypothesis can be summarised as follows: as hummocks develop, they rise above the water table until they are dry enough to support terrestrial species (such as *Calluna*) which produce very little peat, so the hummock ceases to rise and may begin to erode. Within hollows, meanwhile, constant waterlogging ensures deposition of large amounts of peat, so that the hollows infill. Eventually, the hollows will reach the level of former hummocks, which become waterlogged and themselves are converted into hollows; the former hollows, which continue to grow, become hummocks. In due course, these new hummocks will dry out and cease to grow, while the new hollows will infill with peat. By constant repetition of this cycle, a single point will, alternately, be occupied by hummock and hollow. This hypothesis is intuitively very appealing, as it describes an apparently logical progression of bog development, and has been widely presented as an established truth. Unfortunately, as Backéus (1990) points out, there is no evidence for its occurrence and, in all probability, the regeneration cycle does not occur.

7.6d HUMAN INFLUENCE ON SUCCESSION

The raised bog illustrated in Figure 7.10 may be an end point in itself, but, if precipitation is very high and evaporation very low, then expansion into a blanket bog extending over the surrounding land is a possible outcome. Blanket bogs expanded over much of the British Isles and Norway around 5000 BP, at a time of climatic deterioration into cooler, wetter conditions. This, in itself, may have been enough to trigger their development, but the role of human activity in this bog expansion is also implicated (Moore, 1993). Areas that are climatically susceptible to blanket bog expansion may remain dry if there is adequate tree cover; removing trees reduces transpiration losses and interception of rainfall, leading to increased groundwater levels and waterlogging, which favours development of *Sphagnum*. The expansion of blanket bogs in northwest Europe, most of which cover formerly forested areas, was probably enhanced by human activity, cutting and burning tree cover, particularly in areas marginal for blanket mire formation but where trees were under climatic stress.

Attempts at conservation of wetlands can activate successional processes. At the head of the Bay of Fundy in New Brunswick is a series of wetlands which have been contained within embankments, stabilising water levels, in order to create open water habitats for waterfowl. Whereas these wetlands would formerly have dried out for short periods during the summer, allowing decomposition of organic matter and remineralisation of nutrients, this can no longer occur where embankments impede drainage. In one such im-

poundment, Hog Lake, raised water levels since embankments were constructed in 1973 have led to domination by *Typha* × *glauca*, which forms floating mats consisting almost exclusively of this single species. Where these mats form, they insulate the water beneath from summer warming, reducing decomposition rates and nutrient release even further. This, is turn, leads to lower *Typha* vigour and invasion of mats by *Sphagnum*. It is likely that, in due course, *Sphagnum*, which acidifies the water and further suppresses *Typha*, will dominate (Krüsi & Wein, 1988).

7.6e SEASONAL CHANGES IN WETLANDS

Seasonality is a feature of many wetlands, particularly freshwater flood wetlands, whose flooding will be related to seasonal patterns of rainfall. This, in turn, results in seasonal patterns of abundance among wetland organisms. Both terrestrial and aquatic assemblages may occupy the same site, the community changing rapidly in response to water levels.

The vertebrate cycle

Spatial variations in topography enhance diversity, as do temporal changes in water level, particularly in seasonal flood plains where different stages in the flood–drainage cycle favour different groups of species. The movement in and out of floodplain wetlands by river fish has been considered in **Section 2.7c**, but similar migrations occur among terrestrial and semi-aquatic groups. The vertebrate cycle of an idealised north temperate wetland illustrates this well. During high water levels in the winter, the wetland is dominated by aquatic birds, most of which are wintering species which migrate to breeding grounds further north in the spring. As the water level recedes, aquatic species are confined to ever smaller areas but terrestrial grazers and, later, fruit and seed-eating species move in, exploiting the high productivity. When water levels rise once more, aquatic species return. In contrast, terrestrial birds may enter reedbeds in large numbers during migration or in search of food during winter (Doborowski *et al.*, 1993). Floodplain wetlands are not simply the haunt, however, of river or terrestrial species

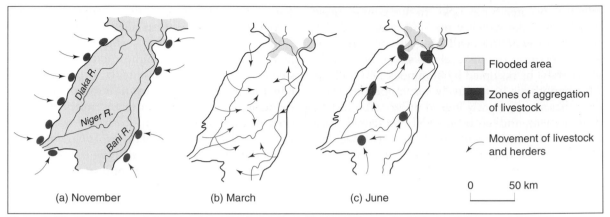

Figure 7.12 The human exploitation cycle: pastoral migration in the Inner Niger Delta. (a) During October and November, herdsmen assemble their cattle along the edges of the floodplain; (b) by March, herds have dispersed across the floodplain, following the receding water; (c) in June, herds reassemble around remaining water holes, ready to move to higher ground as flood waters rise (after Gallais, 1984).

which move in when conditions are appropriate. There are also true wetland species, adapted to cope with the seasonally changing conditions. Examples are amphibians, such as frogs, which require pools of water during the spring for larval development but become more terrestrial as adults, seeking out open water once more in the autumn as a site for hibernation. An alternative strategy, exemplified by the lungfish of tropical Africa and South America, is to spend the dry season in a dormant state, known as aestivation, buried in the ground awaiting the return of the floods. Lungfish are also able to exploit the permanently anoxic waters of the interior of large fringing wetlands (Chapman *et al.*, 1996).

Wetlands of the southeastern USA flood during spring and early summer, leading to a contrasting cycle in which detritus-based food chains predominate during the growing season, when primary production is high, while herbivore pathways dominate over winter, when primary production is low. This is because herbivorous mammals such as deer and rodents are driven away by rising water levels, leaving only specialist semi-aquatic species, such as muskrat (*Ondatra zibethica*); herbivorous birds either migrate to northern breeding grounds or, if resident, shift their diet to take advantage of large numbers of emerging insects. During the summer, therefore, the flooded wetlands are dominated by fish and amphibians, along with aquatic invertebrates, most of which are detritivores or predators, and it is only during the autumn, when water levels recede and, coincidentally, primary production declines, that herbivorous mammals can invade (Harris, 1988).

The human exploitation cycle

The vertebrate cycle has its parallels in human exploitation of wetlands. The Inner Niger Delta in Mali supports 2–3 million head of livestock, which move, along with their human guardians, in an annual cycle dictated by flood water (Figure 7.12). During the rainy season from August to October, the delta is flooded and livestock are grazed on the surrounding higher ground. In October and November they gather around the edge of the delta, ready to move into the newly exposed pasture as the floods recede. At first, they range widely but, as the dry season progresses, they aggregate around permanent water holes and channels, before moving out to higher ground once more as floods return in July (Williams, 1990). In a further analogy to the vertebrate cycle, as the livestock and human pastoralists move out, the fish – and the people who fish for them – return (Welcomme, 1989; Laë, 1995).

Sedentary agriculturalists, too, can exploit the predictability of the seasonal flood. Seasonal floodplains receive an annual input of generally nutrient-rich sediment and, when the soil aerates, can be very fertile. This fertility can be exploited by growing crops during the dry season. Managing the flood water using drainage channels and sluices in levées, to hasten its removal, is a long-established and effective system, and has been practised along the Lower River Nile in Egypt, for example, for thousands of years. Water meadows are a consequence of this technique. The flooding ensures that they are naturally fertilised every year, so they can be very productive and heavily grazed over summer. The result is fertile, botanically rich meadows, with waterlogged drainage ditches supporting a great variety of wildlife, and the value of water meadows to conservation in areas heavily modified by human activity is well understood (Purseglove, 1988).

7.6f SPECIES DIVERSITY

Species diversity in wetlands is determined to a large extent by succession and seasonal change, both of which allow a wide range of species assemblages to coexist in close proximity. Some wetland types can be species-poor, good examples being the large tracts of swamp dominated by a single species, such as reed (*Phragmites australis*) or papyrus (*Cyperus papyrus*), lacking ground vegetation because they are permanently inundated, and impeding submerged vegetation through shading and the large volume of decomposing detritus. A feature of wetland areas, however, is that so often several different habitat types, each with its representative species, are mixed together in a small area. The precise adaptations of different wetland plants to specific degrees of waterlogging contribute to this high species diversity, with very small changes in topography across a small area allowing different species assemblages to coexist (Figure 7.5). The river in Figure 7.1a, for example, has an open water habitat, a fringing wetland, a normally dry levée and a flood wetland, all within a few metres of each other.

Just as the water table produces spatial patterns in wetland biota, so any fluctuations will create temporal patterns. The seasonal changes described in **Section 7.6e** illustrate this well: during any one season, vertebrate species diversity may be low, but when all seasons are considered together, diversity is enhanced by seasonal turnover of species.

7.7 Wetland extent and loss

7.7a EXTENT OF WETLANDS

Calculation of the worldwide extent of wetlands is difficult because they are very scattered and definitions are often hard to apply. Wetlands do not form a discrete biome, so their extent cannot be estimated by delineating an appropriate climatic type. A reasonable estimate would be that wetlands cover about 6% of the Earth's land surface, or around 8.5 million km^2, of which coastal wetlands account for about a quarter of the total area (Williams, 1990). Freshwater wetlands are, however, very unevenly distributed. Their greatest extent is in two climatic zones – the boreal and tundra of the Northern Hemisphere, and more fragmented, but still sizeable, patches in equatorial regions (Figure 7.13a). Aselmann and Crutzen (1989) estimated that approximately half of all natural freshwater wetlands are in an almost continuous expanse of mire across Canada, Alaska and Russia, and a further quarter is aquatic marginal vegetation associated with rivers and floodplains in the Amazon region of South America, these areas accounting for the two peaks of distribution in Figure 7.13a. Outside these regions, wetlands are generally small and scattered. There are exceptions, such as the Florida Everglades in the USA and the Okavango in Botswana, but more typical are those on narrow river floodplains, or small, discrete wetlands in glacial hollows, such as the prairie pothole region of the north-central USA or the border region of Northern Ireland.

To the area covered by natural wetlands must be added cultivated rice paddies, which cover a further 1.3 million km^2, almost 90% of which is in southeast Asia. The distribution of natural wetlands shows a marked trough in northern subtropical latitudes (Figure 7.13a); to a large extent this is expected, because this marks an arid climatic zone, but it is also the latitudinal region with the greatest concentration of rice paddies

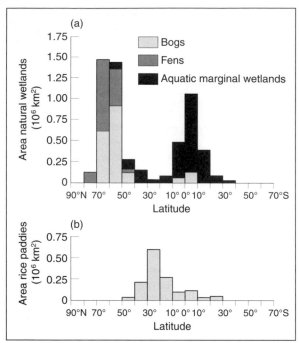

Figure 7.13 Distribution of wetlands by latitude: (a) natural wetlands; (b) rice paddies (from Aselmann & Crutzen, 1989).

(Figure 7.13b), many of which are former natural wetland areas which have been converted to cultivation.

Coastal wetlands, in contrast to freshwater wetlands, show a relatively even distribution around the world's coasts (Chapman, 1977), although saltmarshes are confined to temperate regions and mangals to the tropics, with very few areas of overlap. This distribution is related to climate: mangroves, some species of which grow in excess of 10 m high, easily outcompete saltmarsh plants by overshading, but are very sensitive to frost. In Florida, one of the few places where both wetland types coexist, black mangrove (*Avicennia nitida*) is normally dominant, but is occasionally killed by frost, allowing saltmarsh species to flourish until it recovers (Reimold, 1977).

7.7b WETLAND LOSS

Calculation of the extent of wetlands is further compounded by the scale of their loss, particularly in Europe, North America and southeast Asia. One of the most infamous of the world's lost wet-

lands is the East Anglian Fenland of eastern England, reduced from 3380 km² during the 17th century to around 10 km² today. The USA has had its area of wetland cover reduced from maybe 900 000 km² in the 16th century to around 400 000 km² today, but losses have been unevenly distributed, California and Ohio having lost 91 and 90%, respectively, of their original wetland cover (Anderson, 1996). Such losses occur through active destruction, particularly to create agricultural land, but also indirectly by lowering the water table. The Coto Doñana in southern Spain is one of Europe's largest wetlands, and is protected as a National Park and a series of Natural Areas acting as buffers to development, but extraction of groundwater in the surrounding region has reduced its supply to the extent that its persistence as a wetland is under severe threat.

Natural successional processes lead to the loss of many wetlands to terrestrial environments, but these are countered by creation of new wetlands, particularly along coasts and river floodplains. The process of destruction has, however, been accelerated throughout the world by drainage and reclamation, while, at the same time, natural wetland creation processes are being impeded. As more rivers are impounded and coasts walled, so fewer new wetlands will be created to replace the losses.

7.7c THE VALUE OF WETLANDS

Quite apart from their intrinsic value as high diversity environments, wetlands provide much of benefit to human societies. Their potential role in improving water quality has been considered in **Section 7.3c**, and further benefits are outlined below.

Hydrological benefits

Wetlands associated with rivers reduce storm flows by absorbing excess surface water and releasing it slowly. In this way, flooding is localised in an environment adapted to high water tables, and the potentially damaging effects of floods further downstream are reduced. Removal of wetlands into which excess water can drain, therefore, increases the frequency and mag-

Table 7.2 Change in peak river discharge and number of floods along the Comite River, Louisiana, following wetland loss around Baton Rouge

	Percent change in peak river discharge	Number of annual floods		
	1960s vs 1970s	1951–60	1961–70	1971–78
Upstream of Baton Rouge	−2	2.4	2.6	2.6
Downstream of Baton Rouge	+23	3.8	3.9	5.3

Source: after Stone et al. (1982)

nitude of floods. Table 7.2 shows the effect of increased urbanisation and expansion of agricultural land around Baton Rouge, Louisiana, as wetlands and wet forest have been lost. The total volume of water passing along the Comite River, which drains this area, had not changed, but, as wetland sinks were lost, it became more prone to spates, its water passing through in flushes rather than being stored and released gradually (Stone *et al.*, 1982). In the early 1970s, a series of options was considered for providing flood protection along the lower Charles River, near Boston, Massachusetts: construction of a reservoir capable of holding 68 million m³ of water; extensive embankment of the river or of sensitive areas in the catchment; or protection of 3440 ha of wetlands. The purchase and protection of wetlands was eventually concluded to be an adequate flood control measure, and significantly less expensive than the other options (Wilen & Tiner, 1995).

Wetlands may also be important in recharging aquifers. In southern Florida, for example, the Everglades wetland system overlies a large expanse of porous limestone, the Biscayne aquifer, into which much of the water seeps. The area is very low-lying and channelisation and drainage during the 20th century have disrupted this recharge, allowing intrusion of saline water from the sea, a process compounded by heavy extraction from the aquifer for domestic supply (Wilen & Tiner, 1995).

Saltmarshes play a valuable role in coastal protection, dissipating the energy from storm surges and thereby reducing the requirement for expensive artificial flood defence structures. Saltmarshes are accreting environments, the vegetation slowing water flow over the marsh so that the sediment burden of the incoming tidal waters is deposited. This often leads to a marked change in level at the edge of the vegetated marsh compared to the adjacent tidal flats, this 'micro-cliff' and the extensive areas of gently sloping marsh acting to dissipate wave action and so prevent erosion of the coast at the high water mark. Concern has been expressed that increasing sea levels will cause submergence of the marsh and so reduce its ability to provide coastal defence (Doody, 1992) while, in other areas, establishment of new saltmarshes is being actively encouraged, by flooding coastal meadows, in order to provide a coastal defence function (Davidson *et al.*, 1991).

Natural resources in wetlands

The Inner Niger Delta (**Section 7.6e**; Figure 7.12) is but one of many African wetlands which support large numbers of people, dependent upon raising stock on the productive pasture during the dry season and fishing during the flood period (Williams, 1990). Floodplains and fringe wetland margins provide over one-third of the entire freshwater fish catch in Africa and coastal wetlands are extremely important worldwide as spawning grounds and nursery areas for commercially important marine fish and crustaceans. To these benefits must be added the value of wetlands as sources of wood, reed thatch, peat and many other harvestable products.

Wetlands as refugia

The conservation value of wetlands lies in their intrinsic fauna and flora, and also in their role as refugia for species that have been persecuted in more accessible environments. Wetlands around Lake Victoria in East Africa are dominated by papyrus swamps which may represent an important refugium for native fish threatened by the introduced Nile perch (*Lates niloticus*), a situation described further in **Section 6.7c**. *Lates* is inhibited by low oxygen levels and the structural complexity of the fringes of these wetlands. In contrast, many of the threatened native fish species, having evolved on the fringes of Lake Victoria or in isolated satellite lakes, are naturally predisposed to the oxygen concentrations and can take advantage of the structural diversity of the wetland fringe. Losses of native fish species in Lake Victoria are likely to be very high, but some of those believed to be extinct may persist in adjacent wetlands, either as remnants of formerly more widespread populations or species which have shifted their distribution away from the open water in response to heavy predation pressure (Chapman *et al.*, 1996).

7.8 Summary

Wetlands are areas of land defined by a water table which is permanently or frequently high, leading to waterlogged or flooded soils. Aquatic marginal wetlands are created by rivers, lakes and the sea. Mires are fed by groundwater, overland runoff or precipitation.

Wetlands are characterised by anoxic soils, which often contain toxic chemicals and support bacterial activity which removes nitrates. Aquatic marginal wetlands have nutrient supplies replenished from the parent water body and, if seasonally dry, through decomposition, whereas permanently flooded mires may be nutrient poor.

Wetland plants generally have very specific tolerances to environmental conditions, leading to marked vertical zonation over very small elevational ranges. Their precise requirements ensure that they are very sensitive to fluctuations in water level. *Sphagnum* moss can, however, control the water table to its own advantage, creating mires which often cover large areas. Few vascular plants possess the adaptations required to persist in *Sphagnum* mires.

Seasonally flooded wetlands ('flood wetlands') and those on the edge of open water bodies ('fringe wetlands') are among the most productive environments on Earth, whereas rain-fed mires have very low productivity, but even slow decomposition in the waterlogged conditions leads to a buildup of partially decomposed plant remains – peat.

Grazing is relatively uncommon, although many wetlands are grazed by large aquatic or semi-aquatic mammals. Most primary production is consumed as detritus.

Groundwater fed mires normally develop from infilling a lake or an arm of the sea. There is a clear successional sequence, the end point of which is often *Sphagnum* mire.

Wetland diversity is enhanced by seasonal changes, particularly in those which are seasonally flooded and therefore support terrestrial and aquatic organisms at different times of the year. Human exploitation of wetlands is often seasonal, including grazing livestock on rich pasture during the dry season and fishing during the wet season.

Wetlands absorb excess nutrients and flood water, as well as being a valuable source of natural resources. Losses, particularly to agriculture, have been extensive.

8

The Aquatic System

8.1 Introduction

Aquatic systems are extremely diverse and divisible into a large number of distinguishable types, although the divisions are often across artificial boundaries, the mobility and physical properties of water ensuring much overlap among the various aquatic habitats. There are, of course, differences, recognition of which, as has been carried out here in **Chapters 2** to **7**, is useful, if only for reasons of practicality, but these differences should not be allowed to overshadow their similarities – all are strongly interconnected and generally merge into each other. The fringing wetland dominated by emergent vegetation may look very different to the adjacent open water body but, as Figure 7.8a shows, each merges into the other and, over time, one may become the other (**Section 7.6b**).

Similarities of function and intimate linkages justify the recognition that aquatic habitats together form a single aquatic system, an ecological unit analogous to the physical interactions of the single hydrological cycle. This chapter explores the extensive and intimate linkage between different types of aquatic systems and between geographically separate areas in more detail and then, briefly, considers human exploitation of aquatic communities as an ecological process in its own right.

8.2 Interconnections among aquatic systems

Two processes link all the elements of the aquatic environment – the movement of water around the hydrological cycle and the flux of organic matter, particularly in the form of detritus. These links blur the distinctions between the various habitats and provide a major contrast between the energetics of terrestrial and aquatic ecosystems.

8.2a LINKS BETWEEN AQUATIC HABITATS

The vast majority of the world's aquatic systems are strongly interconnected to other such systems. This is particularly clear in inland waters, where rivers, lakes and wetlands form a continuum of habitat types, often extending into estuarine and coastal systems. Wetlands are rarely separable from other water bodies, either being hydrologically fed and maintained by rivers or themselves being the source of open water systems (**Section 7.1**). Wetlands, in turn, are important in providing energy and nutrients to rivers and lakes. Low order rivers rely upon the terrestrial catchment for energy; higher order rivers depend on export from upstream but also on lateral inputs from their floodplains, as emphasised by the River Continuum Concept (**Section 2.7b**) and the Flood Pulse Concept (**Section 2.7c**), respectively.

There are several spectacularly large and deep lakes in the world, but most are relatively shallow, filling low gradient basins which allow the development of extensive fringing wetlands (Wetzel,

1990) and, indeed, the sedimentation and growth associated with wetlands serves to increase the area they cover (**Section 7.6b**). Large lakes may depend mainly upon pelagic primary production (**Section 6.4**), but most lakes are small and/or shallow enough for macrophytes to be the dominant source of production, particularly those with fringe wetlands (**Section 7.1**). The strong interaction between a lake and its wetland fringe is emphasised by the successional process in which wetlands gradually encroach upon and infill lakes (Figure 7.7).

The freshwater system spills out into coastal areas, where inputs from upstream, in combination with coastal wetlands, provide major fluxes of detritus, which are exploited directly (e.g. **Section 3.4b**) or provide nutrients to stimulate autochthonous primary production. The only aquatic system which is completely self-sufficient, albeit the one which accounts for the vast majority of habitable aquatic volume, is the open ocean. Productivity in the ocean is, however, so low that even relatively small amounts of terrestrially or coastally derived plant detritus or nutrients can have an important effect upon local production (**Section 5.6d**). Within the oceans, there is a vertical connection between the upper illuminated layer and the dark layer beneath: the deep ocean relies upon export of excess production from the photic zone which, in turn, can become starved of nutrients in the absence of upwelling from depths.

8.2b DISPERSAL IN AQUATIC ORGANISMS

Ephemeral habitats such as tree hole pools are apparently independent of all other water bodies but they are connected, at least to each other, in that their inhabitants require adaptations for dispersal and therefore provide a biological link. Dispersal ability is an important criterion for inhabitants of several different types of aquatic systems, and is positively correlated with the life span of the habitat. Estuaries, hydrothermal vents, lakes and ponds are all examples of systems whose inhabitants have generally high powers of dispersal and rapid colonisation rates, in response to the relatively short existence of their habitat units (**Sections 3.6, 5.6b** and **6.5d**). In contrast, oceanic and river species are less well adapted to disperse

between habitats, although perfectly able to redistribute themselves within a given habitat. The ocean is effectively a single unit, with much opportunity for faunal exchange, whereas a river system may support a high proportion of endemics. The few lakes currently in existence which have been present for more than a few hundred thousand years often have high endemicity (**Section 6.5d**), in contrast to the extremely low levels in most lakes, and it is probable that the same would occur in any estuary or hydrothermal vent which could persist for an evolutionarily meaningful time scale.

Segregation of life stages

One of the principal differences between aquatic and terrestrial communities is the spatial segregation of the adult and juvenile phases. Most marine organisms have a dispersive larval stage – even fish species generally produce planktonic larvae which drift with the currents. In fresh waters, insects and amphibians are examples of groups with dispersive terrestrial adult stages, while algae and microcrustacea, among others, disperse through the air by means of dormant spore stages (**Section 6.5d**).

Most aquatic populations are, therefore, highly fragmented, with a sessile or low mobility stage occupying one habitat and a more mobile stage exploiting another habitat and set of resources and dispersing in search of new habitats. Populations of the sessile stage can be regarded as a metapopulation of the species, with the dispersal stages providing the route between them.

Such disjunctures in the life history have a number of ecological consequences. The spatial separation of the adults and larvae means they exploit different resources and so are not usually in competition with each other. The timing of breeding may allow synchronisation with a seasonally abundant food supply, such as the spring phytoplankton bloom (**Sections 4.4c** and **6.4b**) or the pulse allochthonous detrital inputs associated with leaf fall (**Section 2.4b**), while the mobile stage allows colonisation of new areas. In a system with a finite life, or in which there are continually renewed resource patches as a result of disturbance (**Sections 2.5c, 4.5a, 4.6b, 5.6a** and **7.6c**), the advantages to seeking a new patch are obvious.

Migration

Migration is a periodic movement to or from a specific breeding area. Vertebrates, in particular, can migrate over long distances, well known examples including movement of eels to the sea to breed (**Section 3.3a**) and calving migrations of whales (**Section 5.5c**).

Wetland birds provide a connection, through migration, between wetland systems, often connecting freshwater and coastal wetlands. In North America, this has been intensively studied with respect to wildfowl, which are a valuable resource for sport hunting. In general, North American wildfowl breed in the north, in the prairie wetlands of the northern USA and southern Canada, but winter in the south, the breeding and wintering areas being linked by four major flyways (Figure 8.1). Not only does this process connect

---

Figure 8.1 Waterfowl which nest in northern North America follow four main flyways to their wintering grounds in the south of the continent: (1) Atlantic coast flyway; (2) Mississippi flyway; (3) Central flyway; (4) Pacific flyway. Along these routes, all wetlands, however small, are potentially important as stopovers. Note that many of the wintering grounds are coastal, while breeding grounds are fresh water.

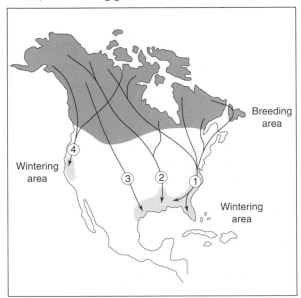

the larger wetland areas of north and south, but along each flyway, any other wetland, however small, takes on a crucial role as a stopover. In the eastern hemisphere, the situation is probably even more complex, but not so well studied because many more countries are involved. Again, the major breeding grounds are in the tundra areas: Siberia, northern Scandinavia, Iceland, Greenland and even eastern Canada. Wintering grounds are many, but fall into four main regions: the many estuaries and mudflats of coastal northwest Europe, and the fewer, but individually larger, wetlands in the Mediterranean, the Middle East and West Africa.

8.2c ENERGY TRANSFERS

A common feature among aquatic systems is the importance of energy inputs which do not derive directly from photosynthesis. Autochthonous primary production is important only in shallow fresh waters and the upper mixed layer of oceans, while allochthonous inputs dominate all other systems. The importance of detritus is most clear in benthic systems, as pelagic systems are generally supported by phytoplanktonic primary production, but even this distinction is blurred by the pelagic zone of deep oceans and lakes, for which the only energy source is detritus rain from the surface layer. Even in systems with high benthic primary production – wetlands, algae-dominated shores, shallow lake littoral (freshwater terminology) or sublittoral (marine terminology) – most energy passes to consumers as detritus rather than direct grazing.

Detritus transport in the aquatic system

The dependence of the aquatic system upon detritus is enhanced by transport between its various components, most obviously in the sinking of POM from the surface to the deep ocean or the hypolimnion of lakes, and in downstream transport along rivers and out into the estuary or open sea (**Sections 2.7b and 5.4b**). In both cases, detritus undergoes modification as it progresses, much of this through the activity of intermediate consumers (including conditioning), and its nutritional value for macroconsumers is determined by its residence time in the aquatic system.

Detrital transport in low order rivers is mainly from benthos to benthos, with the pelagic phase simply being downstream flushing (although microorganisms living on or in the detrital matter presumably do not distinguish between these states; once established, they will persist whether the detrital particle is on the bed or in the water column). Only in larger rivers does autochthonous planktonic production become important, although, even here, benthos are heavily dependent upon POM transported from upstream. In shallow seas, too, the marine littoral fauna is dominated by sessile benthos dependent upon POM brought in by currents. In lentic and oceanic systems, transport is generally from pelagic production, via deep pelagic consumption, to benthos, where it is finally mineralised. Resuspension does, however, occur (e.g. **Section 5.4b**) and, although much of this will sink to the bed, it is also utilised by pelagic consumers. Consumption by benthic detritivores can generate DOM which provides resources, via the microbial loop, for plankton, while grazing or physical disturbance of macrophytes or epilithic algae adds DOM and nutrients to the pelagic system.

8.3 Human exploitation as an ecological factor

Perhaps one of the clearest demonstrations of the common features shared by aquatic habitats is their response to human exploitation. Human impacts upon the aquatic system are well documented, if poorly explained, and similar human processes can have very similar effects in very different aquatic habitats. Anthropogenic impacts on the aquatic system arise from extraction and addition of materials, the former including impacts arising from harvesting living resources as well as the removal of non-living resources, while additions are usually of waste material, including accidental discharges. Examples of profound changes wrought upon aquatic habitats include physical barriers to water movement (**Sections 2.7e** and **3.7c**), artificial sedimentation (**Section 4.8b**), modification of water chemistry (**Sections 2.3c** and **6.7a**), introduction of alien species (**Section 6.7c**) and complete destruction (**Section 7.7b**).

8.3a ECOLOGICAL EFFECTS OF EXPLOITATION

People have exploited aquatic organisms for food for almost as long as they have exploited terrestrial animals and plants. The history of most fisheries is one of discovery, exploitation until the stock collapses and then switching to a new stock, while the harvesting process, particularly when it has developed technologically, is often equally damaging to the habitat of the target species. This is not just a recent phenomenon: even in classical times, stocks were collapsing due to overexploitation (Desse & Desse-Berset, 1993) and, as early as the 12th century, Edward II of England banned the use of a new trawl from the Thames Estuary because of the devastating effect it was having on the estuarine fishery.

The ecological effects of fishing are most apparent in coastal seas, where some species have been driven to local economic extinction (including cod on the Grand Banks off Newfoundland) or where the physical scars of destructive fishing practices are readily observed (Figure 4.16). Initially the targeted species undergo changes – large individuals become rarer and the size distribution shifts – which leads to a more efficient use of the natural productivity of the species and therefore higher yields. If, however, this encourages greater levels of fishing, then the stock goes into decline and changes in the strength of its interactions with competitors, prey and natural predators introduce further ecosystem effects, particularly the expansion of opportunistic species to exploit under-utilised resources. While the change in stock sizes and population size structure are well documented, our knowledge of ecosystem function is so recent, and exploitation so widespread, that we are unable to say for sure what changes have actually occurred at the ecosystem level (ICES, 1995). It has been suggested that the demise of populations of large demersal fish, such as cod and haddock, in areas like the North Sea (**Box 4.2**) has allowed an increase in populations of smaller, more rapidly reproducing species such as whiting and pout, which are now exploited by industrial fisheries. The switch from a fishery providing food for direct human consumption to an industrial fishery has, therefore, been driven by ecosystem changes, arising from exploitation. If this is the case, then it may be an example of the system maintaining its productivity but switching to a different 'stable state', as has been suggested for the Antarctic (**Section 5.7d**). Freshwater fisheries often differ from this pattern in that the decline of a target species will encourage introduction of an exotic species as a replacement, before the system can find an alternative stable state (e.g. **Sections 6.7b** and **6.7c**).

8.3b WASTE DISPOSAL

An old adage of wastewater engineering states that 'the solution to pollution is dilution'. Bodies of water such as lakes and the seas are often seen as providing the necessary dilution while flowing watercourses provide an obvious – and cheap – conduit for waste transport. The range of wastes disposed of into water is immense – heat, sewage, urban wastewater, agricultural wastes, oil, heavy metals, organic toxins, radionuclides and persistent particulates, such as plastics, to name some of the most important. Physical impacts of these inputs include the direct smothering effect of wastes on the benthos, absorption of light, and alterations in the nature of the sediments. Physiological effects include direct toxicity and the effects of altered O_2 saturation, pH, salinity, etc., arising from the presence of the waste.

Ecological effects of waste disposal vary, according to the contaminant added, so that, for example, solid particulate wastes smother the bed at the disposal site, often leading to anoxic conditions (Bamber, 1984) but have little effect further afield, while persistent organohalides and heavy metals accumulate in body tissues over time, and are concentrated as they pass up the food chain from prey to predator. Therefore, concentrations in predators, which may spend only a short time near the disposal site, can be high – leading to mortality or sublethal effects such as reduced reproductive viability. Organic wastes may have sudden, devastating effects, if added at high concentrations, but are less persistent as they can be degraded by microbial activity.

The huge volume of the deep ocean and the capacity for water and biological processes to absorb and deal with a range of pollutants has led to the proposal that discharge into the deep oceans would be an effective means of waste disposal (Angel, 1996). Such decisions should not, however, be made on ecological grounds alone; the deep sea is perhaps the last pristine environment on Earth – so should we fill it with our rubbish?

Ecological impacts of man on aquatic systems are incredibly diverse – the range of species exploited, the different methods used, the variety of wastes discharged, the types of minerals extracted. The spatial extent of mineral extraction operations and of waste disposal makes their effects relatively easy to monitor and quantify: in general, such effects are small scale and transient, recovery eventually occurring after the impact stops. The changes wrought by man as a top predator are more difficult to quantify: human activity has certainly impacted prey populations, but the extent of ecosystem changes resulting from this, and the permanence of such changes, remain to be resolved. The challenge for aquatic ecologists in the future will be to apply the basic ecological principles to aquatic systems so that all human impacts on them can be managed in a sustainable way.

8.4   Summary

All aquatic habitats are interconnected. Even apparently physically isolated water bodies are connected through dispersive abilities of their inhabitants. Dispersal is an important component of aquatic biota, most species having a relatively (or absolutely) sessile or non-mobile life phase and a dispersive life phase. Migration provides another mechanism whereby aquatic organisms connect geographically separate habitats.

It is difficult to identify any fundamental ecological distinctions between aquatic habitats. Any distinctions mask so much overlap in function and interconnection that aquatic habitats should be considered to be a single aquatic system, analogous to the single hydrological cycle.

Human activity acts as an ecological process in most aquatic habitats, exploitation of biological resources and waste disposal into aquatic environments being the major human impacts. Effects of waste disposal and mineral extraction are relatively easy to quantify, whereas long-term effects of exploitation are more difficult to predict.

References

Adams, P. (1990) *Saltmarsh Ecology*. Cambridge University Press, Cambridge.

Allan, J.D. (1995) *Stream Ecology. Structure and Function of Running Waters*. Chapman and Hall, London.

Allison, P.A., C.R. Smith & H. Kukert (1991) Deep water taphonomy of a vertebrate carcass: a whale skeleton in the bathyal Santa Catalina Basin. *Paleobiology*, **17**, 78–89.

Ambrose, W.G. (1984a) Role of predatory infauna in structuring marine soft-bottom communities. *Marine Ecology Progress Series*, **17**, 109–115.

Ambrose, W.G. (1984b) Influence of residents on the development of a marine soft-bottom community. *Journal of Marine Research*, **42**, 633–654.

Anderson, I. (1996) World's wetlands sucked dry. *New Scientist*, 30 March, 9.

Angel, M.V. (1991) Variations in time and space: is biogeography relevant to studies of long time-scale change? *Journal of the Marine Biological Association of the UK*, **71**, 191–206.

Angel, M.V. (1994) Patterns in marine pelagic systems. In Giller, P.S., A.G. Hildrew & D.G. Raffaelli (eds) *Aquatic Ecology. Scale, Pattern and Process*. 34th Symposium of the British Ecological Society, pp. 403–439. Blackwell Science, Oxford.

Angel, M.V. (1996) Waste disposal in the deep ocean. In Summerhayes, C.P. & S.A. Thorpe (eds) *Oceanography: an Illustrated Guide*, pp. 338–345. Manson, London.

Aselmann, I. & P.J. Crutzen (1989) Global distribution of natural freshwater wetlands and rice paddies, their net primary productivity, seasonality, and possible methane emissions. *Journal of Atmospheric Chemistry*, **8**, 307–358.

Attrill, M.J., P.M. Ramsay, R.M. Thomas & M.W. Trett (1996) An estuarine biodiversity hot-spot. *Journal of the Marine Biological Association of the UK*, **76**, 161–175.

Attrill, M.J. & R.M. Thomas (1996) Long term distribution patterns of mobile estuarine invertebrates (Ctenophora, Cnidaria, Crustacea: Decapoda) in relation to hydrological parameters. *Marine Ecology Progress Series*, **143**, 25–36.

Azam, F., T. Fenchel, J.G. Field, J.S. Gray, L.A. Meyerreil & F. Thingstad (1983) The ecological role of water-column microbes in the sea. *Marine Ecology Progress Series*, **10**, 257–263

Backéus, I. (1990) The cyclic regeneration on bogs – a hypothesis that became an established truth. *Striae*, **31**, 33–35.

Badri, A., J. Giudicelli & G. Prévot (1987) Effets d'une crue sur la communauté d'invertébrés benthiques d'une rivière méditerranéenne, Le Rdat (Maroc). *Acta Oecologia, oecologia generalis*, **8**, 481–500.

Baird, D., P.R. Evans, H. Milne & M.W. Pienowski (1985) Utilization by shorebirds of benthic invertebrate production in intertidal areas. *Oceanography and Marine Biology, an Annual Review*, **23**, 573–597.

Balls, H., B. Moss & K. Irvine (1989) The loss of submerged plants with eutrophication. I. Experimental design, water chemistry, aquatic plant and phytoplankton biomass in experiments carried out in Norfolk Broadland. *Freshwater Biology*, **22**, 71–87.

Bamber, R.N. (1984) The benthos of a marine fly-ash dumping ground. *Journal of the Marine Biological Association of the UK*, **64**, 211–226.

Barnes, H. & S.M. Marshall (1951) On the variability of replicate plankton samples and some application of 'contagious' series to the statistical distribution of catches over restricted periods. *Journal of the Marine Biological Association of the UK*, **30**, 233–263.

Barr, R., P.G. Watson, C.R. Ashcroft, B.E. Barnett & C. Hilton (1990) Humber Estuary – a case study. *Hydrobiologia*, **195**, 127–143.

Barry, M.J. & I.A.E. Bayley (1985) Further studies on predator induction of crests in Australian *Daphnia* and the effects of crests on predation. *Australian Journal of Marine and Freshwater Research*, **36**, 519–539.

Bénech, V. & M. Peñáz (1995) An outline on lateral fish migrations within the Central Delta of the Niger River, Mali. *Hydrobiologia*, **303**, 149–157.

Bergman, M.J.N. & M. Hup (1992) Direct effects of beam trawling on macrofauna in a sandy sediment in the southern North Sea. *ICES Journal of Marine Science*, **49**, 5–11.

Berner, E.K. & R.A. Berner (1987) *The Global Water Cycle*. Prentice-Hall, Englewood Cliffs, New Jersey.

Berrie, A.D. (1976) Detritus, micro-organisms and animals in fresh water. In Anderson, J.M. & A. Macfadyen (eds) *The Role of Terrestrial and Aquatic Organisms in Decomposition Processes*. 17th Symposium of the British Ecological Society, pp. 323–338. Blackwell, Oxford.

Berrie, A.D. (1992) The chalk-stream environment. *Hydrobiologia*, **248**, 3–9.

Beukema, J.J. (1992) Expected changes in the Wadden Sea benthos in a warmer world – lessons from periods with mild winters. *Netherlands Journal of Sea Research*, **30**, 73–79.

Bilby, R.E. & G.E. Likens (1980) Importance of organic debris dams in the structure and function of stream ecosystems. *Ecology*, **61**, 1107–1113.

Blom, C.W.P.M. & L.A.C.J. Voesenek (1996) Flooding: the survival strategies of plants. *Trends in Ecology and Evolution*, **11**, 290–295.

Boar, R.R. & C.E. Crook (1985) Investigations into the causes of reedswamp regression in the Norfolk Broads. *Verhandlungen der Internationale Vereinigung für Theoretische und Angewandte Limnologie*, **22**, 2916–2919.

Bondarenko, N.A., N.E. Guselnikova, N.F. Logacheva & G.V. Pomazkina (1996) Spatial distribution of phytoplankton in Lake Baikal, Spring 1991. *Freshwater Biology*, **35**, 517–523.

Bravard, J.P., A.L. Roux, C. Amoros & J.L. Reygrobellet (1992) The Rhône River: a large alluvial temperate river. In Calow, P. & G.E. Petts (eds) *The Rivers Handbook*, Volume 1, pp. 426–447. Blackwell Science, Oxford.

Brenchley, G.A. (1981) Disturbance and community structure: an experimental study of bioturbation in marine soft-bottom environments. *Journal of Marine Research*, **39**, 767–790.

Brinson, M.M. (1988) Strategies for assessing the cumulative effects of wetland alteration on water quality. *Environmental Management*, **12**, 655–662.

Brittain, J.E. & T.J. Eikeland (1988) Invertebrate drift – a review. *Hydrobiologia*, **166**, 77–93.

Brock, R.H. (1977) Occurrence and variety of fishes in mixo-haline ponds of the Kono, Hawaii, coast. *Copeia*, 1977(1), 134–138.

Buchanan, J.B. (1993) Evidence of benthic pelagic coupling at a station off the Northumberland coast. *Journal of Experimental Marine Biology and Ecology*, **72**, 1–10.

Burgis, M.J. & P. Morris (1987) *The Natural History of Lakes*. Cambridge University Press, Cambridge.

Cadée, G.C. (1990) Feeding traces and bioturbation by birds on a tidal flat, Dutch Wadden Sea. *Ichnos* 30, 173–180.

Cameron, W.M. & D.W. Pritchard (1963) Estuaries. In Hill, M.N. (ed.) *The Sea*, Volume 2, pp. 306–324. John Wiley & Sons, New York.

Canfield, D.E., J.V. Shireman, D.E. Cole, W.T. Haller, C.E. Watkins & M.J. Maceina (1984) Prediction of chlorophyll-*a* concentrations in Florida lakes: importance of aquatic macrophytes. *Canadian Journal of Fisheries and Aquatic Sciences*, **41**, 497–501.

Carpelan, L.H. (1958) The Salton Sea: physical and chemical characteristics. *Limnology and Oceanography*, **3**, 373–386.

Carpenter, E.J. & R.R.L. Guillard (1971) Intraspecific differences in nitrate half-saturation constants for three species of marine phytoplankton. *Ecology*, **52**, 183–185.

Carpenter, S.R., J.F. Kitchell & J.R. Hodgson (1985) Cascading trophic interactions and lake productivity. *Bioscience*, **35**, 634–639.

Carpenter, S.R. & D.M. Lodge (1986) Effects of submerged macrophytes on ecosystem processes. *Aquatic Botany*, **26**, 341–370.

Carrick, H.J., F.J. Aldridge & C.L. Schelske (1993) Wind influences phytoplankton biomass and composition in a shallow, productive lake. *Limnology and Oceanography*, **38**, 1179–1192.

Cassie, R.M. (1959) Micro-distribution of plankton. *New Zealand Journal of Science*, **2**, 398–409.

Cassie, R.M. (1963) Micro-distribution of plankton. *Oceanography and Marine Biology, an Annual Review*, **1**, 223–252.

Chapman, J.L. & M.J. Reiss (1992) *Ecology, Principles and Applications*. Cambridge University Press, Cambridge.

Chapman, L.J., C.A. Chapman & M. Chandler (1996)

Wetland ecotones as refugia for endangered fishes. *Biological Conservation*, 78, 263–270.

Chapman, V.J. (ed.) (1977) *Ecosystems of the World 1. Wet Coastal Ecosystems*. Elsevier, Amsterdam.

Chauvet, E. & A.-M. Jean-Louis (1988) Production de litière de la ripisylve de la Garonne et apport au fleuve. *Acta Oecologia, oecologia generalis*, 3, 265–279.

Chavez, F.P., K.R. Buck, K. Coale, J.H. Martin, G.R. DiTullio, N.A. Welschmeyer, A.C. Jacobsen & R.T. Barber (1991) Growth rates, grazing, sinking, and iron limitation of equatorial Pacific phytoplankton. *Limnology and Oceanography*, 36, 1816–1833.

Cheng, L. (ed.) (1976) *Marine Insects*. North-Holland, Amsterdam.

Cherrill, A.J. & R. James (1987) Character displacement in *Hydrobia*. *Oecologia*, 71, 618–623.

Clark, C.W. & D.A. Levy (1988) Diel vertical migrations by juvenile sockeye salmon and the antipredation window. *American Naturalist*, 131, 271–290.

Clark, R.B. (1997) *Marine Pollution*, 4th edition. Oxford University Press, Oxford.

Clark, S. & A.J. Edwards (1994) The use of artificial reef structures to rehabilitate reef flats degraded by coral mining in the Maldives. *Bulletin of Marine Science*, 55, 726–746.

Clarke, M.R. & J. D. Stevens (1974) Cephalopods, blue sharks and migration. *Journal of the Marine Biological Association of the UK*, 54, 949–957.

Clymo, R.S. (1987) The ecology of peatlands. *Science Progress* (Oxford), 71, 593–614.

Clymo, R.S. & P.M. Hayward (1982) The ecology of *Sphagnum*. In Smith, A.J.E. (ed.) *Bryophyte Ecology*, pp. 229–289. Chapman and Hall, London.

Cole, G.A. (1975) *Textbook of Limnology*. Mosby, St Louis, Missouri.

Connell, J.H. (1961) The influence of interspecific competition and other factors on the distribution of the barnacle *Chthalamus stellatus*. *Ecology*, 42, 710–723.

Connell, J.H. (1978) Diversity in tropical rainforests and coral reefs. *Science*, 199, 1302–1309.

Connor, V.M. & J.F. Quinn (1984) Stimulation of food species growth by limpet mucus. *Science*, 225, 843–844.

Cooper, D.J., A.J. Watson & P.D. Nightingale (1996) Large decrease in ocean-surface CO_2 fugacity in response to *in-situ* iron fertilization. *Nature*, 383, 511–513.

Cortes, E. & S.H. Gruber (1990) Diet, feeding-habits and estimates of daily ration of young lemon sharks, *Negaprion-brevirostris* (poey). *Copeia*, 1, 204–218.

Coulter, G.W. (1994) Lake Tanganyika. In Martens, K., B. Goddeeris & G. Coulter (eds) *Speciation in Ancient Lakes. Archiv für Hydrobiologie, Ergebnisse der Limnologie*, 44, 13–18.

Crane, K., B. Hecker & V. Golubev (1991) Hydrothermal vents in Lake Baikal. *Nature*, 350, 281.

Cryer, M.G., G. Pierson & C.R. Townsend (1986) Reciprocal interactions between roach (*Rutilus rutilus* L.) and zooplankton in a small lake: prey dynamics and fish growth and recruitment. *Limnology and Oceanography*, 31, 1022–1038.

Cuffney, T.F., J.B. Wallace & G.J. Lugthart (1990) Experimental evidence quantifying the role of benthic invertebrates in organic matter dynamics of headwater streams. *Freshwater Biology*, 23, 281–299.

Cummins, K.W. (1974) Structure and function of stream ecosystems. *Bioscience*, 24, 631–641.

Cummins, K.W., C.E. Cushing & G.W. Minshall (1995) Introduction: an overview of stream ecosystems. In Cushing, C.E., K.W. Cummins & G.W. Minshall (eds) *River and Stream Ecosystems. Ecosystems of the World*, 22, pp 1–8. Elsevier, Amsterdam.

Cyr, H. & M. Pace (1992) Grazing by zooplankton and its relationship to community structure. *Canadian Journal of Fisheries and Aquatic Sciences*, 49, 1455–1465.

Dame, R.F. (1994) The net flux of materials between marsh–estuarine systems and the sea: the Atlantic coast of the United States. In Mitsch, W.J. (ed.) *Global Wetlands: Old World and New*, pp 295–302. Elsevier, Amsterdam.

Dame, R.F. & J.C. Lefeuvre (1994) Tidal exchange: import–export of nutrients and organic matter in New and Old World salt marshes: conclusions. In Mitsch, W.J. (ed.) *Global Wetlands: Old World and New*, pp. 303–305. Elsevier, Amsterdam.

Danielopol, D.L. (1989) Groundwater fauna associated within riverine aquifers. *Journal of the North American Benthological Society*, 8, 18–35.

Davidson, N.C., D. d'A. Laffoley, J.P. Doody, L.S. Way, J. Gordon, R. Key, M.W. Pienkowski, R. Mitchell & K.L. Duff (1991) *Nature Conservation and Estuaries in Great Britain*. Nature Conservancy Council, Peterborough.

Davis, C.S., M.B. Gallagher & A.R. Solow (1992) Micro-aggregation of oceanic plankton observed by towed video microscopy. *Science*, 257, 230–232.

Dayton, P.K. (1984) Processes structuring some marine communities: are they general? In Strong, D.R., Jr,

D. Simberloff, L.G. Abele & A.B. Thistle (eds) *Ecological Communities: Conceptual Issues and the Evidence*, pp. 181–197. Princeton University Press, Princeton, New Jersey.

Dayton, P.K. & R.R. Hessler (1972) Role of biological disturbance in maintaining diversity in the deep sea. *Deep-Sea Research*, **19**, 199–208.

Dayton, P.K., S.F. Thrush, M.T. Agardy & R.J. Hofman (1995) Environmental effects of marine fishing. *Aquatic Conservation: Marine and Freshwater Enviornments*, **5**, 205–232.

DeAngelis, D.L. & J.C. Waterhouse (1987) Equilibrium and non-equilibrium concepts in ecological models. *Ecological Monographs*, **57**, 1–21

Deming, J.W., A.L. Reysenbach, S.A. Macko & C.R. Smith (1997) Evidence for the microbial basis of a chemoautotrophic invertebrate community at a whale fall on the deep seafloor: bone-colonizing bacteria and invertebrate endosymbionts. *Microscopy Research and Technique*, **37**, 162.

Denman, K.L. (1994) Scale determining biological–physical interactions in oceanic food webs. In Giller, P.S., A.G. Hildrew & D.G. Raffaelli (eds) *Aquatic Ecology. Scale, Pattern and Process*. 34th Symposium of the British Ecological Society, pp. 377–403. Blackwell Science, Oxford.

Denny, M.W. (1987) Life in the maelstrom: the biomechanics of wave swept rocky shores. *Trends in Ecology and Evolution*, **2**, 61–66.

Denny, P. (1995) Wetlands of Africa. Eastern Africa. In Whigham, D.F., D. Dyjová & S. Hejný (eds) *Wetlands of the World I: Inventory, Ecology and Management*, pp. 1–31. Kluwer, Dordrecht.

Descy, J.P., V. Gosselain & F. Evrard (1994) Respiration and photosynthesis of river phytoplankton. *Verhandlungen der Internationale Vereinigung für Theoretische und Angewandte Limnologie*, **25**, 1555–1560.

Desse, J. & N. Desse-Berset (1993) Pêche et surpêche en Méditerranée: le temoinage des os. In Desse, J. & F. Audoin-Rouzeau (eds) *Exploitation des Animaux Sauvages à Travers le Temps*, pp. 327–339. Editions APDCA, Juan-les-Pins.

DeWalt, R.E. & J.H. Olive (1988) Effects of eroding glacial silt on the benthic insects of Silver Creek, Portage County, Ohio. *Ohio Journal of Science*, **88**, 154–159.

Dick, J.T.A., D.E. Irvine, & R.W. Elwood (1990) Differential predation by males on moulted females may explain the competitive displacement of *Gammarus duebeni* by *G. pulex* (Crustacea: Amphipoda). *Behavioural Ecology and Sociobiology*, **26**, 41–45.

Doborowski, K.A., A. Kozakiewicz & B. Leznicka (1993) The role of small mammals and birds in transport of matter through the shore zone of lakes. *Hydrobiologia*, **251**, 81–93.

Dobson, M., H. Cariss & B. Murray (1997) Effects of a flash flood on channel morphology and some insects of a small stony stream in the Peak District, Derbyshire. *Freshwater Forum*, **9**, 2–13.

Dobson, M. & A.G. Hildrew (1992) A test of resource limitation among shredding detritivores in low order streams in southern England. *Journal of Animal Ecology*, **61**, 69–78.

Dodson, S. (1989) Predator-induced reaction norms. *Bioscience*, **39**, 447–452.

Doody, J.P. (1992) Sea defence and nature conservation: threat or opportunity? *Aquatic Conservation: Marine and Freshwater Ecosystems*, **2**, 275–283.

Dugdale, R.C & J.J. Goering (1967) Uptake of new and regenerated forms of nitrogen in primary productivity. *Limnology and Oceanography*, **12**, 196–206.

Dumont, H.J. (1994) Ancient lakes have simplified pelagic food webs. In Martens, K., B. Goddeeris & G. Coulter (eds) *Speciation in Ancient Lakes. Archiv für Hydrobiologie Ergebnisse der Limnologie*, **44**, 223–234.

Eagle, R.A., P.A. Hardiman, M.G. Norton, R.S. Nunny, & M.S. Rolfe (1979) The field assessment of effects of dumping wastes at sea. 5: The disposal of solid wastes off the north-east coast of England. Fisheries Research Technical Paper **51**, Ministry of Agriculture, Fisheries & Food, Marine Laboratory, Lowestoft.

Eckman, J.E. (1985) Flow disruption by an animal-type mimic affects sediment bacterial colonization. *Journal of Marine Research*, **43**, 419–435.

Edwards, A.J. & S.C. Clark (1992) Rehabilitation of coral reef flats using precast concrete. *Concrete*, **26**, 16–19.

Ehrenfeld, J.G. & J.P. Schneider (1991) *Chamaecyperis thyoides* wetlands and suburbanization: effects on hydrology, water quality and plant community composition. *Journal of Applied Ecology*, **28**, 467–490.

Elliott, J.M. (1967) Invertebrate drift in a Dartmoor stream. *Archiv für Hydrobiologie*, **63**, 202–237.

Ellis, J.R., M.G. Pawson & S.E. Shackley (1996) The comparative feeding ecology of six species of shark and four species of ray (Elasmobranchii) in the north east Atlantic. *Journal of the Marine Biological Association of the UK*, **76**, 87–106.

Elser, J.J. & R.P. Hassett (1994) A stoichiometric analysis of the zooplankton–phytoplankton interaction in marine and freshwater ecosystems. *Nature*, **370**, 211–214.

Elser, M.M., C.N. von Ende, P. Sorrano & S.R. Carpenter (1987) *Chaoborus* populations: response to food web manipulation and potential effects on zooplankton communities. *Canadian Journal of Zoology*, **65**, 2846–2852.

Enright, J.T. (1977a) Diurnal vertical migration: adaptive significance and timing. Part 1. Selective advantage; a metabolic model. *Limnology and Oceanography*, **22**, 856–872.

Enright, J.T. (1977b) Diurnal vertical migration: adaptive significance and timing. Part 2. Test of the model, details of timing. *Limnology and Oceanography*, **22**, 873–886.

Epifano, C.E., A.K. Masse & R.W. Garvine (1989) Transport of Blue Crab larvae by surface currents off Delaware Bay, USA. *Marine Ecology Progress Series*, **54**, 35–41.

Fenchel, T. (1975) Character displacement and co-existence in mud snails (Hydrobiidae). *Oecologia*, **20**, 19–32.

Fenchel, T. & L.H. Kofoed (1976) Evidence for exploitative interspecific competition in mud snails (Hydrobiidae). *Oikos*, **27**, 367–376.

Findlay, S., K. Schoeberl & B. Wagner (1989) Abundance, composition, and dynamics of the invertebrate fauna of a tidal freshwater wetland. *Journal of the North American Benthological Society*, **8**, 140–148.

Flecker, A.S. & J.D. Allan (1988) Flight direction in some Rocky Mountain mayflies (Ephemeroptera), with observations of parasitism. *Aquatic Insects*, **10**, 33–42.

Fojt, W. (1994) The conservation of British fens. *British Wildlife*, **5**, 355–366.

Fraser, D., D. Arthur, J.K. Morton & B.K. Thompson (1980) Aquatic feeding by moose *Alces alces* in a Canadian lake. *Holarctic Ecology*, **3**, 218–223.

Fraser, J.H. (1962) The role of ctenophores and salps in zooplankton production and standing crop. *Rapports et Procès-Verbaux des Réunions Conseil Permanent International pour l'Exploration de la Mer*, **153**, 121–123.

Fraser, W.R., W.Z. Trivelpiece, D.G. Ainley & S.G. Trivelpiece (1992) Increases in Antarctic penguin populations – reduced competition with whales or a loss of sea ice due to environmental warming. *Polar Biology*, **11**, 525–531.

Frid, C.L.J. & N.V. Huliselan (1996) Far field control of long term changes in Northumberland (NW North Sea) coastal zooplankton. *ICES Journal of Marine Science*, **53**, 972–977.

Frid, C.L.J. & R. James (1988) The role of epibenthic predators in structuring the marine invertebrate community of a British coastal salt marsh. *Netherlands Journal of Sea Research*, **22**, 307–314.

Frid, C.L.J., L.C. Newton & J.A. Williams (1994).The feeding rates of *Pleurobrachia* (Ctenophora) and *Sagitta* (Chaetognatha), with notes on the potential seasonal role of planktonic predators in the dynamics of North Sea zooplankton communities. *Netherlands Journal of Aquatic Ecology*, **28**, 181–191.

Gage, J.D. (1996) Why are there so many species in deep sea sediments? *Journal of Experimental Marine Biology and Ecology*, **200**, 257–286.

Gage, J.D. & P.A. Tyler (1991) *Deep-Sea Biology: A Natural History of Organisms at the Deep-Sea Floor*. Cambridge University Press, Cambridge.

Gaines, S. & J. Roughgarden (1985) Larval settlement rate: a leading determinant of structure in an ecological community of the marine intertidal zone. *Proceedings of the National Academy of Science*, **82**, 3707–3711.

Gallagher, E.D., P.A. Jumars & D.D. Trueblood (1983) Facilitation of soft-bottom benthic succession by tube builders. *Ecology*, **64**, 1200–1216.

Gallais, J. (1984) *Hommes du Sahel*. Flammarion, Paris.

Garthe, S., C.J. Camphuysen & R.W. Furness (1996) Amounts discarded by commercial fisheries and their significance as food for seabirds in the North Sea. *Marine Ecology Progress Series*, **136**, 1–11.

Gaskin, D.E. (1982) *The Ecology of Whales and Dolphins*. Heinemann, London.

George, D.G. & A.H. Taylor (1995) UK lake plankton and the Gulf Stream. *Nature*, **378**, 139.

Gersberg, R.M., B.V. Elkins, S.R. Lyon & C.R. Goldman (1986) Role of aquatic plants in wastewater treatment by artificial wetlands. *Water Research*, **20**, 363–368.

Gessner, M.O. & E. Chauvet (1994) Importance of stream microfungi in controlling breakdown rates of leaf litter. *Ecology*, **75**, 1807–1817.

Giangrande, A., S. Geraci & G. Belmonte (1994) Life-cycle and life history diversity in marine invertebrates and the implications for community dynamics. *Oceanography and Marine Biology, an Annual Review*, **32**, 305–333.

Gibbard, P.L. (1988) The history of the great northwest European rivers during the past three million years. *Philosophical Transactions of the Royal Society of London B*, **318**, 559–602.

Gibert, J., D.L. Danielopol & J.A. Stanford (eds) (1994) *Groundwater Ecology*. Academic Press, London.

Giller, P.S. & N. Sangpradub (1993) Predatory foraging behaviour and activity patterns of larvae of two species of limnephilid cased caddis. *Oikos*, **67**, 351–357.

Giller, P.S., N. Sangpradub & H. Twomey (1991) Catastrophic flooding and macroinvertebrate community structure. *Verhandlungen der Internationale Vereinigung für Theoretische und Angewandte Limnologie*, **24**, 1724–1729.

Gislason, H. (1994) Ecosystem effects of fishing activities in the North Sea. *Marine Pollution Bulletin*, **29**, 520–527.

Golani, D. & B. Galil (1991) Trophic relationships of colonizing and indigenous goatfishes (Mullidae) in the eastern Mediterranean with special emphasis on decapod crustaceans. *Hydrobiologia*, **218**, 27–33.

Golley, F., H.T. Odum & R.F. Wilson (1962) The structure and metabolism of a Puerto Rican red mangrove forest in May. *Ecology*, **43**, 9–19.

Golubev, G.N. (1996) Caspian and Aral Seas: two different paths of environmental degradation. *Verhandlungen der Internationale Vereinigung für Theoretische und Angewandte Limnologie*, **26**, 159–166.

Gophen, M., P.B.O. Ochumba & L.S. Kaufman (1995) Some aspects of perturbation in the structure and biodiversity of the ecosystem of Lake Victoria (East Africa). *Aquatic Living Resources*, **8**, 27–41.

Gordon, N.D., T.A. McMahon & B.L. Finlayson (1992) *Stream Hydrology, an Introduction for Ecologists*. John Wiley & Sons, Chichester.

Goudie, A. (1992) *Environmental Change*, 3rd edition. Oxford University Press, Oxford.

Graça, M.A.S., L. Maltby & P. Calow (1993) Importance of fungi in the diet of *Gammarus pulex* and *Asellus aquaticus*. I: feeding strategies. *Oecologia*, **93**, 139–144.

Grassle, J.F. & J.P. Grassle (1974) Opportunistic life histories and genetic systems in marine benthic polychaetes. *Journal of Marine Research*, **32**, 253–284.

Grassle, J.F. & N.J. Maciolek (1992) Deep-sea species richness: regional and local diversity estimates from quantitative bottom samples. *American Naturalist*, **139**, 313–341.

Grassle, J.F. & L.S. Morse-Porteous (1987). Macrofaunal colonisation of disturbed deep-sea environments and the structure of deep-sea benthic communities. *Deep-Sea Research*, **34**, 1911–1950.

Gray, A. (ed.) (1992) *The Ecological Impact of Estuarine Barrages*. British Ecological Society, Ecological Issues No. 3. Field Studies Council, Shrewsbury.

Greenwood, P.H. (1994) Lake Victoria. In Martens, K., B. Goddeeris & G. Coulter (eds) *Speciation in Ancient Lakes. Archiv für Hydrobiologie, Ergebnisse der Limnologie*, **44**, 19–26.

Greve, W. (1981) Invertebrate predator control in a coastal marine ecosystem. The significance of *Beroe gracilis* (Ctenophora). *Kieler Meeresforschungen* (Sonderheft), **5**, 211–217.

Hairston, N.G., F.E. Smith & L.B. Slobodkin (1960) Community structure, population control, and competition. *American Naturalist*, **94**, 421–425.

Hall, R.J., G.E. Likens, S.B. Fiance & G.R. Hendrey (1980) Experimental acidification of a stream in the Hubbard Brook Experimental Forest, New Hampshire. *Ecology*, **61**, 976–989.

Hall, S.J., D. Raffaelli & S.F. Thrush (1994) Patchiness and disturbance in shallow water benthic assemblages. In Giller, P.S., A.G. Hildrew & D.G. Raffaelli (eds) *Aquatic Ecology. Scale, Pattern and Process*. 34th Symposium of the British Ecological Society, pp. 333–377. Blackwell Science, Oxford.

Harden-Jones, F.R. (1968) *Fish Migration*. Edward Arnold, London.

Hardy, A.C. (1956) *The Open Sea – Its Natural History: The World of Plankton*. Houghton-Mifflin, Boston, Massachusetts.

Harris, L.D. (1988) The nature of cumulative impacts on biotic diversity of wetland invertebrates. *Environmental Management*, **12**, 675–693.

Harris, R.P. (1987) Marine plankton communities. In Gee, J.H.R. & P.S. Giller (eds) *Organization of Communities Past and Present*, pp. 327–346, Blackwell Science, Oxford.

Hart, D.D. (1985) Causes and consequences of territoriality in a grazing stream insect. *Ecology*, **66**, 404–413.

Hawkins, S.J., R.G. Hartnoll, J.M. Kain & T.A. Norton (1992). Plant–animal interactions on hard substrata in the North-east Atlantic. In John, D.M., S.J. Hawkins & J.H. Price (eds) *Plant–Animal Interactions in the Marine Benthos*, pp. 1–32. Clarendon Press, Oxford.

Hay, M.E. (1981) Herbivory, algal distribution and the maintenance of between-habitat diversity on a tropical fringing reef. *American Naturalist*, **118**, 520–540.

Hay, M.E., T. Colburn & D. Downing (1983) Spatial and temporal patterns in herbivory on a Caribbean fringing reef: the effects on plant distribution. *Oecologia* (Berlin), **58**, 299–308.

Healey, M.C. & J. Richardson (1996) Changes in the productivity base and fish populations of the lower Fraser River associated with historical changes in human occupation. *Archiv für Hydrobiologie* (Supplement), **113** (Large Rivers 10), 279–290.

Hecky, R.E., F.W.B. Bugenyi, P.B.O. Ochumba, J.F. Talling, R. Mugidde, M. Gophen & L. Kaufman (1994) Deoxygenation of the deep water of Lake Victoria, East Africa. *Limnology and Oceanography*, **39**, 1476–1481.

Herman, L., M.F. Peacock, M.P.Yunker & C.J. Madsen (1975) Bottlenosed dolphin double-slit pupil yields equivalent aerial and underwater diurnal acuity. *Science* **189**, 650–652.

Hildrew, A.G., M.K. Dobson, A. Groom, J. Lancaster & S.D. Rundle (1991) Flow and retention in the ecology of stream invertebrates. *Verhandlungen der Internationale Vereinigung für Theoretische und Angewandte Limnologie*, **24**, 1742–1747.

Hildrew, A.G. & J.M. Edington (1979) Factors facilitating the coexistence of hydropsychid caddis larvae (Trichoptera) in the same river system. *Journal of Animal Ecology*, **48**, 557–576.

Hildrew, A.G. & P.S. Giller (1994) Patchiness, species interactions and disturbance in the stream benthos. In Giller, P.S., A.G. Hildrew & D.G. Raffaelli (eds) *Aquatic Ecology. Scale, Pattern and Process*. 34th Symposium of the British Ecological Society, pp. 21–62. Blackwell Science, Oxford.

Hildrew, A.G. & C.R. Townsend (1980) Aggregation, interference and foraging by larvae of *Plectrocnemia conspersa* (Trichoptera: Polycentropodidae). *Animal Behaviour*, **28**, 553–560.

Hill, A.E. (1991) A mechanism for horizontal zooplankton transport by vertical migration in tidal currents. *Marine Biology*, **111**, 485–492.

Hogg, E.H. & R.W. Wein (1988) The contribution of *Typha* components to floating mat buoyancy. *Ecology*, **69**, 1025–1031.

Holland, D.G. & J.P.C. Harding (1984) Mersey. In Whitton, B. (ed.) *Ecology of European Rivers*, pp. 114–144. Blackwell, Oxford.

Howells, G. & T.R.K. Dalziel (eds) (1992) *Restoring Acid Waters: Loch Fleet 1984–1990*. Elsevier, London.

Hughes, J.M.R. & P.J. Johnes (1995) Overview of the ecology and management of British wetlands. In Hughes, J.M.R. & A.L. Heathwaite (eds) *Hydrology and Hydrochemistry of British Wetlands*, pp. 317–323. John Wiley & Sons, Chichester.

Hughes, T.P. (1994) Catastrophes, phase shifts and large-scale degradation of a Caribbean coral reef. *Science*, **265**, 1547–1551.

Humpesch, U.H. (1992) Ecosystem study Altenwörth: impacts of a hydroelectric power-station on the River Danube in Austria. *Freshwater Forum*, **2**, 33–58.

Hutchinson, G.E. (1961) The paradox of the plankton. *American Naturalist*, **95**, 137–145.

Hylleberg, J. (1975) Selective feeding by *Abarenicola pacifica* with notes on *Abarenicola vagabunda* and a concept of gardening in lugworms. *Ophelia*, **14**, 113–137.

Hynes, H.B.N. (1970) *The Ecology of Running Waters*. Liverpool University Press, Liverpool.

ICES (1995) Report of the study group on the ecosystem effects of fisheries. ICES Co-operative Research Report, **200**. ICES, Copenhagen.

Irvine, K., B. Moss & H. Balls (1989) The loss of submerged plants with eutrophication. II. Relationships between fish and zooplankton in a set of experimental ponds, and conclusions. *Freshwater Biology*, **22**, 89–107.

Iversen, T.M., J. Thorup & J. Scriver (1982) Inputs and transformations of allochthonous particulate organic matter in a headwater stream. *Holarctic Ecology*, **5**, 10–19.

Iwakuma, T. & Y. Masayuki (1983) Fate of the univoltine chironomid, *Tokunagayusurika akamusi* (Diptera: Chironomidae), at emergence in Lake Kasumigaura, Japan. *Archiv für Hydrobiologie*, **99**, 37–59.

Jacobsen, D. & K. Sand-Jensen (1995) Variability of invertebrate herbivory on the submerged macrophyte *Potamogeton perfoliatus*. *Freshwater Biology*, **34**, 357–365.

Jensen, K.T. & C. Andre (1993) Field and laboratory experiments on interactions among an infaunal polychaete, *Nereis diversicolor* and two amphipods, *Corophium volutator* and *Corophium arenarium*: effects of survival, recruitment and migration. *Journal of Experimental Marine Biology and Ecology*, **168**, 259–278.

John, D.M., C. Lévêque & L.E. Newton (1993) Western

Africa. In Whigham, D.F., D. Dyjová & S. Hejny (eds) *Wetlands of the World I: Inventory, Ecology and Management*, pp. 47–78. Kluwer, Dordrecht.

Johnson, D.R. & B.S. Hester (1989) Larval transport and its association with recruitment of blue crabs to Chesapeake bay. *Estuarine, Coastal and Shelf Science*, **28**, 459–472.

Jónasson, P.M. (1996) Limits for life in the lake ecosystem. *Verhandlungen der Internationale Vereinigung für Theoretische und Angewandte Limnologie*, **26**, 1–33.

Jones, R.I., J.M. Young, A.M. Hartley & A.E. Bailey-Watts (1996) Light limitation of phytoplankton development in an oligotrophic lake – Loch Ness, Scotland. *Freshwater Biology*, **35**, 533–543.

Judd, A. & M. Hovland (1989) The role of chemosynthesis in supporting fish stocks in the North Sea. *Journal of Fish Biology*, **35** (Supplement A), 329–330.

Junk, W.J., P.B. Bayley & R.E. Sparks (1989) The Flood Pulse Concept in river–floodplain systems. In Dodge, D.P. (ed.) *Proceedings of the International Large River Symposium*, pp. 110–127. Canadian Special Publications in Fisheries and Aquatic Sciences, **106**.

Jurasz, C. M. & V. P. Jurasz (1979) Feeding modes of the humpback whale, *Megaptera novaeangliae*, in southeastern Alaska. *Scientific Report of the Whales Research Institute*, 2239–2243.

Kaiser, M.J. & B.E. Spencer (1994) Fish scavenging behaviour in recently trawled areas. *Marine Ecology Progress Series*, **112**, 41–49.

Kaiser, M.J. & B.E. Spencer (1996) The behavioural response of scavengers to beam trawl disturbance. In Greenstreet, S.P.R. & M.L. Tasker (eds) *Aquatic Predators and Their Prey*, pp. 117–123. Blackwell Science, Oxford.

Kalikhman, I., I. Ostrovsky, P. Wallie, M. Gophen & Y.Z. Yacobi (1995) Distribution fields for aquatic ecosystem components: methods of identification of correlation zones. *Freshwater Biology*, **34**, 317–328.

Kiørboe, T. (1993) Turbulence, phytoplankton cell size and the structure of pelagic food webs. Advances in Marine Biology, **29**, 1–72.

Kitching, J.A. & F.J. Ebling (1967) Ecological studies at Lough Ine. *Advances in Ecological Research*, **4**, 197–291.

Kosarev, A.N. & E.A. Yablonskaya (1994) *The Caspian Sea*. SPB Academic Publishing, The Hague.

Kovats, Z.E., J.J.H. Ciborowski & L.D. Corkum (1996) Inland dispersal of adult aquatic insects. *Freshwater Biology*, **26**, 265–276.

Kratz, T.K. & C.B. DeWitt (1986) Internal factors control peatland–lake ecosystem development. *Ecology*, **67**, 100–107.

Krüsi, B.O. & R.S. Wein (1988) Experimental studies on the resiliency of floating *Typha* mats in a freshwater marsh. *Journal of Ecology*, **76**, 60–72.

Künitzer, A., D. Basford, J.A. Craeymeersch, J.M. Dewaramez, J. Dörjes, G.C.A. Duineveld, A. Eletheriou, C. Heip, P. Herman, P. Kingston, U. Niermann, E. Rachor, H. Rumohr & P.A.J. deWilde (1992). The benthic fauna of the North Sea: species distribution and benthic assemblages. *ICES Journal of Marine Science*, **49**, 127–143.

Laë, R. (1995) Climatic and anthropogenic effects on fish diversity and fish yields in the Central Delta of the Niger River. *Aquatic Living Resources*, **8**, 43–58.

Lalli, C.M. & Parsons, T.R. (1993) *Biological Oceanography: an Introduction*. Butterworth-Heinemann, Oxford.

Lampert, W. (1989) The adaptive significance of diel vertical migration in zooplankton. *Functional Ecology*, **3**, 21–27.

Lancaster, J. (1990) Predation and drift of lotic macroinvertebrates during colonization. *Oecologia* (Berlin), **85**, 48–56.

Lancaster, J. & L.R. Belyea (1997) Nested heirarchies and scale-dependence of mechanisms of flow refugium use. *Journal of the North American Benthological Society*, **16**, 221–238.

Lancaster, J. & A.G. Hildrew (1993) Flow refugia and the microdistribution of lotic macroinvertebrates. *Journal of the North American Benthological Society*, **12**, 385–393.

Lang, J.C. (1973) Interspecific aggression by scleractinian corals. 2. Why the race is not only to the swift. *Bulletin of Marine Science of the Gulf and Caribbean*, **23**, 260–279.

Laprise, J. & J.J. Dodson (1994) Environmental variability as a factor controlling spatial patterns in the distribution and species diversity of zooplankton in the St Lawrence Estuary (Canada). *Marine Ecology Progress Series*, **107**, 67–81.

Law, R. & D.R. Grey (1989) Life history evolution and sustainable yields from populations with age-specific cropping. *Evolutionary Ecology*, **3**, 343–359.

Laws, R.M. (1985) The ecology of the Southern Ocean. *American Scientist*, **73**, 26–40.

Lefeuvre, J.C., G. Bertru, F. Butrel, L. Brient, V. Creach, Y. Gueuné, J. Levasseur, A. Marlotti, A. Radureau, C. Retière, B. Savouré & O. Troccazl

(1994) Comparative studies on salt marsh processes: Mont Saint Michel Bay, a multi-disciplinary study. In Mitsch, W.J. (ed.) *Global Wetlands: Old World and New*, pp. 215–234. Elsevier, Amsterdam.

Lévêque, C. (1995) Role and consequences of fish diversity in the functioning of African freshwater ecosystems: a review. *Aquatic Living Resources*, **8**, 59–78.

Levinton, J.S. (1995) *Marine Biology: Function, Biodiversity and Ecology*. Oxford University Press, Oxford.

Lewis, M.R., Jr (1988) Primary production in the Orinoco River. *Ecology*, **69**, 679–692.

Long, S.P. & C.F. Mason (1983) *Saltmarsh Ecology*. Blackie, Glasgow.

Longhurst, A.R. & D. Pauly, (1987) *Ecology of Tropical Oceans*, Academic Press, London.

Lowe-McConnell, R. (1994) The changing ecosystem of Lake Victoria, East Africa. *Freshwater Forum*, **4**, 76–89.

Lubchenco, J. (1980) Algal zonation in the New England rocky intertidal community: an experimental analysis. *Ecology*, **61**, 333–344.

Lutz, R.A., L.W. Fritz & D.C. Rhoads (1985) Molluscan growth at deep sea hydrothermal vents. *Bulletin of the Biological Association of Washington*, **6**, 199–210.

Lynch, M. (1980) The evolution of cladoceran life histories. *Quarterly Review of Biology*, **55**, 23–42.

MacIntyre, S. & J.M. Melack (1988) Frequency and depth of vertical mixing in an Amazon floodplain lake (L. Calado, Brazil). *Verhandlungen der Internationale Vereinigung für Theoretische und Angewandte Limnologie*, **23**, 80–85.

MacIntyre, S. & J.M. Melack (1995) Vertical and horizontal transport in lakes: linking littoral, benthic and pelagic habitats. *Journal of the North American Benthological Society*, **14**, 616–630.

Mackas, D.L. & C.M. Boyd (1979) Spectoral analysis of zooplankton spatial heterogeneity. *Science*, **204**, 62–64.

Maddock, L., G.T. Boalch & D.S. Harbour (1981) Populations of phytoplankton in the Western English Channel between 1964 and 1974. *Journal of the Marine Biological Association of the UK*, **61**, 565–583.

Maguire, B., Jr (1963) The passive dispersal of small aquatic organisms and their colonization of isolated bodies of water. *Ecological Monographs*, **33**, 161–185.

Malmer, N., B.M. Svensson & B. Wallén (1994) Interactions between *Sphagnum* mosses and field layer vascular plants in the development of peat-forming systems. *Folia Geobotanica et Phytotaxonomica* (Praha), **29**, 483–496.

Malmqvist, B., S. Rundle, C. Brönmark & A. Erlandsson (1991) Invertebrate colonisation of a new, man-made stream in southern Sweden. *Freshwater Biology*, **26**, 307–324.

Mann, K.H. (1982) *Ecology of Coastal Waters. A Systems Approach*. Blackwell Scientific, Oxford.

Margulis, L. & K.V. Schwarz (1988) *Five Kingdoms. An illustrated Guide to the Phyla of Life on Earth*. 2nd edition. W.H. Freeman, New York.

Martill, D.M., A.R.I. Cruikshank & M.A. Taylor (1991) Dispersal via whale bones. *Nature*, **351**, 193.

Martin J.H., K.H. Coale, K.S. Johnson *et al.* (1994) Testing the iron hypothesis in ecosystems of the equatorial Pacific Ocean. *Nature*, **371**, 123–129

Martin, P. (1994) Lake Baikal. In Martens, K., B. Goddeeris & G. Coulter (eds) *Speciation in Ancient Lakes. Archiv für Hydrobiologie Ergebnisse der Limnologie*, **44**, 3–11.

Mason, B.J. (ed.) (1990) *The Surface Waters Acidification Programme*. Cambridge University Press, Cambridge.

Mason, C.F. (1996) *Biology of Freshwater Pollution*, 3rd edition. Longman, Harlow.

McAuliffe, J.R. (1984) Competition for space, disturbance, and the structure of a benthic community. *Ecology*, **65**, 894–908.

McCann, L.D. & L.A. Levin (1989) Oligochaete influence on settlement, growth and reproduction in a surface deposit feeding polychaete. *Journal of Experimental Marine Biology and Ecology*, **131**, 233–253.

McGown, J.A. & P.W. Walker (1985) Dominance and diversity maintenance in an oceanic ecosystem. *Ecological Monographs*, **55**, 103–118.

McLachlan, A. & E. Jaramillo (1995) Zonation on sandy beaches. *Oceanography and Marine Biology, an Annual Review*, **33**, 305–335.

McLaren, I. (1969) Effects of temperature on the growth of zooplankton and the adaptive value of vertical migration. *Journal of the Fisheries Research Board, Canada*, **20**, 685–727.

McLaren, I. (1974) Demographic strategy of vertical migration by a marine copepod. *American Naturalist*, **108**, 91–108.

McLusky, D.S. (1989) *The Estuarine Ecosystem*, 2nd edition. Blackie, Glasgow.

Meijer, M.-L., M.W. de Haan, A.W. Breukelaar & H. Buiteveld (1990) Is reduction of the benthivorous fish an important cause of high transparency following biomanipulation in shallow lakes? *Hydrobiologia*, **200/201**, 303–315.

Menge, B.A. (1976) Organisation of the New England rocky intertidal community: role of predation, competition and environmental heterogeneity. *Ecological Monographs*, **46**, 355–393.

Menge, B.A. & J.P. Sutherland (1976) Species diversity gradients: synthesis of the roles of predation, competition and temporal heterogeneity. *American Naturalist*, **110**, 351–369.

Menge, B.A. & J.P. Sutherland (1987) Community regulation: variation in disturbance, competition, and predation in relation to environmental stress and recruitment. *American Naturalist*, **130**, 730–757.

Miller, C.B., B.W. Frost, B. Booth, P.A. Wheeler, M.R. Landry & N.A. Welschmeyer (1991a) Ecological processes in the subarctic Pacific: iron limitation cannot be the whole story. *Oceanography*, **4**, 71–78.

Miller, C.B., B.W. Frost, B. Booth, P.A. Wheeler, M.R. Landry, N.A. Welschmeyer & T.M. Powell (1991b) Ecological dynamics in the subarctic Pacific: a possibly iron-limited ecosystem. *Limnology and Oceanography*, **36**, 1600–1615.

Milner, A.M. (1987) Colonization and ecological development of new streams in Glacier Bay National Park, Alaska. *Freshwater Biology*, **18**, 53–70.

Milner, A.M. (1994) Colonization and succession of invertebrate communities in a new stream in Glacier Bay National Park, Alaska. *Freshwater Biology*, **32**, 387–400.

Minshall, G.W., K.W. Cummins, R.C. Petersen, C.E. Cushing, D.A. Bruns, J.R. Sedell & R.L. Vannote (1985) Developments in stream ecosystem theory. *Canadian Journal of Fisheries and Aquatic Sciences*, **42**, 1045–1055.

Mitchell, R. & P.K. Probert (1983) Environmental and nature conservation aspects of tidal power proposals for the Severn Estuary (UK). *Water Science and Technology*, **16**, 269–279.

Mitsch, W.J. (1996) Managing the world's wetlands – preserving and enhancing their ecological functions. *Verhandlungen der Internationale Vereinigung für Theoretische und Angewandte Limnologie*, **26**, 139–147.

Moe, S.R. (1994) The importance of aquatic vegetation for the management of the barasingha *Cervus duvauceli* in Nepal. *Biological Conservation*, **70**, 33–37.

Moore, P.D. (1993) The origin of blanket mire, revisited. In Chambers, F.M. (ed.) *Climate Change and Human Impacts on the Landscape*, pp. 217–224. Chapman and Hall, London.

Moore, P.D. & D.J. Bellamy (1974) *Peatlands*. Elek Science, London.

Moreira, F. (1997) The importance of shore birds to energy fluxes in a food web of a south European estuary. *Estuarine, Coastal and Shelf Science*, **44**, 67–78.

Moreno, C.A., J.P. Sutherland & F.H. Jara (1984) Man as a predator in the intertidal zone of southern Chile. *Oikos*, **46**, 359–364.

Morrison, B.R.S. (1990) Recolonisation of four small streams in central Scotland following drought conditions in 1984. *Hydrobiologia*, **208**, 261–267.

Moss, B. (1990) Engineering and biological approaches to the restoration from eutrophication of shallow lakes in which aquatic plant communities are important components. *Hydrobiologia*, **200/201**, 367–377.

Moss, B. & M. Timms (1989) Predation, sediment stability and food availability as determinants of the benthic invertebrate fauna in two shallow lakes. *Hydrobiologia*, **185**, 249–257.

Müller, K. (1954) Investigations on the organic drift in north Swedish streams. *Annual Report of the Institute of Freshwater Research, Drottningholm*, **35**, 133–148.

Mulligan, H.F., A. Baranowski & R. Johnson (1976) Nitrogen and phosphorus fertilisation of aquatic vascular plants and algae in replicated ponds. I. Initial response to fertilisation. *Hydrobiologia*, **48**, 109–116.

Murdoch, W.W. (1966) Community structure, population control and competition – a critique. *American Naturalist*, **100**, 219–226.

Neill, W.E. (1990) Induced vertical migration in copepods as a defence against invertebrate predation. *Nature*, **345**, 524–526.

Neill, W.E. (1994) Spatial and temporal scaling and the organization of limnetic communities. In Giller, P.S., A.G. Hildrew & D.G. Raffaelli (eds) *Aquatic Ecology. Scale, Pattern and Process*. 34th Symposium of the British Ecological Society, pp. 189–231. Blackwell Science, Oxford.

Nelson-Smith, A. (1977) Estuaries. In Barnes, R.S.K. (ed.) *The Coastline*, John Wiley & Sons, London.

North Sea Task Force (1993) *North Sea Quality Status Report*. Olsen & Olsen, Fedensborg, Denmark.

Nybacken, J.W. (1988) *Marine Biology: An Ecological Approach*. Harper Collins, New York.

Nyström, P. & J.A. Strand (1996) Grazing by a native and an exotic crayfish on aquatic macrophytes. *Freshwater Biology*, **36**, 673–682.

Ogden, J.C., R.A. Brown & N. Salesky (1973). Grazing by the echinoid *Diadema antillarum* Philippi: formation of the halos around West Indian patch reefs. *Science*, **182**, 715–717.

Oresland, V. (1987) Feeding of the chaetognaths *Sagitta elegans* and *Sagitta setosa* at different seasons in Gullmarsfjorden, Sweden. *Marine Ecology Progress Series*, **39**, 69–79.

Orme, A.R. (1975) Ecologic stress in a subtropical coastal lagoon: Lake St Lucia, Zululand. *Geoscience and Man*, **12**, 9–22.

Ott, J.A. & R. Novak (1989) Living at the interface: Meiofauna at the oxygen/sulphide boundary of marine sediments. In Ryland, J.S. & P.A. Tyler (eds) *Reproduction, Genetics and Distribution of Marine Organisms*, pp. 415–422. Olsen & Olsen, Fedensborg, Denmark.

Ott, J.A., R. Novak, F. Schiemer, U. Hentschel, M. Nebelsick & M.F. Polz (1991) Tackling the sulfide gradient: a novel strategy involving marine nematodes and chemoautotrophic ectosymbionts. *Marine Ecology*, **12**, 261–279.

Paine, R.T. (1966) Food web complexity and species diversity. *American Naturalist*, **100**, 6–75.

Palmer, M.A., A.E. Bely & K.E. Berg (1992) Response of macroinvertebrates to lotic disturbance: test of the hyporheic refuge hypothesis. *Oecologia*, **89**, 182–194.

Parsons, T.R., M. Takahashi & B. Hargrave (1984) *Biological Oceanographic Processes*, 3rd edition. Pergamon Press, Oxford.

Pearce, F. (1994) Dam truths about the Danube. *New Scientist*, 17 September, 27–31.

Pearce, F. (1995) Poisoned waters. *New Scientist*, 21 October, 29–33.

Pieczynska, E. (1993) Detritus and nutrient dynamics in the shore zone of lakes: a review. *Hydrobiologia*, **251**, 49–58.

Piedade, M.T.F., W.J. Junk & S.P. Long (1997) Nutrient dynamics of the highly productive C_4 macrophyte *Echinochloa polystachya* on the Amazon floodplain. *Functional Ecology*, **11**, 60–65.

Pimm, S.L. & R.L. Kitching (1987) The determinants of food chain lengths. *Oikos*, **50**, 302–307.

Pinay, G. & H. Décamps (1988) The role of riparian woods in regulating nitrogen fluxes between the alluvial aquifer and surface water: a conceptual model. *Regulated Rivers: Research and Management*, **2**, 507–516.

Pingree, R.D. (1978) Mixing and stabilisation of phytoplankton distributions on the Northwest European Continental shelf. In Steele, J.H. (ed.) *Spatial Patterns in Plankton Communities*, pp. 181–220. Plenum Press, New York.

Polz, M.F., R. Felbeck, M. Nebellsick & J.A. Ott (1991) Chemotrophic, sulfur-oxidising symbiotic bacteria in marine nematodes. *Applied Environmental Microbiology*, **24**, 313–329.

Por, F.D. (1978) *Lessepsian Migration. The Influx of Red Sea Biota into the Mediterranean by Way of the Suez Canal*. Ecological Studies, **23**. Springer-Verlag, Berlin.

Priscu, J.C. (1995) Phytoplankton nutrient deficiency in lakes of the McMurdo dry valleys, Antarctica. *Freshwater Biology*, **34**, 215–227.

Probert, P.K. (1984) Disturbance, sediment stability and trophic structure of soft-bottom communities. *Journal of Marine Research*, **42**, 893–921.

Purseglove, J. (1988) *Taming the Flood*. Oxford University Press, Oxford.

Raffaelli, D.G., A. Conacher, H. McLachlan & C. Emes (1989a) The role of epibenthic crustacean predators in an estuarine food web. *Estuarine, Coastal and Shelf Science*, **28**, 149–160.

Raffaelli, D.G. & S. Hawkins (1996) *Intertidal Ecology*. Chapman and Hall, London.

Raffaelli, D., S. Hull & H. Milne (1989b). Long-term changes in nutrients, weed mats and shorebirds in an estuarine system. *Cahiers du Biologie Marine*, **30**, 259–270.

Raffaelli, D.G. & H. Milne (1987) An experimental investigation of the effects of shorebird and flat fish predation on estuarine invertebrates. *Estuarine, Coastal and Shelf Science*, **24**, 1–13.

Ramsay, K., M.J. Kaiser & R.N. Hughes (1996) Changes in hermit crab feeding patterns in response to trawling disturbance. *Marine Ecology Progress Series*, **144**, 63–72.

Rankin, J.C. & J.A. Davenport (1981). *Animal Osmoregulation*. Blackie, Glasgow.

Ratcliffe, D.A. & P.H. Oswald (eds) (1988) *The Flow Country. The Peatlands of Caithness and Sutherland*. Nature Conservancy Council, London.

Raymont, J.E.G. (1983) *Plankton and Productivity in the Oceans. Volume 2. Zooplankton*. Pergamon Press, Oxford.

Reeve, M.R. & M.A. Walter (1978) Nutritional ecology of ctenophores: a review of recent research. *Advances in Marine Biology*, **15**, 249–287.

Reid, P.C., C. Lancelot, W.W.C. Gieskes, E. Hagmeier & G. Weichert (1991) The phytoplankton of the North Sea and its dynamics: a review. *Netherlands Journal of Sea Research*, **26**, 295–331.

Reimold, R.J. (1977) Mangals and salt marshes of

eastern United States. In Chapman, V.J. (ed.) *Ecosystems of the World 1. Wet Coastal Ecosystems*, pp. 157–166. Elsevier, Amsterdam.

Reise, K. (1978) Experiments on epibenthic predation in the Wadden Sea. *Helgolander wissenschaftliche Meeresuntersuchungen*, **31**, 55–101.

Remane, A. & C. Schlieper (1971) *Biology of Brackish Water*. E. Schweizerbart'sche, Stuttgart.

Reynolds, C.S. (1987) Community organisation in the freshwater plankton. In Gee, J.H.R. & P.S. Giller (eds) *Organization of Communities, Past and Present*. 27th Symposium of the British Ecological Society, pp. 297–325. Blackwell Science, Oxford.

Reynolds, C.S. (1988) Potamoplankton: paradigms, paradoxes and prognoses. In Round, F.E. (ed.) *Algae and the Aquatic Environment*, pp. 285–311. Biopress, Bristol.

Rhoads, D.C. & L.F. Boyer (1983) The effects of marine benthos on physical properties of sediment: a successional perspective. In McCall, P.L. & M.J.S. Tevesz (eds) *Animal–Sediment Relations*, pp. 3–52. Plenum, New York.

Rhoads, D.C. & D.K. Young (1970) The influence of deposit-feeding organisms on sediment stability and community trophic structure. *Journal of Marine Research,* **28**, 150–178.

Ribbink, A.J. (1994) Biodiversity and speciation of freshwater fishes with particular reference to African cichlids. In Giller, P.S., A.G. Hildrew & D.G. Raffaelli (eds) *Aquatic Ecology. Scale, Pattern and Process*. 34th Symposium of the British Ecological Society, pp. 261–288. Blackwell Science, Oxford.

Rice, A.L. & P.J.D. Lambshead (1994) Patch dynamics in the deep-sea benthos: The role of a heterogeneous supply of organic matter. In Giller, P.S., A.G. Hildrew & D.G. Raffaelli (eds) *Aquatic Ecology. Scale, Pattern and Process*. 34th Symposium of the British Ecological Society, pp. 469–497. Blackwell Science, Oxford.

Rice, D.W. (1989) Sperm whale – *Physeter macrocephalus* Linnaeus, 1758. In Ridgway, S.H. & R. Harrison (eds) *Handbook of Marine Mammals*, Volume 4: *River Dolphins and the Larger Toothed Whales*, pp. 177–234. Academic Press, London.

Robertson, A.L., J. Lancaster & A.G. Hildrew (1995) Stream hydraulics and the distribution of microcrustacea: a role for refugia? *Freshwater Biology*, **33**, 469–484.

Roff, J.C., K. Middlebrook & F. Evans (1988) Long-term variability in North Sea zooplankton off the Northumberland coast: productivity of small copepods and analysis of trophic interaction.

Journal of the Marine Biological Association of the UK, **68**, 143–164.

Rosas, F.C.W. (1994) Biology, conservation and status of the Amazon manatee *Trichechus inunguis*. *Mammal Review*, **24**, 49–59.

Ross, S.M. (1995) Overview of the hydrochemistry and solute processes in British wetlands. In Hughes, J.M.R. & A.L. Heathwaite (eds) *Hydrology and Hydrochemistry of British Wetlands*, pp. 133–181. John Wiley & Sons, Chichester.

Roughgarden, J., S.D. Gaines & S.W. Pacala (1987) Supply side ecology: the role of physical transport processes. In Gee, J.H.R. & P.S. Giller (eds) *Organisation of Communities Past and Present*, pp. 491–518. Blackwell Science, Oxford.

Rowell, T.A. (1986) The history of drainage at Wicken Fen, Cambridgeshire, England, and its relevance to conservation. *Biological Conservation*, **35**, 111–142.

Russell, F.S., A.J. Southward, G.T. Boalch & E.I. Butler (1971) Changes in the biological conditions in the English Channel off Plymouth during the last half century. *Nature*, **234**, 468–470.

Rydin, H. (1993) Mechanisms of interactions among *Sphagnum* species along water-level gradients. *Advances in Bryology*, **5**, 153–185.

Ryther, J.H. (1981) Mariculture, ocean ranching and other culture based fisheries. *Bioscience*, **31**, 223–230.

Sale, P.F. (1984) The structure of communities of fish on coral reefs and the merit of a hypothesis testing manipulative approach to ecology. In Strong, D.R., Jr, D. Simberloff, L.G. Abele & A.B. Thistle (eds), *Ecological Communities: Conceptual Issues and the Evidence*, pp. 478–490. Princeton University Press, Princeton, New Jersey.

Sanders, H.L. (1968) Marine benthic diversity: a comparative study. *American Naturalist*, **102**, 243–282.

Scheer, B.T. (1945) The development of marine fouling communities. *Biological Bulletin*, **89**, 103–121.

Schindler, D.W. & E.J. Fee (1974) Experimental Lakes area: whole-lake experiments in eutrophication. *Journal of the Fisheries Research Board of Canada*, **31**, 937–953.

Schofield, K., C.R. Townsend & A.G. Hildrew (1988) Predation and the prey community of a headwater stream. *Freshwater Biology*, **20**, 85–95.

Schriver, P., J. Bogestrand, E. Jeppesen & M. Sondergaard (1995) Impact of submerged macrophytes on fish–zooplankton–phytoplankton interactions: large scale enclosure experiments in a shallow eutrophic lake. *Freshwater Biology*, **33**, 255–270.

Scott, W.B. & E.J. Crossman (1964) *Fishes Occurring in the Fresh Waters of Insular Estuaries in Newfoundland*. Canadian Department of Fisheries, Ottawa.

Sedell, J.R., J.E. Ridley & F.J. Swanson (1989) The River Continuum Concept: a basis for the expected ecosystem behaviour of very large rivers? In Dodge, D.P. (ed.) *Proceedings of the International Large River Symposium*, pp. 49–55. Canadian Special Publications in Fisheries and Aquatic Sciences, **106**.

Sharp, G.D. (1978) Behavioural and physiological properties of tuna and their effects on vulnerability to fishing gear. In Sharp, G.D. & A.E. Dixon (eds) *The Physiological Ecology of Tuna*, pp. 397–450. Academic Press, New York.

Sharp, G.D. & R.C. Francis (1976) Vulnerability of tunas as a function of environmental profiles. In *Maguro Gyogyo Kyogikay Gijiroku, Suisancho-Enyo Suisan Kenkyusho (Proceedings of the Tuna Fishery Research Conference)*, pp. 124–133. Fisheries Agency-Far Seas Fishery Research Laboratory, Japan

Sherr, E.B. & B.F. Sherr (1991) Planktonic microbes: tiny cells at the base of the ocean's food webs. *Trends in Ecology and Evolution*, **6**, 50–54.

Simpson, R.L., D.F. Whigham & R. Walker (1978) Seasonal patterns of nutrient movement in a freshwater tidal marsh. In Good, R.E., D.F. Whigham, R.L. Simpson & C.G. Jackson, Jr (eds) *Freshwater Wetlands. Ecological Processes and Management Potential*. Academic Press, New York.

Smith, C.R. (1992) Whale falls: chemosynthesis on the deep seafloor. *Oceanus*, **35**, 74–78.

Smith, C.R., H. Kukert, R.A. Wheatcroft, P.A. Jumars & J.W. Deming (1989). Vent fauna on whale remains. *Nature*, **341**, 27–28.

Soetaert, K. & P. van Rijswijk (1993) Spatial and temporal patterns of the zooplankton in the Westerhelde Estuary. *Marine Ecology Progress Series*, **97**, 47–59.

Sousa, W.P. (1979) Disturbance in marine intertidal boulder fields: the non-equilibrium maintenance of species diversity. *Ecology*, **60**, 1225–1239.

Sousa, W.P. (1984) The role of disturbance in natural communities. *Annual Review of Ecology and Systematics*, **15**, 353–391.

Southward, A.J. (1974) Changes in the plankton community of the Western English Channel. *Nature*, **249**, 180–181.

Stanford, J.A. & J.V. Ward (1988) The hyporheic habitat of river ecosystems. *Nature*, **335**, 64–66.

Stavn, R.H. (1971) The horizontal–vertical distribution hypothesis: Langmuir circulation and *Daphnia* distributions. *Limnology and Oceanography*, **16**, 453–466.

Steele, J.H. (1976) Patchiness. In Cushing, D.H. & J.J. Walsh (eds) *The Ecology of the Seas*, pp. 98–115. Blackwell, Oxford.

Stich, H.-B. & W. Lampert (1981) Predator evasion as an explanation of diurnal vertical migration by zooplankton. *Nature*, **293**, 396–398.

Stockner, J.G. & K.G. Porter (1988) Microbial food webs in freshwater planktonic ecosystems. In Carpenter, S.R. (ed.) *Complex Interactions in Lake Communities*, pp. 69–83. Springer-Verlag, New York.

Stokes, T.K.A., R. Law & J. McGlade (eds) (1993) *The Exploitation of Evolving Populations*. Springer-Verlag, New York.

Stone, J.H., L.M. Bahr, Jr, J.W. Day & R.M. Darnell (1982) Ecological effects of urbanization on Lake Pontchartrain, Louisiana, between 1953 and 1978, with implications for management. In Lee, J.A. & M.R.D. Seaward (eds) *Urban Ecology*. 2nd European Ecological Symposium, pp. 243–252. Blackwell Scientific, Oxford.

Stoner, J.H., A.S. Gee & K.R. Wade (1984) The effects of acidification on the ecology of streams in the upper Tywi catchment in west Wales. *Environmental Pollution* (Series A), **35**, 125–157.

Strong, D.R., L.A. Szyzka & D. Simberloff (1979) Tests of community wide character displacement against null hypotheses. *Evolution* **33**, 897–913.

Sutcliffe, D.W. (1984) Quantitative aspects of oxygen uptake in *Gammarus* (Crustacea: Amphipoda): a critical review. *Freshwater Biology*, **14**, 443–489.

Svensson, B.M. (1995) Competition between *Sphagnum fuscum* and *Drosera rotundifolia*: a case of ecosystem engineering. *Oikos*, **74**, 205–212.

Takamura, K., Y. Sugaya, N. Takamura, T. Hanazato, M. Yasuno & T. Iwakuma (1989) Primary production of phytoplankton and standing crops of zooplankton and zoobenthos in hypertrophic Lake Teganuma. *Hydrobiologia*, **173**, 173–184.

Talling, J.F. (1986) The seasonality of plankton in African lakes. *Hydrobiologia*, **138**, 139–160.

Talling, J.F. (1993) Comparative seasonal changes, and inter-annual variability and stability, in a 26-year record of total phytoplankton biomass in four English lakes. *Hydrobiologia*, **268**, 65–98.

Taylor, A.H. (1995) North–south shifts in the Gulf

Stream and their climatic connection with the abundance of zooplankton in the UK and its surrounding seas. *ICES Journal of Marine Science*, **200**, 711–722.

Thorson, G. (1950) Reproductive and larval ecology of marine bottom invertebrates. *Biological Reviews*, **25**, 1–45.

Thorson, G. (1957) Bottom communities (sublittoral or shallow shelf). *Memoirs of the Geological Society of America*, **67**, 461–534.

Thrush, S.F. (1991) Spatial patterns in soft-bottom communities. *Trends in Ecology and Evolution*, **6**, 75–78.

Thrush, S.F., R.D. Pridmore, J.E. Hewitt, & V.J. Cummings (1992) Adult infauna as facilitators of colonization on intertidal sandflats. *Journal of Experimental Marine Biology and Ecology*, **159**, 253–265.

Townsend, C.R., A.G. Hildrew & J. Francis (1983) Community structure in some southern English streams: the influence of physicochemical factors. *Freshwater Biology*, **13**, 521–544.

Trémolieres, M., D. Carbienier, R. Carbienier, I. Eglin, F. Robach, J.M. Sanchez-Perez, A. Schnitzler & D. Weiss (1991) Zones inondables, végétation et qualité de l'eau en milieu alluvial rhenan: l'Ile de Rhinau, un site de recherches intégrées. *Bulletin d'Ecologie*, **22**, 317–336.

Tunnicliffe, V., J.F. Garrett & H.P. Johnson (1990) Physical and biological factors affecting the behaviour and mortality of hydrothermal vent tubeworms (vestimentiferans). *Deep Sea Research*, **37A**, 103–125.

Turner, S.J. & C. D. Todd (1993) The early development of epifaunal assemblages on artificial substrata at two intertidal sites on an exposed rocky shore in St. Andrews Bay, NE Scotland. *Journal of Experimental Marine Biology and Ecology*, **166**, 251–272.

Tyler, M.A. & H.H. Seliger (1978). Annual sub-surface transport of a red tide dinoflagellate to its bloom area: water circulation patterns and organisms distributions in Chesapeake Bay. *Limnology and Oceanography*, **23**, 227–246.

UK Department of the Environment (1994) *Biodiversity: The UK Action Plan*. HMSO, London.

Underwood, A.J. & E.J. Denley (1984) Paradigms, explanations and generalisations in models for the structure of intertidal communities on rocky shores. In Strong, D.R., Jr, D. Simberloff, L.G. Abele & A.B. Thistle (eds) *Ecological Communities:*

Conceptual Issues and the Evidence, pp. 151–180. Princeton University Press, Princeton, New Jersey.

Usinger, R.L. (1957) Marine insects. *Memoirs of the Geological Society of America*, **67**, 1177–1182.

van Breeman, N. (1995) How *Sphagnum* bogs down other plants. *Trends in Ecology and Evolution*, **10**, 270–275.

van der Hage, J.C.H. (1996) Why are there no insects and so few higher plants, in the sea? New thoughts on an old problem. *Functional Ecology*, **10**, 546–547.

van Es, F.B. (1977) A preliminary carbon budget for part of the Ems Estuary: the Dollard. *Helgolander wissenschaftliche Meeresuntersuchungen*, **30**, 283–291.

Vannote, R.L., G.W. Minshall, K.W. Cummins, J.R. Sedell & C.E. Cushing (1980) The River Continuum Concept. *Canadian Journal of Fisheries and Aquatic Science*, **37**, 130–137.

Vasquez, J.A. (1995) Ecological effects of brown seaweed harvesting. *Botanica Marina*, **38**, 251–257.

Vervier, Ph., M. Dobson & G. Pinay (1993) Role of interaction zones between surface and ground waters in DOC transport and processing: considerations for river restoration. *Freshwater Biology*, **29**, 275–284.

Vinogradov, M.E., I.I. Gitelzon & Y.I. Sorokin (1970) The vertical structure of a pelagic community in the tropical ocean. *Marine Biology*, **6**, 187–194.

Wafar, S., A.G. Untawale & M. Wafar (1997) Litter fall and energy flux in a mangrove ecosystem. *Estuarine, Coastal and Shelf Science*, **44**, 111–124.

Walker, D. (1970) Direction and rate in some British post-glacial hydroseres. In Walker, D. & R.G. West (eds) *Studies in the Vegetational History of the British Isles*, pp. 117–139. Cambridge University Press, Cambridge.

Waringer, J.A. (1987) Spatial distribution of Trichoptera larvae in the sediments of an Austrian mountain stream. *Freshwater Biology*, **18**, 469–482.

Watson, D.C. & T.A. Norton (1985) Dietary preferencs of the common periwinkle, *Littorina littorea* (L.). *Journal of Experimental Marine Biology and Ecology*, **88**, 193–211.

Watson, G.F., M. Davies & M.J. Tyler (1995) Observations on temporary waters in northwestern Australia. *Hydrobiologia*, **299**, 53–73.

Weber, W. (1995) Estimation of cod discards caused by the fishery on roundfish in the German Bight

1982–1994. ICES CM 1995/B+G+H+J+K:6, ICES, Copenhagen.

Welcomme, R.L. (1989) Review of the present state of knowledge of fish stocks and fisheries of African rivers. In Dodge, D.P. (ed.) *Proceedings of the International Large River Symposium*, pp. 515–532. Canadian Special Publications in Fisheries and Aquatic Sciences, **106**.

Wendt, P.H., D.M. Knott & R.F. van Dolah (1989) Community structure of the sessile biota on five artificial reefs of different ages. *Bulletin of Marine Science*, **44**, 1106–1122.

Wetherbee, B.M. & S.H. Gruber (1990) The effects of ration level on food retention time in juvenile lemon sharks, *Negaprion brevirostris*. *Environmental Biology of Fishes*, **29**, 59–65.

Wetzel, R.G. (1990) Land–water interfaces: metabolic and limnological regulators. *Verhandlungen der Internationale Vereinigung für Theoretische und Angewandte Limnologie*, **24**, 6–24.

Wheeler, A. (1977) The origin and distribution of the freshwater fishes of the British Isles. *Journal of Biogeography*, **4**, 1–24.

Whitlatch, R.B. & R.N. Zajac (1985) Biotic interactions among estuarine infaunal opportunistic species. *Marine Ecology Progress Series*, **21**, 299–311.

Wiafe, G. & C.L.J. Frid (1996) Short term temporal variation in coastal zooplankton communities: the relative importance of physical and biological mechanisms. *Journal of Plankton Research*, **18**, 1485–1501.

Wiebe, P.H. (1970) Small-scale spatial distribution in oceanic zooplankton. *Limnology and Oceanography*, **15**, 205–217.

Wildish, D.J. (1977) Factors controlling marine and estuarine sublittoral macrofauna. *Helgolander wissenschaftliche Meeresuntersuchungen*, **30**, 445–454.

Wilen, B.O. & R.W. Tiner (1995) Wetlands of the United States. In Whigham, D.F., D. Dyjová & S. Hejný (eds.) *Wetlands of the World I: Inventory, Ecology and Management*, pp. 515–636. Kluwer, Dordrecht.

Williams, D.D. (1996) Environmental constraints in temporary fresh waters and their consequences for the insect fauna. *Journal of the North American Benthological Society*, **15**, 634–650.

Williams, D.D. & B.W. Feltmate (1992) *Aquatic Insects*. CAB International, Wallingford, UK.

Williams, M. (1990) Understanding wetlands. In Williams, M. (ed.) *Wetlands: a Threatened Landscape*, pp. 1–41. Blackwell, Oxford.

Williams, W.D. (1996) The largest, highest and lowest lakes of the world: saline lakes. *Verhandlungen der Internationale Vereinigung für Theoretische und Angewandte Limnologie*, **26**, 61–79.

Wilson, W.H. (1986) Importance of predatory infauna in marine soft-sediment communities. *Marine Ecology Progress Series*, **32**, 35–40.

Witte, F., T. Goldschmidt, P.C. Goudswaard, W. Ligtvoet, M.J.P. van Oijen & J.H. Wanink (1992) Species extinction and concomitant ecological changes in Lake Victoria. *Netherlands Journal of Zoology*, **42**, 214–232.

Wolff, W.J. (1977) A benthic food budget for the Grevelingen Estuary, the Netherlands, and a consideration of the mechanisms causing high benthic secondary production in estuaries. In Coull, B.C. (ed.) *Ecology of Marine Benthos*, pp. 267–280. University of South Carolina Press, Charleston, SC.

Woodin, S.A. (1976) Adult–larval interactions in dense infaunal assemblages: patterns of abundance. *Journal of Marine Research*, **34**, 25–41.

Woodin, S.A. (1981) Disturbance and community structure in a shallow water sand flat. *Ecology*, **62**, 1052–1066.

World Resources Institute (1992) *World Resources 1992–93*. Oxford University Press, Oxford.

Zaret, T.M. & R.T. Paine (1973) Species introduction in a tropical lake. *Science*, **182**, 449–455.

Zaret, T.M. & J.S. Suffren (1976) Vertical migration in zooplankton as a predator avoidance mechanism. *Limnology and Oceanography*, **21**, 804–813.

Glossary

AABW – Antarctic Bottom Water. Deep oceanic water which downwells off Antarctica (see **Section 1.2b**).

Abiotic – referring to the non-living component of the environment; e.g. climate, temperature, pH (cf. **Biotic**).

Abyssal – referring to the deep ocean, 4000–6000 m in depth.

Acidification – increase in the acidity of water. Normally refers to anthropogenic activity.

Acidity – the concentration of alkalinity-buffering ions in water. Normally refers to the concentration of hydrogen ions, expressed as pH (see **Section 1.3c**).

Advect – to move laterally within a water column.

Alga (plural **algae**) – photosynthetic organism in the phylum Protoctista. Includes unicellular forms (e.g. diatoms) and multicellular forms (e.g. seaweeds).

Alkalinity – the concentration of acidity-buffering ions in water (see **Section 1.3c**).

Allochthonous – originating from outside a given site; e.g. allochthonous detritus (cf. **Autochthonous**).

Alluvium – sediment deposited by a river. **Alluvial terrace** – see **Section 2.2e**.

Amphibyte – an organism whose life cycle involves stages in both groundwater and surface environments (see **Section 2.7d**).

Amplitude – the difference in height between the crest or the trough of a wave and mean water level (see **wave**).

Anadromy – see **Diadromy**.

Anoxic – deprived of oxygen.

Anaerobic – in the absence of oxygen.

Anthropogenic – caused by human activity.

Athalassic – referring to saline lakes whose saline water derives from non-marine sources.

Attenuation – reduction in intensity of light by absorption or reflection as it passes through water.

Aufwuchs – see **Biofilm**.

Autochthonous – originating from within a given site; e.g. autochthonous primary production (cf. **Allochthonous**).

Autotroph – an organism that obtains energy from inorganic substances through primary production (cf. **Heterotroph**).

Bedload – sediment, transported by water flow, which moves by rolling or sliding and generally, therefore, remains in contact with the bed.

Benthic – referring to organisms living on or in the bed of a water body. **Benthos** – collective term for such organisms (see **Section 1.6a**).

Biofilm – the layer of bacteria, algae, FPOM and extracellular bacterial secretions which develops on solid surfaces in water. Occasionally referred to as 'aufwuchs'.

Biogenic – created by biological activity.

Biome – a climatically determined vegetation zone defined by structural vegetation type rather than the actual plant species present; e.g. hot desert, tropical rainforest, tundra.

Biota – the living organisms within an area.

Biotic – referring to living components of the environment, or to products derived from living components; e.g. detritus (cf. **Abiotic**).

Biotic Index – a water quality scoring system based upon the presence of living organisms (see **Section 2.3c**).

Bioturbation – disturbance caused by biological activity.

Boundary layer – a layer of high shear stress created by friction between a moving fluid and a stationary surface. Its upper limit occurs where the speed of the current is no longer influenced by the presence of the solid surface and may, in slow-flowing water bodies, extend to the surface. See **Current**.

BP – years before present. Used to denote dates which have been inferred from radiocarbon dating, for which the 'present day' is 1950.

Broadcast breeding – production of a dispersive reproductive stage, e.g. spores, planktonic larvae.

Catadromy – see **Diadromy**.

Channelisation – engineering a channel to make it straighter and more homogeneous in structure than the natural channel.

Chemosynthesis – see **Primary production**.

Conditioning – the process by which detritus becomes more palatable to macroinvertebrates through the activity of decomposers.

Conductivity – a measure of salinity of water, through its ability to conduct electricity. Can be used to determine concentration of solutes in water (see **Section 1.3a**).

Coriolis force – the apparent force which deflects fluids moving over the surface of the rotating Earth from a linear to a circular trajectory (see **Box 1.1**).

CPOM – coarse particulate organic matter. Detrital particles retained by a 1 mm sieve (see **Section 1.4c**).

Current – movement of water within a water body. **Current velocity** – the speed of movement of water, normally expressed as m s^{-1}. The presence of a viscous (or laminar) sublayer, a layer of zero flow between a solid surface and a moving fluid, means that there must also be a gradient in current velocity, creating the boundary layer, close to the bed, where the change is most rapid. In a river, current velocity is measured at a point 0.6 of the depth of the channel.

CWD – coarse woody debris. Large pieces of wood of terrestrial origin (see **Section 1.4c**).

Cyanobacteria – 'blue-green algae': photosynthetic bacteria formerly known as Cyanophyta and classed as algae.

Dead zone – a portion of the river channel where current is reduced by the presence of a barrier to free water movement (see **Section 2.3e**).

Deep ocean – see **Hypolimnion**.

Demersal – living adjacent to, and in association with, the sea floor, e.g. demersal fish.

Detritus – particulate organic matter derived from formerly living organisms.

Diadromy – referring to a life cycle which involves stages in both freshwater and marine habitats. **Anadromy** – migration from the sea to fresh water to breed; **catadromy** – migration from fresh water to the sea to breed (see **Section 4.3a**).

Dimictic – referring to a lake whose mixing cycle has two periods of stratification per year. (see **Section 6.2b**).

Discharge – the total volume of water moving past a point, usually expressed in m^3 s^{-1} (or cumecs – cubic metres per second), or, for low discharges, l s^{-1}. For a river, discharge (Q) may be approximated from $Q = WDU$ where W = stream width, D = mean depth and U = current velocity.

Disturbance – a discrete event which removes, damages or impairs the normal function of organisms.

DOC – dissolved organic carbon (see **Section 1.4c**).

DOM – dissolved organic matter (see **Section 1.4c**).

Downwelling – the movement of surface water into the body of the water column (see **Section 1.2b**).

Drift – passive movement with the current of a water body (see **Section 2.3d**).

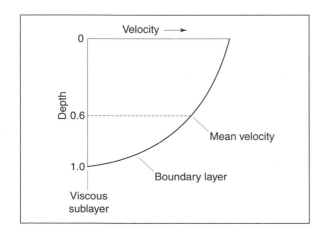

DVM – diet vertical migration (see **Box 5.4**; **Section 5.7a**).

ENSO – El Niño Southern Oscillation (see **Section 5.7c**)

Epibenthic – attached to or living on the bed of a water body.

Epifauna – benthos living or active on the surface of the substrate (*cf*. infauna).

Epilimnion – the surface layer of a stratified water body, above the thermocline. A limnological term equivalent to the mixed layer in marine systems (see **Box 1.3**).

Epilithic – attached to stones.

Epiphytic – attached to plants. **Epiphyte** – an organism growing on a plant.

Euhydrophyte – a fully submerged macrophyte, including those with floating leaves.

Euphotic zone – see **Photic zone**.

Euryhaline – tolerant of a wide range of salinities (see **Section 3.3a**).

Eutrophic – referring to water containing high concentrations of nutrients, relative to an oligotrophicormesotrophicwaterbody.**Eutrophication** – the increase in nutrient concentrations in a water body, normally used to refer to the effects of anthropogenic pollution (see **Box 6.2**).

Evaporation – the transition of a liquid or solid phase into a gaseous state. Can be used to refer to loss of surface water to the atmosphere.

Evapotranspiration – the sum of water lost from the land through evaporation and transpiration.

Flocculation – aggregation of small particles into larger particles (see **Section 3.2b**).

Floodplain – the area flooded by a river with a predictable, normally seasonal frequency (see **Section 2.2d**).

Fluvial – referring to flowing water.

FPOM – fine particulate organic matter. Detritus passing through a 1 mm sieve, but retained by a 0.45 μm sieve (see **Section 1.4c**).

Glide (Run) – a stretch of river where flow is rapid but not turbulent (see **Section 2.2c**)

Groundwater – water in sediments beneath the Earth's surface.

Hadal - referring to the deep ocean beneath 6000 m depth.

Halocline – a zone of abrupt change in salinity.

Heterotroph – an organism that obtains its energy from eating other living organisms or their by-products (*cf*. **Autotroph**).

Holoplankton – see **Plankton**.

Hydrology – the study of water and its properties on the Earth's surface, including atmospheric water and groundwater.

Hydrosphere – the waters on the Earth's surface, including all water bodies which act as habitat for biota.

Hypertrophic – extremely eutrophic.

Hypolimnion – the deep layer of a stratified lake, below the thermocline. A limnological term equivalent to the deep ocean in marine systems (see **Box 1.3**).

Hyporheic – referring to the sediments and interstitial water beneath a water body (**Section 2.3e**). **Hyporheos** – organisms inhabiting this zone.

Hypotonic – a solution of lower osmotic pressure (i.e. a relative term).

Infauna – benthos living within the bed sediments, rather than on its surface (*cf*. epifauna).

Interstitial – between the particles of sediments.

Isohaline – at the same salinity.

Karst – limestone dominated landscape, typically containing caves and associated subterranean aquatic habitats.

Labile – easily assimilated or modified.

Laminar sublayer – see **Current**.

Levée – a raised embankment along the edge of a river.

Limnology – the study of inland waters.

Littoral zone (1) – in lakes, that part of the water body in which the photic zone extends to the bed. Also referred to as the **lake littoral**.

Littoral zone (2) – in the sea, the intertidal zone.

Ma – millions of years ago.

Macrofauna (**macroinvertebrates**) – animals retained on a 0.5 mm (500 μm) sieve.

Macrophyte – a large multicellular photosynthesising organism; generally applied to vascular plants but also refers to multicellular algae.

Maximum Sustainable Yield (MSY) – the greatest harvest of a wild living resource (e.g. fish) that can be taken each year while still leaving a viable population to harvest the following year.

Meiofauna – animals retained on a 10 μm sieve but which pass through a 500 μm sieve.

Meroplankton – see **Plankton**.

Mesotrophic – referring to water containing a

concentration of nutrients intermediate between that of a eutrophic and an oligotrophic water body (see **Box 6.2**).

Metapopulation – a group of spatially distinct populations of a species which are linked by dispersal of individuals between them.

MHW – mean high water. The average height on the seashore to which the water rises at high tide. **MHWS** – the average height of high tides during spring tides; **MHWN** – the average height of high tides during neap tides (see Figure 4.1).

Microphyte – small, single-celled or filamentous photosynthesiser – algae and autotrophic bacteria. **Microphytobenthos** – microphytes inhabiting the bed of a water body.

Minerotrophic – see **Mire**.

Mire – a wetland whose water supply is independent of surface water bodies. **Minerotrophic** – referring to a mire fed by groundwater or overland flow. **Ombrotrophic** – referring to a mire fed only by rainwater and atmospheric inputs.

Mixed layer – see **Epilimnion**.

MLW – mean low water. The average height on the seashore to which the water falls at low tide. **MLWS** – the average height of low tides during spring tides; **MLWN** – the average height of low tides during neap tides (see Figure 4.1).

Monomictic – referring to a lake whose mixing cycle has one period of stratification per year. (see **Section 6.2b**).

NADW – North Atlantic Deep Water. Deep oceanic water which downwells in the North Atlantic (see **Section 1.2b**).

Nauplius (plural **nauplii**) – the free-swimming first stage of certain crustaceans.

Nekton – organisms living within the water column which are able to swim or otherwise move independently of the current (see **Section 1.6a**).

Neuston – organisms inhabiting the surface film of water (see **Section 1.6a**).

Nutricline – a region of rapid change in concentration of one or more nutrients.

Nutrient cycle – the pathway followed by a nutrient as it changes from an inorganic to an organic form and back. **Nutrient spiral** – a condition in which the cycle is completed only when the nutrient has moved to a different geographical location (see **Section 2.7a**).

Oceanography – the study of marine systems.

Oligohaline – tolerant only of low salinities (see **Section 4.3a**).

Oligomictic – referring to a lake with infrequent, aseasonal mixing (see **Section 6.2b**).

Ombrotrophic – see **Mire**.

Osmoconformer – a species whose internal salt concentrations fluctuate in response to changes in the external medium (see **Section 3.3a**).

Osmoregulation – maintaining constant internal salt concentrations despite fluctuations in the external medium (see **Section 3.3a**).

Oxycline – a region of rapid change in oxygen concentration.

Paludification – development of a peat mire on dry land.

Pelagic – referring to the water column, as opposed to its bed or edges.

Periphyton – unicellular algae attached to sediment surface layers.

pH – see **Acidity**.

Photic zone (Euphotic zone) – the depth of water to which sunlight penetrates in sufficient quantity to support photosynthesis. The bottom of the photic zone is defined as the depth at which only 1% of light intensity at the surface remains.

Photosynthesis – see **Primary production**.

Phytoplankton – see **Plankton**.

Plankter – an individual member of the plankton.

Plankton (planktonic) – organisms inhabiting the pelagic zone which have no independent means of propulsion, or are too small and weak to swim in the horizontal plane (**Section 1.6a**). **Holoplankton** – organisms which spend their entire lives as members of the plankton. **Meroplankton** – organisms which spend only part of their life cycle as members of the plankton. **Phytoplankton** – the photosynthesising component of the plankton, mainly single-celled algae but including autotrophic bacteria. **Potamoplankton** – phytoplankton species which are endemic to river systems. **Zooplankton** – animal components of the plankton.

Pleistocene – the geological period incorporating the most recent Ice Ages. It began around 1.6 Ma and ended with the onset of the Holocene, or Recent, period about 10 000 BP.

POC – particulate organic carbon (see **Section 1.4c**).

Polymictic – referring to a lake with frequent but aseasonal mixing (see **Section 6.2b**).

POM – particulate organic matter (see **Section 1.4c**).

Pool – a stretch of river where flow is relatively slow (see **Section 2.2c**).

Potamoplankton – see **Plankton**.

Precipitation (1) – water that falls from the atmosphere to the surface of land or sea, including rain, snow, etc.

Precipitation (2) – the process by which a substance dissolved in water separates out of solution and becomes a solid.

Primary production – production of organic compounds from inorganic components, using energy fixed from an external source.

    Photosynthesis – primary production in which energy is obtained from sunlight.

    Chemosynthesis – primary production in which energy is derived from chemical oxidation of simple inorganic compounds.

Protoctist – a member of the kingdom Protoctista, which includes algae and single celled heterotrophs formerly classified as 'Protozoa'.

    Protist – a single celled protoctist; often applied only to heterotrophs, distinguishing them from single celled algae.

Pycnocline – a region of rapid change in density.

Redox – an abbreviation for reduction–oxidation, a chemical reaction in which an atom or ion loses electrons to another atom or ion. **Redox Discontinuity Layer** (**RDL**) – the layer at which a sediment changes from an oxygenated to an anoxic state.

Refractory – not readily assimilated and therefore slow to decompose (*cf.* **Labile**).

Rheotaxis – movement of an organism in response to current.

Rheotrophic – relying upon current to provide food.

Riffle – a stretch of river where flow is relatively rapid and turbulent (see **Section 2.2c**).

Riparian – referring to the bank of a river.

Run – see **Glide**.

Runoff – rainfall which is not absorbed by soil, but passes into surface water bodies.

Salinity – the concentration of dissolved ions in water (see **Section 1.3a**).

Seston – suspended particles in water, including both living (plankton) and non-living (tripton) components.

Shear stress – the effect of a series of forces of different magnitude acting simultaneously at different parts of an object.

Sill – a shallow ridge which separates relatively deep parts of a water body (see **Box 3.1**).

Solute – a substance dissolved in another substance.

Stenohaline – adapted to a narrow range of salinities (see **Section 3.3a**)

Stratification – development of discrete vertical layers within a water body (see **Box 1.3**).

Stygobyte – an organism which is a permanent inhabitant of groundwater, including caves.

Succession – directional change through time at a site by means of colonisation and local extinction (note that succession is a controversial process with several, often contradictory, definitions in ecology).

Taxon (plural **taxa**) – organisms classed together within the same taxonomic group (differs from species in that the taxonomic group may be genus, family, order, etc.).

Terrestrialisation – conversion of open water to dry land through successional processes.

Terrigenous – derived from land.

Thalassic – referring to saline lakes whose water is marine in origin (e.g. coastal lagoons).

Thermocline – a region of rapid temperature change, e.g. the zone between the epilimnion (or mixed layer) and hypolimnion (or deep ocean).

Tidal limit – the point furthest up an estuary (i.e. inland) at which periodic vertical displacement of the water surface by tides can be detected.

Tidal range – the height difference in sea level between high and low water at a given point.

Transpiration – transfer of water from soil to the atmosphere by living plants.

Tripton – non-living particles suspended in water.

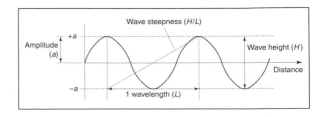

Turbidity – the concentration of suspended particles in water.

Upwelling – the appearance at the surface of a water mass previously within the depths of the water body (see **Section 1.2b**).

Water mass – a body of water characterised by certain values of its conservative properties (i.e. those not altered except by mixing), e.g. salinity, temperature.

Wave – a periodic displacement in a medium, normally used to refer to the succession of peaks and troughs on the surface of a water body. Temporally, there are two components to a wave. **Period** (T) – the time interval between successive peaks (or troughs) passing a fixed point. **Frequency** (f) – the number of peaks (or troughs) passing a fixed point per second.

Zooplankton – see **Plankton**.

Organism Index

Subject Index

channel form, rivers 31–3
channelisation 35, 41
chemoautotrophy 19, 69, 123, 124, 144
chemosynthesis 18, 112
Chesapeake Bay (USA) 66
chloride 9, 10, 11, 13, 15–16
chlorinity 9
chlorophyll maximum 88
circulation
  atmospheric 2, 5, 6, 109
  deep ocean 3, 5–6, 109, 110
  estuarine 57–60
  horizontal 75
  hydrothermal 113–14
  negative estuarine 60
  residual 57, 60, 66–7
  surface ocean 3, 4, 6, 109
  vertical 112
classification
  aquatic organisms 23–6
  lakes 135–6
  nutrient status 142
  rivers 31, 32
  wetlands 158–61
coarse particulate organic matter see CPOM
coarse woody debris see CWD
coastal fronts 111
coastal zone 21, 23, 79–107, 108, 186
cold core ring 109, 114
collector-filterers 24–5
collector-gatherers 24–5, 69
collectors 24, 44, 51, 52
colonisation 184
  artificial surfaces 86, 102
  coastal hard substrates 86, 101
  coastal soft sediments 98, 101
  detritus 68
  freshwaters 21–2
  marine species into estuaries 65
  ocean floor 123
  rivers 45, 46–7
  sea from freshwaters 22–3
  sea from land 22–3
  wetlands 169
Colonisation Cycle Hypothesis 47
Colorado River (USA) 151
Comite River (USA) 181
community structure 26–8
  coastal hard substrates 91–5
  coastal pelagic zone 98–101
  coastal soft sediments 95–8
  coastal zone 85
  coral reefs 101–2
  estuaries 71–3
  lakes 147–51
  ocean floor 122–5

ocean pelagic 116–22
rivers 44–6
Sphagnum mires 170–2
wetlands 170–2
compensation point 16, 17, 18
competition 1, 22, 27–8, 184, 186
  coastal hard substrates 92–3, 94, 101
  coastal soft sediments 97–8
  coral reefs 94–5
  estuaries 71–2
  lakes 144
  ocean pelagic zone 120–1
  rivers 44–5
  wetlands 170, 171
competitive release 71
conditioning 43, 68, 169, 185
  role of macrofauna 43–4, 68
  role of microbial activity 43, 68, 69
conductivity 10
continental plates 132
continental shelf 2, 6–8, 108, 110, 122, 130
continental slope 2, 6–8, 128
coral reefs 6, 87, 94–5, 91, 98, 101, 105, 106, 122
Coriolis force 4, 5, 60
Coto Doñana (Spain) 180
CPOM 43
Crater Lake (USA) 135
critical depth 16, 17, 18, 111
currents 4, 27, 109, 186
  coastal 83–4
  deep ocean 5, 139
  geostrophic 4
  near bottom 115, 123
  ocean 110, 132
  river 35, 36, 37
  turbidity 8
CWD 20
Cyanobacteria 16, 88, 114, 146, 155
Cyanophyta 16
cyclonic gyre 109
cyclonic ring 110, 120
cyclonic systems 5, 108
cyclonic wind 6

dams 49–51, 75, 136, 151
  beaver 152
Danube Delta (Romania) 158
dead zones 39–40, 41, 134
debris flows 7, 8
decomposition 15
  effect on oxygen concentration 69–70, 110, 142, 154
  large carcasses 124
  regenerating nutrients 112

wetlands 160–2, 166, 169, 175, 177
Decoy Lake (UK) 173
Dee Estuary (UK) 73
deep circulation 138
deep ocean 19, 117, 125, 139, 184, 185, 187
deltas 31, 54
demersal fish 186
denitrification 162, 163, 166, 167
deoxygenation 44, 69, 97, 110, 124, 139, 152, 154, 157, 161
deposit feeders 25, 65, 71, 97, 98, 115
deposition zone 30, 31, 33
desiccation 150
detritivores 23, 24, 42, 68–9, 115, 125, 144, 155, 169, 178, 186
detritus 19–20, 87, 183, 184, 187
  deep ocean 123
  estuaries 68–70, 71
  lakes 147
  oceans 114, 126
  rivers 34, 42–4, 51, 52
  wetlands 163–4, 169, 172, 174, 178, 184
detritus flux
  oceans 115
  rivers 42–3
detritus transformation 43, 68
detritus transport 185–6
diadromous fish 21–2
discharge 102, 162
  rivers 14, 30, 33, 34, 46
dispersal 23, 47, 49, 53, 64, 184–5
  aerial 184
  between hydrothermal vents 123–4
  between river catchments 46–7, 49
  estuaries 65–6
  flight 47, 49
  overland 150
  plankton 125, 184
  planktonic stage 23
  role of whale carcasses 124
dissolved organic carbon see DOC
dissolved organic matter see DOM
disturbance 27–8, 73, 86, 91–2, 95–7, 98, 184, 186
  coastal soft sediments 95–7
  fishing activity 105
  floods as 38–41
  lakes 154
  ocean bed 123
  rivers 38–41, 45, 46, 47
DOC 26, 44, 68, 146
Dollard Estuary (Netherlands) 70
DOM 26, 115, 186

downwelling 5, 6, 109, 116, 118
drainage 159
drift 37–8, 44 ,47, 49
Dugdale and Goering model 88

East Pacific Rise 8, 113
ebb tide 56, 57, 77, 81
Ekman currents 6
Ekman layer 4
Ekman spiral 4
El Nino Southern Oscillation *see*
    ENSO
Elbe Estuary (Germany) 75
endemism
    ancient lakes 151, 155–7, 184
    ocean trenches 122
    rivers 184
energy budgets estuaries 70
energy transfer 115, 147
English Channel 100
ENSO 95, 126–8
epibenthos 63, 87
epifauna 23, 65, 71
epilimnion 19, 137, 138, 140, 141,
    143–5
epilithic algae 45
epiphytic algae 23, 42, 167
Equatorial Counter Current 3
erosion zone 30, 31
estuaries 1, 8, 22, 31, 56–78, 87,
    96, 164, 166, 169, 184, 185
estuarine flushing 76
Estuarine Tank Model 76
euhydrophytes 165
euphotic zone 17
euryhaline organisms 62
eutrophic water 142, 153
eutrophication 75, 88, 152–4, 155,
    157, 167–8
    effect on oxygen concentration
    75, 155
evaporation 2, 8, 9, 30–1, 59, 79,
    83, 136, 140, 174
evapotranspiration 159, 160, 161
Everglades (USA) 167, 179, 181
exploitation 186–7
extraction, water 65

feeding plasticity, in benthos 24–5
fens 158, 159–60, 161, 172, 173
    rheotrophic 169
Fens, East Anglian (UK) 152, 180
filamentous algae 75
filter feeders 20, 25, 52, 61, 68–9,
    86, 97–8, 115, 121, 122, 125,
    147
fine particulate organic matter *see*
    FPOM
Finger Lakes (USA) 135

fish ladders 77
fish passes 77
fisheries 186
    coastal 103–6
    coastal demersal 104
    coastal pelagic 104
    deep ocean 129
    effect of ENSO 127
    industrial 104, 187
    non-target species 103
    oceans 129
    target species 103
    tuna 118
fishing 103–5, 106, 153, 186
    disturbance by 97, 186
    dynamite 91, 106
    Inner Niger Delta 178, 181
    Lake Victoria 155–7
fjords 59
Flathead River (USA) 53
floating islands 165, 166
floating mats 177
flocculation 61
flood cycles 33, 34
Flood Pulse Concept 52, 183
flood refugia 38–9
flood tides 56, 57, 77, 81, 162
floodplain 31, 34, 52, 53, 138,
    159, 162, 163, 167, 168–9,
    172, 178, 181, 183
    as a flood refugium 39, 41
floods 33, 34, 45, 52, 158, 160,
    162, 164, 172, 176, 177,
    178–9, 180–1
    effect on river biota 27, 37,
    38–40, 54
Flow Country (UK) 176
Flugströmmen (Sweden) 47
flyways 185
food webs
    lakes 156
    pelagic 25–6, 122, 128–9
founder control 45, 97–8
founders 45, 97
FPOM 43, 44, 51, 68, 147
Fraser River (Canada) 54
fresh water 14, 15, 20, 21, 22, 61,
    79
    adaptation to 64
    colonisation 20
    estuaries 57–60, 64–5, 66,
    73–4, 75, 76
freshwater composition 13, 14
freshwater organisms
    estuaries 62
    saline lakes 141–2
freshwaters, coastal wetlands 166
fringing communities 23, 24
functional groups 24–6

fungal activity 43

gardening behaviour 69, 101
Gatun Lake (Panama) 154–5
geostrophic current 4
glacial ice 2, 4, 8, 46, 135, 152
Glacier Bay (USA) 46
glaciers 2, 134, 135
Glenfinnish River (Ireland) 38, 39
glide 33
global warming 114
Goose Creek (USA) 39
Grand Banks 186
gravel bars 33, 44, 47
grazer-scrapers 24, 42
grazers 18, 25, 46, 94, 98, 101,
    123
grazing 89, 95, 105, 119, 177,
    185, 186
    as a limiting factor 18
    lakes 145, 147–51
    wetlands 169–70
Great Lakes (East Africa) 9, 151
Great Lakes (North America) 9,
    135
Great Salt Lake (USA) 137
Great Slave Lake (Canada) 135
Grevelingen Estuary (Netherlands)
    67, 71
groundwater 2, 8, 9, 23, 30, 31,
    33–4, 53, 134, 136–7,
    159–60, 161, 162, 167, 180
Guadeloupe River (USA) 33
Gulf of California 79, 130
Gulf Stream 100–1
guyots 8
Gwendoline Lake (Canada) 149
gyres 6

hadal zone 108
Hairston–Smith–Slobodkin model
    27–8
halocline 57, 58, 60, 83, 91
halophytes 166
harvesting
    coastal waters 103–5
    rocky shores 92
    seaweeds 92
HAT 81
Highest Astronomical Tides *see*
    HAT
Hog Lake (Canada) 177
hollows 171
holoplankton 23
hover 168
Hudson River (USA) 169
human exploitation cycle 178
human impacts 186–7
    coastal zone 101–2, 103–6

methane gas seeps 123
MHW 82, 166
MHWS 82, 166
microbial activity 161, 187
  role in detritus processing 43,
    65, 68, 115
microbial community 65, 115
microbial loop 25, 26, 146, 186
microflora 167
microorganisms 23–4, 35, 43, 68,
    69, 115, 167
microphytes
  benthic 23
  rivers 41
microphytobenthos 23, 66, 67, 68,
    70
microplankton 26
microzooplankton 122
Mid-Atlantic Ridge 8, 113, 132
mid-ocean ridges 113, 123
migration 185
  birds 71, 73
  diel vertical 125, 127, 148
  exporting energy 71
  fish 22, 73, 77, 155
  lateral 53, 163, 170, 177
  ocean scale 120, 121
  ontogenetic 117, 125
  planktonic stage 66
  rivers 53
  role of estuaries 64, 66, 71, 73, 77
  seasonal 117, 120
  vertical 66, 90, 117, 125–5, 149
mires 159–60, 162
  blanket 169
  ombrotrophic 159, 166, 168,
    169, 175
  raised 169
  rheotrophic 158, 175,
mixed layer 19
monsoon 3, 59, 125
monsoon wind 5
mosses 135
mudflats 71, 72, 74, 185

NADW 6, 110
Namaluta (Indonesia) 94
nanoplankton 26, 89
neap tides 81, 82
near-bed flow 87
nekton 23, 25
  ocean pelagic 125
net-phytoplankton 25
neuston 23, 24
nitrate 168
  as a limiting factor 16, 18, 88,
    114, 144, 145, 162, 166
nitrification/nitrogen fixing 145,
    162, 163, 167

Norfolk Broads (UK) 136, 147,
    153, 168
North Atlantic 4, 6, 86, 88,
    89–90, 108, 146
North Atlantic Deep Water see
    NADW
North Atlantic gyre 125
North Pacific 103
North Sea 49
  benthos 95–7
  eutrophication 88
  fishery 103–4, 105, 106, 186–7
  pollution 75
  primary production 90, 91
  zooplankton 99–101
nursery areas, estuaries as 73
nutricline 139
nutrient cycling 51, 153
nutrient depletion 90, 137–40, 184
nutrient enrichment 90, 145, 153,
    170
nutrient limitation 17, 18, 88,
    89–91, 114, 146–7
nutrient
  recirculation 114
  recycling 75, 88, 144–5
  release 177
  resuspension 115
  spiralling 51
  status
    classification 142
    defining 142
  transfer 71, 167
nutrients 41, 51, 52, 70, 75, 90–1,
    94, 99, 109, 110, 112, 114,
    138, 142, 144, 152
  as limiting factors 127, 141,
    144–5
  coastal zone 184
  lakes 141, 144–5
  oceans 114
  role of vertebrates 167
  upwelling 118, 122
  wetlands 159–60, 162–3,
    166–7, 169, 171
Nyanza Gulf (Kenya) 56

Oaken Clough (UK) 43
ocean basin 7
ocean bed 6–8
ocean floor 109, 110, 112, 113,
    122–5, 130, 132
ocean ridges 8, 132
oceans 2, 4–8, 108–33, 138, 184,
    185, 186
  evolution 129–32
Okavango Delta (Botswana) 9,
    179
oligohaline organisms 62

oligomictic lakes 138, 139
oligotrophic waters 122, 142, 143,
    144, 153
osmoconformers 63
osmoregulation 20, 22, 62–3, 64,
    166–7
osmotic stress 68
overturn 138, 147
oxycline 156
oxygen 14–15, 18, 20, 35, 51, 53,
    84, 109, 123, 139–40, 147,
    161–2, 182
  as a limiting factor 68
  concentration 14–15
oxygenation 69, 110, 139, 142

Pacific Ocean 7, 8, 95, 103, 108,
    114, 117–18, 120, 122, 124,
    126–7, 128, 129, 130
  formation 130–1
Panthalassa Ocean 130–2
papyrus swamps 155, 168
partially mixed estuaries 60, 75
particulate organic carbon see POC
particulate organic matter see
    POM
patchiness 27, 184
  coastal zones 92, 98
  in plankton distribution 118–9
  nutrients 145
  ocean detritus 126
  ocean floor 123, 124–5
  rivers 35–6
peat 141, 160, 170, 174, 175, 182
peatlands 160
pelagic community 25
  lakes 136, 144–7
  rivers 35
pelagic organisms 23
pelagic system 185
pelagic zone 4
  lakes 155, 175
periphyton 23, 24
  rivers 42
Petersen's communities 95–6
pH 15, 16, 26, 35, 36, 141, 160,
    187
phagocytosis 25
phosphate 114, 142, 153, 167
  as a limiting factor 16, 18, 143,
    144
photic zone 17, 18, 88, 102, 108,
    114, 115, 116–22, 149, 184
photo-inhibition 16
photosynthesis a 14, 15, 16–18,
    87, 89, 108, 112, 185
  coastal 87
  effect on oxygen concentration
    139–40

tolerance 71, 72
saltmarshes 22, 66, 67, 68, 70, 72, 98, 125, 159, 162, 163–4, 166–7, 180, 181
  energy budgets 70
Salton Sea (USA) 150
salt wedge estuaries 57, 61
San Fransisco Bay (USA) 60
sand dunes 72
sandy shores 82–3, 85–6
Sargasso Sea 114, 125
scavengers 25, 97, 103, 123, 125
scavenging 103, 106
Scheldt Estuary (Netherlands) 75
schwingmoors 175, 176
sea grass beds 75
sea level change 8, 73, 77, 181
Sea of Galilee (Israel) 147
seafloor spreading 113, 129
seamounts 8, 110, 129
seawater 9–10, 11–13, 15, 16, 20, 21
  composition 11–13, 16
Secchi depth 17, 142
secondary production
  estuaries 71
  lakes 146–7
  oceans 115
  wetlands 169–70
sedge fen 174
sedge peat 174
sediment transfer zone 30, 31
sedimentation
  coastal 95
  estuaries 60–2, 65, 74, 75
  lakes 49–50, 151
  wetlands 164, 172–3, 184
sediments 8, 23, 96, 124, 135, 187
  carbonate 110, 122
  coastal 72, 82, 84, 87, 98, 101–2
  estuaries 68–9, 75, 77
  intertidal 56, 84, 87
  lakes 141, 151–3
  ocean bed 110, 112, 122, 125
  pelagic 8, 110, 112
  poorly sorted 84
  resuspension 115
  rivers 30–1, 33–4, 35, 39, 46, 49, 51, 53–4
  siliceous 110, 122
  terrigenous 7, 112
  well sorted 84
  wetlands 174, 175
  wetlands 163, 165, 167, 168, 172
seiches 139
Selenga River (Russia) 143
seston 20
Severn bore 57
Severn Estuary (UK) 56, 75

Severn Tidal Barrage (UK) 77
sewage 41, 44, 69, 75, 152, 187
shelf break fronts 111
shredders 24–5, 43, 44, 52, 68
Shreve method 32
silicate 10, 11, 13, 114
  as a limiting factor 18, 91, 144, 145
sills 58, 110
siltation 101
Silver Creek 49
slides 7, 8
slumps 7
soda lakes 15
solar tides 80–1
Solimoes River (Brazil) 138
Somali Current 3
Southern Ocean 114, 121, 129
species diversity 20–3, 27
  coral reefs 95
  effect of disturbance 27
  effect of nutrients 145
  estuaries 72–3
  freshwater 21
  lakes 150–1
  marine 21
  ocean floor 122–3
  reefs 95
  rivers 35, 36, 46
  wetlands 170, 179
Sphagnum bog 136, 166, 170–2, 174, 176–7
splash zone 82
spring blooms 88, 90, 146, 184
spring tides 81, 82, 166
St Lawrence Estuary (Canada) 64
stability time hypothesis 122–3
stenohaline organisms 62
storm surge barrier 75, 77
storms 27, 82, 83, 85, 86, 91, 139, 166, 180
Strahler method 32
Straits of Gibraltar 132
stratification 18, 19
  lakes 137–40, 142–6
  oceans 101, 108–10, 112, 114, 115
stream order 31, 32
stygobytes 53
sublittoral 82, 83, 91, 94, 185
substrate, hard coastal 84, 86–7
subtidal 82, 87
  primary production in 67
succession
  coastal zone 86, 92, 101–2
  cyclical 176–7
  estuaries 73–4
  lakes 151–2, 184
  ocean bed 123

rivers 47
  wetlands 172–7, 180
sudd 166
Suez Canal 132
summer bloom 99–100
supply side ecology 94, 95
supralittoral 82, 91
suspension feeders 25, 97
Sverdrup's model 17
swamp 160–1
  floating 165

Tagus Estuary (Portugal) 71
tectonic movement 22
tectonically formed estuaries 60
Tees Estuary (UK) 74, 75
temperature, as a limiting factor 146
terrestrialisation 73
Tethys Ocean 22, 130–2
Thames Barrier (UK) 75
Thames Estuary (UK) 65, 72, 75, 186
thermocline 6, 17, 19, 83, 88, 89, 108, 109, 114
  daily 108
  effect of ENSO 127, 128
  lakes 137–9, 145
  oceans 108, 106
tidal bore 57
tidal cycle 64, 65, 80–1, 84–5
tidal energy 111
tidal flats 65, 74
tidal range 56–7, 62, 77
tides 79–83, 181
  estuaries 56–7, 77
  formation 79–81
  in freshwaters 70
top down control 152, 154
toxins/toxicity, created by anoxia 162, 164–5
trade winds 127, 128
transpiration 2, 171, 177
trenches, deep ocean 7, 8, 108, 110, 112, 122
tripton 20
trophic cascade 103, 150, 152, 154
trophic group
  amensalism hypothesis 97
  mutual exclusion hypothesis 97
Tullanavert (UK) 173
turbidity, lakes 153
turbidity current 8
turbidity maximum 62, 65
Tyne Estuary (UK) 75

ultra-oligotrophic waters 142
upwelling 3, 6

lakes 138, 141
oceans 109–10, 116, 118, 120, 122, 127, 184

varzea 168, 170
vertebrate cycle 177–8
vertical mixing, lakes 138, 143–4
viscous layer 35

Wadden Sea 88, 96
Wash, The (UK) 74
waste disposal
coastal zone 102
estuaries 75–6
water chemistry 9–16
lakes 140–1
wetland soils 161–2, 163
water column 108
water masses 108–9, 129
water meadows 179
water quality
effect of wetlands 167–8
rivers 34–5, 36–7, 44, 48

water table 34, 54, 84, 158, 160–2, 166, 169, 171, 174–5
wave action 83, 84, 95, 115, 153
waves 19, 27, 83–4, 85–6, 91, 95
coastal 83–6
estuaries 57
Weddell Sea 6
well-mixed estuaries 75
wetlands 2, 16, 33, 135, 152, 158–82, 185
aquatic marginal 158–9, 162, 172, 176
coastal 6, 9, 159, 162, 166, 176, 179, 180, 184
effect on water quality 167–8
flood 158–9, 160, 176, 177, 179
freshwater 70, 179
fringe 159–60, 162–3, 164, 168, 169, 178, 179, 181, 183, 184
minerotrophic 159
riparian 159
riverine 159
saline 22, 70, 158–82

whale carcasses 124, 125
whaling 103, 128–9
Wolf Point Creek (USA) 47
woody debris 42

zonation
coastal hard substrates 82–3, 92–3
rivers 31, 35–6, 37
sandy shores 84–5
Sphagnum bogs 171
wetlands 164–6
zooplankton 23, 25–6
coastal pelagic 88, 90–1, 99–101
estuaries 64
lakes 145–8
ocean pelagic 115, 118, 119, 124–5
rivers 53
zooxanthellae 91, 94–5